K.

MATHEMATICAL
STATISTICS

Dr. Albert A. Bennett, Editor

PRENTICE-HALL MATHEMATICS SERIES

JOHN E. FREUND

Professor of Mathematics
Arizona State University

MATHEMATICAL STATISTICS

PRENTICE-HALL, INC. Englewood Cliffs, N. J.

Current printing (last digit):
16 15 14 13 12 11

Library of Congress Catalog Card Number 62–9287

Printed in the United States of America

56219–C

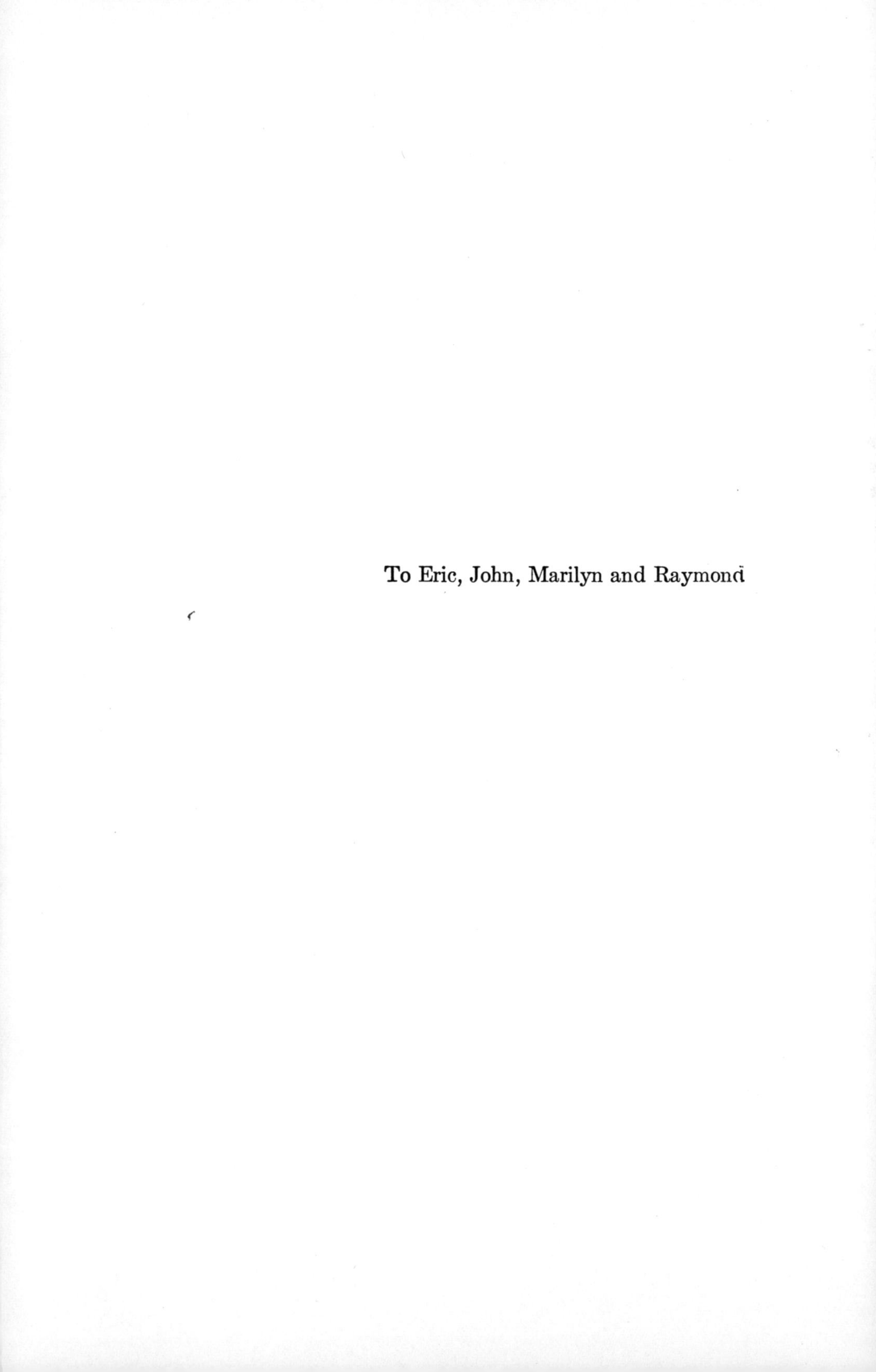

To Eric, John, Marilyn and Raymond

Preface

This book has been written for an introductory two-semester or three-quarter course in mathematical statistics with the prerequisite of a standard undergraduate course in calculus. The first seven chapters, dealing with an introduction to probability, basic distribution theory, and some limit theorems, can also serve for a semester course in probability theory. The treatment of probability is rigorous in so far as discrete (finite or countably infinite) sample spaces are concerned. Some of the difficulties arising in the continuous case are pointed out in Section 5.1; it is felt that a rigorous treatment of general probability spaces is better left for a more advanced course.

One of the major problems in writing a text on mathematical statistics is to find a suitable balance between theory and application. Ultimately, of course, such a balance can only reflect the author's personal preference, as is evidenced by existing texts ranging from the purely theoretical to the largely applied. Although there is emphasis in this text on the mathematics of statistics, it is hoped that it will, nevertheless, aid the reader in developing an early appreciation for applications. It is for this reason that the author has included special sets of applied problems in Sections 3.2.4 and 5.3.5 and the material on decision making in Sections 4.6 and 6.6. Although the treatment of statistical inference is fairly traditional, an introduction to the fundamental concepts of decision theory and some simple illustrations are given in Section 9.1.

Since the language of statistics is not always acceptable to pure mathematicians, the author had to make some compromises while attempting to write this book in the language of modern mathematics. So far as symbolism is concerned, boldface type is used for random variables in order to distinguish between functions and the values which they assume.

The author would like to express his appreciation for the many helpful suggestions which he received from his students, colleagues, and friends.In particular, the author is indebted to Dr. Irwin Miller, who taught with a preliminary draft of this book. The author would also like to express his appreciation to the editorial staff of Prentice-Hall, Inc., for their courteous cooperation in the production of this book and, above all, to his wife for putting up with the many inconveniences which are unavoidable while one is engaged in writing a book.

Finally, the author would like to express his appreciation and indebtedness to the McGraw-Hill Book Company for permission to reproduce the material in Tables I and II from their *Handbook of Probability and Statistics with Tables*; to Professor R. A. Fisher and Messrs. Oliver and Boyd, Ltd., Edinburg, for permission to reproduce the material in Table IV from their book *Statistical Methods for Research Workers*; and to Professor E. S. Pearson and the *Biometrika* trustees for permission to reproduce the material in Tables V and VI.

JOHN E. FREUND

Contents

MATHEMATICAL
STATISTICS

Chapter 1

Introduction

1.1 Introduction

In recent years, the growth of statistics has made itself felt in practically every phase of human activity. Statistics no longer consists merely of the collection of data and their presentation in charts and tables, it is now considered to encompass the entire science of decision making in the face of uncertainty. This covers enormous ground since uncertainties are met when we flip a coin, when we experiment with a new drug, when we determine life insurance premiums, when we inspect manufactured products, when we compare the merits of different missiles, rate the abilities of human beings, make executive decisions, and so forth. It would be presumptuous to say that statistics, in its present state of development, can handle *all* situations involving uncertainties, but new methods are being developed constantly and modern mathematical statistics can, at least, provide the framework for looking at these situations in a logical and systematic fashion. In other words, probability and statistics provide the *models,* the underlying mathematical formulations, to study situations involving uncertainties just as calculus provides the *models,* the underlying mathematical formulations, to describe the concepts of Newtonian physics.

Historically speaking, the origin of probability theory dates back to the 17th century. It seems that the Chevalier de Méré, claimed to have been an ardent gambler, was baffled by some questions concerning a game of chance.* He consulted the French mathematician Blaise Pascal (1623–1662), who in turn wrote about this matter to Pierre Fermat (1601–1665); it is this correspondence which is generally considered the origin of modern probability theory.

The 18th century saw a rapid growth of the mathematics of probability as it applies to games of chance, but it was not until the work of Karl Gauss (1777–1855) and Pierre Laplace (1749–1827) that this theory found applications in other fields. Noting that the theory developed for "heads and tails" or "red and black" in games of chance applied also to situations where the outcomes are "life or death" or "boy or girl", probability theory was applied to actuarial mathematics and to some phases of social science. Later, statistical concepts were introduced into physics by L. Boltzmann, J. Gibbs, and J. Maxwell, and in this century the methods of probability and statistics have found applications in all phases of human endeavor which in some way involve an element of uncertainty or risk. The names which are connected most prominently with the growth of 20th century mathematical statistics are those of R. A. Fisher, J. Neyman, E. S. Pearson, and A. Wald. References to the particular contributions made by these statisticians will be made later in the text.

Since the subjects of probability and statistics can be presented at various levels of mathematical refinement and with various patterns of emphasis, let us point out briefly that the mathematical background expected of the reader is a basic course in differential and integral calculus, including some elementary material on partial differentiation, multiple integration, and series. So far as emphasis is concerned, Chapters 2 through 7 are devoted primarily to the mathematical concepts and techniques which are required to develop the statistical methods treated in Chapters 8 through 14. Chapters 2 and 5 provide a formal introduction to probability based on the concepts of sets, while the other chapters of the first half of the book deal with what might be called basic *distribution theory*. Chapters 8 through 14 contain an introduction to the most fundamental and the most widely used methods of statistics, with emphasis on their theoretical foundation.

* Essentially, his question was how to divide the stakes if two players start but fail to complete a game, in which the winner is the one who wins three matches out of five.

1.2 Fundamental Problems of Probability

Directly or indirectly, probability plays a role in all problems of science, business, and everyday life, which somehow involve an element of uncertainty. In view of this, it is unfortunate that the term "probability", itself, is difficult to define and controversial.

In the study of probability there are essentially three kinds of problems. First there is the question of what we *mean* when we say that a probability is 0.82, 0.25, and so forth; then there is the question of *how to obtain* numerical values of probabilities; and finally there is the question of how known or assumed values of probabilities can be used to determine others, namely, the formal *calculus of probability*. Most of the early chapters of this book will be devoted to the last kind of problem; the problem of how to obtain probabilities will be touched upon in Chapters 9 and 10, dealing with the general problem of estimation.

Philosophical arguments about the various meanings which have been attached to the word "probability" make interesting reading, but in view of our interests and objectives in this book, we shall limit our discussion to the so-called *objectivistic* view. Accordingly, we shall *interpret* probabilities in terms of relative frequencies, or to be more exact as *limits of relative frequencies*. When we say "the probability that a man aged 50 will live to be 65 is 0.72", we mean that if present conditions prevail, 72 per cent of all men aged 50 will live to be 65; when we say "the probability that it will rain tomorrow in Detroit is 0.27", we mean that in the long run it will rain there on that date 27 per cent of the time. The proportion of the time that an event takes place is called its relative frequency, and the relative frequency with which it takes place in the long run is interpreted as its probability.

When we say "the probability of getting heads with a balanced coin is 0.50", this means that in the long run we will get 50 per cent heads and 50 per cent tails; it does not mean that we must necessarily get 5 heads and 5 tails in 10 flips or 50 heads and 50 tails in 100.

It is important to note that the mathematical theory of probability and statistics, which is the subject matter of this book, does not depend on philosophical arguments concerning the meaning of "probability"; there is general agreement concerning the postulates

The Probability of an event E is the limit of its relative frequency of occurrence as the number of trials increases without bound and definitions given in Chapters 2 and 5. Questions of meaning arise only when mathematical theories are applied, and *when it comes to applications, the frequency interpretation of probability is the one that is held by many, probably most, statisticians.*

1.3 Probabilities and Sets

Probabilities invariably refer to the occurrence or non-occurrence of some event. We assign a probability to the *event* that a coin will come up heads, to the *event* that a given candidate will be elected governor of his state, to the *event* that it will not rain on the day of the company's picnic, to the *event* that a missile will hit its target, and so forth. To treat the subject of probability in a rigorous fashion, it will thus be necessary to explain what we mean by "event", and we shall do so by representing events with *sets*, usually *sets of points*.

Figure 1.1

For example, if we consider the flip of a coin, the outcomes, the *events* of getting head or tail, can be represented by the two points of Figure 1.1, where 0 stands for tail (0 heads) and 1 for head (1 head). Similarly, the outcomes of the roll of a die can be represented by the six points of Figure 1.2.

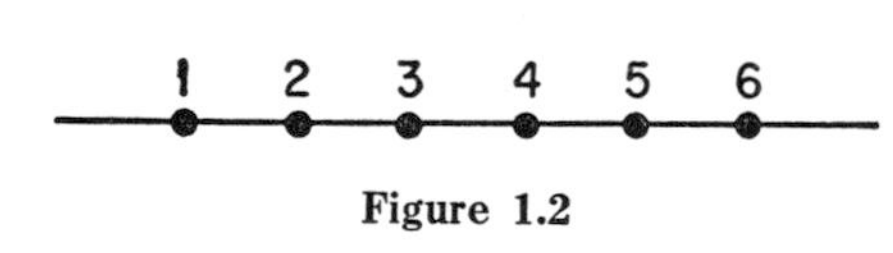

Figure 1.2

To consider a slightly more complicated example, the outcomes of an experiment consisting of two flips of a coin can be represented

Figure 1.3

by the points of Figure 1.3, provided one is interested only in the total number of heads. An alternate way of representing the outcomes by means of points is shown in Figure 1.4, where 0 and 1 again stand for tail and head, and the two coordinates represent the two flips of the coin. It should be noted that in Figure 1.4 the event of getting 1 head and 1 tail is represented by the set of two points inside the dotted line.

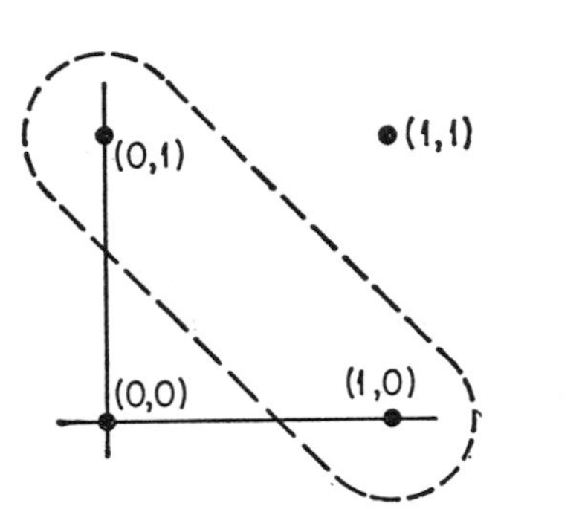

Figure 1.4

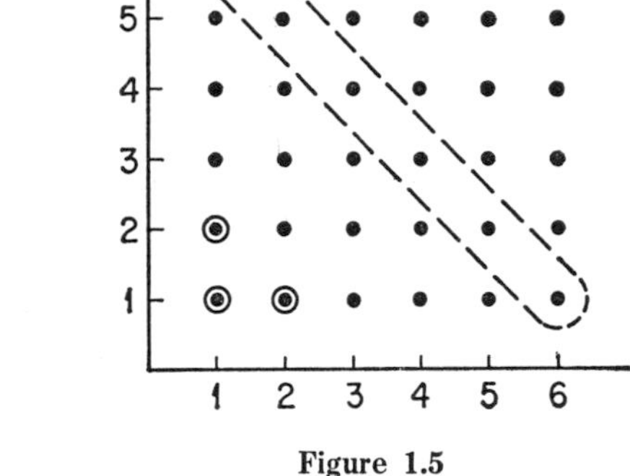

Figure 1.5

Referring to an experiment which consists of rolling a pair of dice (one red and one green), the event of rolling a 7 is represented by the set of six points inside the dotted line of Figure 1.5, and the event of rolling 2, 3, or 12 is represented by the set of four points which are circled in Figure 1.5.

Since sets play such an important role in the theory of probability, some of the basic concepts of set theory will be introduced in Chapter 2. Although the proofs of many theorems in probability theory require knowledge of the *Algebra of Sets*, it will be seen that they can also be justified quite readily by means of simple diagrams. Knowledge of the Algebra of Sets (or *Boolean Algebra* as it is also called) is, thus, desirable, but not absolutely essential.

Throughout this section we used the term "set" without giving it a definition, understanding tacitly that it stands for a collection, group, or class of points or other kinds of objects. Indeed, it is customary to leave this term undefined, subject to the qualification that sets must obey the rules set down in Section 2.1.3.

The objects that belong to a set are usually referred to as its *members* or its *elements*, and sets are sometimes specified by actually listing the individual elements. Thus, the set which consists of the different outcomes of a roll of a die may be indicated as $\{1, 2, 3, 4, 5, 6\}$; and similarly {apple pie, ice cream, chocolate cake, rice pudding} is a set of four desserts. It should be noted that when the elements of a set are thus listed, their order does not matter; $\{1, 2, 3\}$ and $\{2, 3, 1\}$ represent the same set consisting of the first three positive integers.

Instead of listing the elements, which is often impracticable or even impossible, sets can also be specified by giving a rule according to which one can decide whether any given object does or does not belong to a set. We can thus speak of the set of *all college students* without having to list them all, by specifying that a person belongs to this set if and only if he (or she) is enrolled in an institution of higher learning. Similarly, we speak of the set of *prime numbers*, specifying that a positive integer greater than 1 belongs to this set if it has no factors other than itself and 1.

Chapter 2

Probability–The Discrete Case

2.1 Discrete Sample Spaces

A set whose elements represent all possible outcomes of an experiment is generally called a *sample space* for the experiment and it will be denoted by the letter S. Using the word "experiment" rather loosely, we are referring here to any situation which permits a variety of outcomes involving somehow an element of chance. Instead of "sample space", the terms "universal set", "universe of discourse", and "possibilities space" are also used.

The fact that the sample space which represents a given experiment need not be unique is illustrated by Figures 1.3 and 1.4; both of these sample spaces represent the outcomes of an experiment consisting of two flips of a coin, the difference being in what we mean by "outcome". *Generally speaking, it is desirable to use sample spaces whose elements represent outcomes which do not permit further subdivision; that is, an individual element of the sample space should not represent two or more outcomes which are distinguishable in some fashion.* This is true for the sample space of Figure 1.4, but not for that of Figure 1.3. Following this convention avoids many of the difficulties and paradoxes which hampered the early development of the theory of probability.

Sample spaces are usually classified according to the *number of elements* which they contain and also according to the *dimension* of the geometrical configuration in which they are displayed. Thus, Figure 1.1 is a one-dimensional representation of the outcomes of a flip of a coin and Figure 1.4 is a two-dimensional representation of the outcomes of two flips of a coin. If a sample space contains a finite number of elements or as many as there are whole numbers, namely, an unending sequence, it is said to be *discrete*. The sample spaces of Figures 1.1 through 1.5 have 2, 6, 3, 4, and 36 elements, respectively, they are all finite and discrete, and so is the three-dimensional sample space of Figure 2.1, whose 8 elements (points)

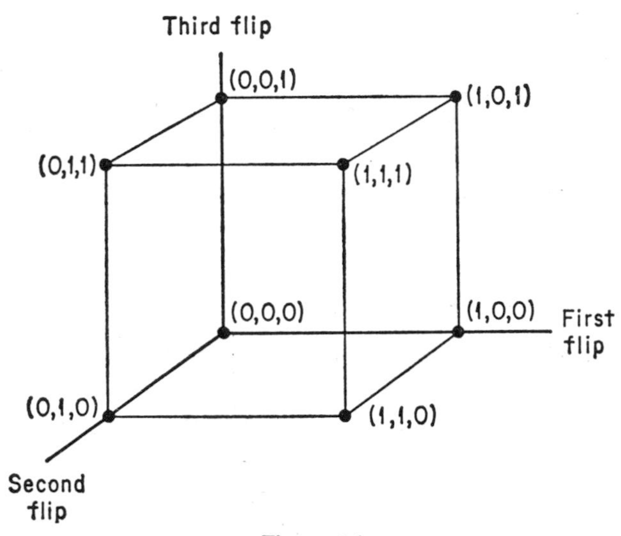

Figure 2.1

represent the possible outcomes of an experiment consisting of three flips of a coin. (The three coordinates represent the successive flips and 0 and 1 again stand for tail and head.) If a coin is flipped until *head* appears *for the first time*, the possible outcomes are: the first head appears on the *first* flip, the first head appears on the *second* flip, it appears on the *third* flip, the *fourth* flip, the *fifth* flip, ... The sample space for this experiment contains infinitely many elements, but only as many as there are whole numbers and according to our definition it is also *discrete*.

If the elements (points) of a sample space constitute a continuum, for example, all the points on a line, all the points on a line segment, all the points in a plane, and so forth, the sample space is said to be *continuous*. Continuous sample spaces are required whenever the outcomes of experiments are measurements of physical properties such as temperature, height, speed, length, ..., which are measured on a continuous scale. The remainder of this chapter as well as Chapters 3 and 4 will be devoted to problems involving sample spaces that are discrete; the continuous case will be introduced in Chapter 5.

2.1.1 *Subsets and events*

Set A is called a *subset* of set B, if and only if each element of A is also an element of B. Thus, in Figure 1.5 the six points inside the dotted curve constitute a subset of the sample space and so do the four points which are drawn heavier than the other thirty-two. According to this definition *each set is a subset of itself*; furthermore, *the empty set ϕ, the set which has no elements, is considered to be a subset of every set.* Thus, the set of all 8 points of Figure 2.1 is a subset of the sample space which represents three flips of a coin, and the set of all points representing, for example, the event of getting 5 heads in 3 flips of a coin, obviously an empty set, is a subset of this sample space in a somewhat trivial sense.

Using the concepts of sample space and subset, let us now state more formally that *all events with which we are concerned in probability are represented by subsets of appropriate sample spaces.* In other words, "event" is the non-technical term and "subset of a sample space" or merely "subset" is the corresponding mathematical counterpart. Thus, in Figure 2.1 the subset which consists only of the point (0, 0, 0) represents the event of getting 3 tails in 3 flips of a coin; the subset which consists of the points (1, 0, 0), (0, 1, 0), and (0, 0, 1) represents the event of getting 1 head and 2 tails; $\{(0, 1, 1), (1, 0, 1), (1, 1, 0)\}$ represents the event of getting 2 heads and 1 tail; $\{(1, 1, 1)\}$ represents the event of getting 3 heads; and the entire sample space represents the event of getting 0, 1, 2, or 3 heads.

Similarly, if 6 candidates are running for a given office, one and only one is to be elected, and A, B, C, D, E, and F stand for the outcomes that Mr. Allen, Mrs. Bond, Mr. Cole, Mr. Day, Miss Evans, or Mrs. Foster is elected, then $\{A, C, D\}$ represents the event that a male is elected to the office, $\{B, F\}$ represent the event that a married female is elected, and $\{E\}$ represents the event that an unmarried female is elected. We have given this second example primarily to stress the fact that the concepts which we have introduced do not apply only to sets of points—they apply also to sets whose elements are other kinds of objects. (On the other hand, we *could* have identified the outcomes with 6 points, say, those of Figure 1.2, in which case point sets would represent the various events.)

2.1.2 *Operations on sets*

In the following it will be assumed that the sets on which certain operations are performed belong to a given sample space S and that the new sets thus obtained belong to the same sample space S. To help visualize these operations, it is convenient to represent sets geometrically as in Figure 2.2. Here the entire sample space is represented by a rectangle and given subsets are represented by regions inside the rectangle. Thus, if the rectangle of Figure 2.2 represents the sample space for one roll of a pair of dice, the shaded circle might represent the event, subset, of getting 7 or 11.

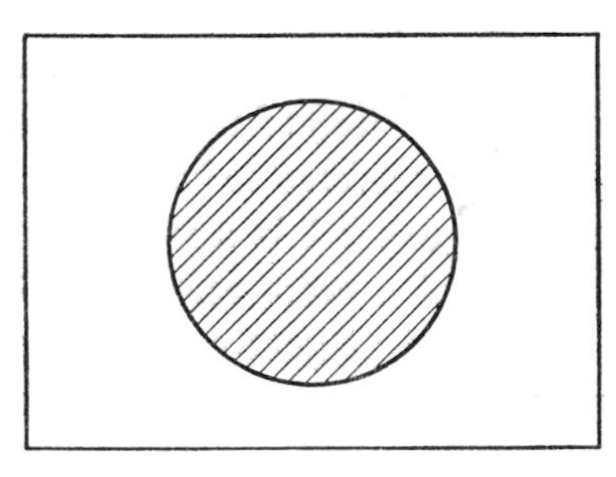

Figure 2.2

The *union*, or *logical sum*, of two sets A and B is the set which consists of all elements, each of which belongs to A or to B or to both. The union of two sets A and B is written $A \cup B$, which is sometimes read "A cup B", and it is represented by the shaded region of Figure 2.3. (Other notations used for the union of A and B are $A + B$ and A *or* B, the "or" being the "inclusive or" meaning A *or* B *or both.*) If the rectangle of Figure 2.3 represents the sample space for 5 flips of a coin, A represents the event of getting 2 heads and 3 tails and B represents the event of getting 4 heads and 1 tail,

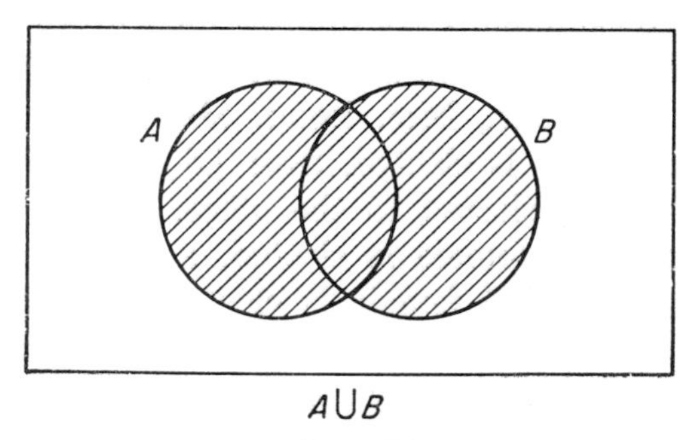

$A \cup B$

Figure 2.3

then $A \cup B$ represents the event of getting 2 or 4 heads in 5 flips of a coin.

Referring again to the six candidates of the example on page 9, suppose that Mr. Allen is married and that Mr. Cole and Mr. Day are bachelors. Then, $\{A, C, D\}$ represents the event that the candidate who is elected is male, $\{A, B, F\}$ represents the event that the candidate who is elected is married, and the union of these two sets, $\{A, B, C, D, F\}$, represents the event that the person who is elected is male, married, or both. It should be noted that when we so to speak "add" the sets $\{A, C, D\}$ and $\{A, B, F\}$, each of which has 3 elements, their union has only the 5 elements A, B, C, D, and F. When listing the elements of a set each element is listed (counted) only once and when talking about the elements of a set it will always be assumed that they are distinct.

The *intersection*, or *logical product*, of two sets A and B is the set which consists of all elements, each of which belongs to both A and B. The intersection of two sets A and B is written $A \cap B$, which is sometimes read "A cap B," and it is represented by the shaded region of Figure 2.4. (Other notations used for the intersection of A and B are $A \cdot B$, AB, and A *and* B.) If A and B again represent the events of getting, respectively, 2 and 4 heads in 5 flips of a coin, then $A \cap B$ is empty—it represents the event of getting (at the same time) 2 heads and 4 heads in 5 flips of a coin. With reference to the 6 candidates, the intersection of $\{A, C, D\}$, representing the event that the candidate who is elected is male, and $\{A, B, F\}$, representing the event that the candidate who is elected is married, is the set $\{A\}$, since Mr. Allen is the only one among the 6 candidates who is a married male.

It should be noted that if circles (or other regions) representing two sets are drawn as in Figure 2.5, this assumes automatically that

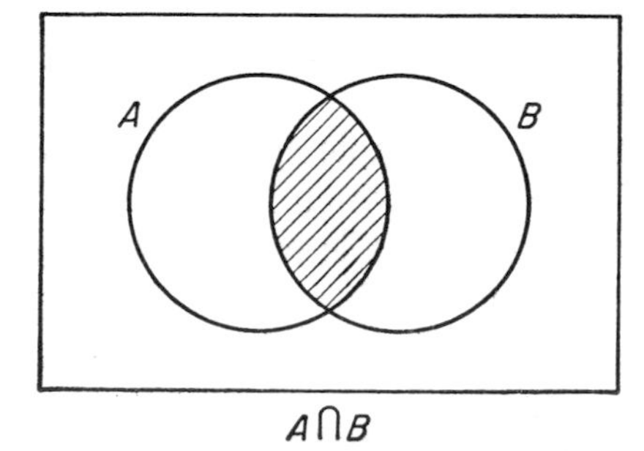

Figure 2.4

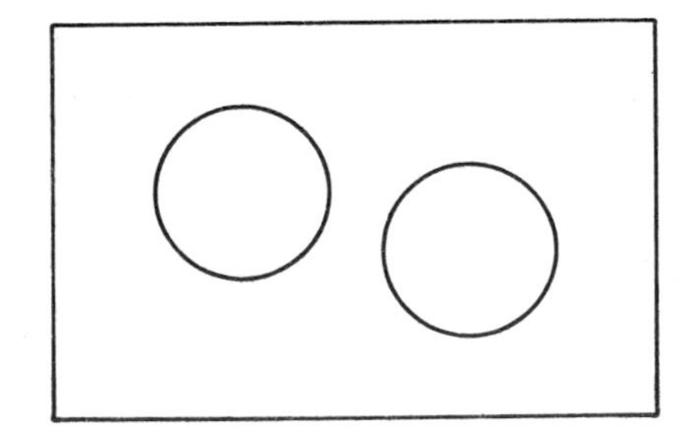

Figure 2.5

the intersection of the two sets is empty. In order to avoid such assumptions, particularly when they are uncalled for, the circles should always be drawn as in Figures 2.3 and 2.4, called *Venn diagrams*. Although Figure 2.4 includes a region representing the intersection of the two sets, this does not imply that the intersection cannot be empty. As a matter of fact, it was empty in our first example concerning the 5 flips of a coin.

Two sets A and B are said to be *disjoint* if and only if they have no elements in common, that is, if and only if their intersection is empty. Thus, sets A and B are disjoint if they represent the events of getting 2 heads and 4 heads, respectively, in 5 flips of a coin; they are *not* disjoint if A represents the event that the first of two flips of a coin yields head and B represents the event that the second of the two flips yields head.

In probability theory it is customary to refer to two events which are represented by disjoint subsets of the sample space as *mutually exclusive.** Getting 2 heads in 5 flips of a coin and getting 4 heads are, thus, mutually exclusive events; and referring again to the 6 candidates, the events that the candidate who is elected is male or female are mutually exclusive while the events that the candidate who is elected is married or male are not.

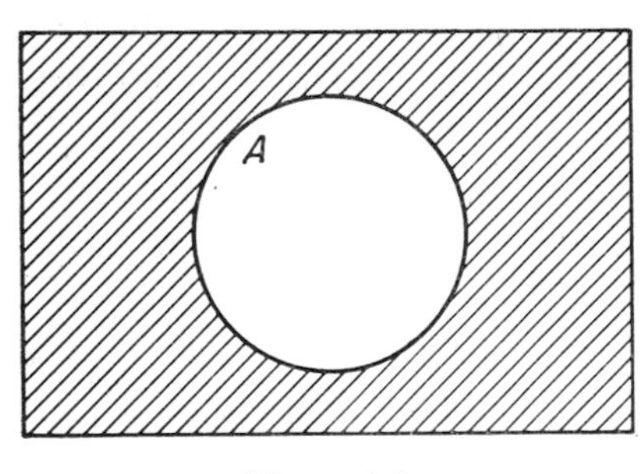

Figure 2.6

Extending the definitions of "disjoint" and "mutually exclusive" to more than two sets and the events which they represent, sets A_1, A_2, A_3, . . . , are said to be disjoint (and the events which they represent are said to be mutually exclusive) if and only if they have pairwise no elements in common. Getting 0, 1, 2, 3, 4, or 5 heads in 5 flips of a coin are, thus, mutually exclusive events.

The *complement* of a set A relative to a sample space S is the set which consists of all elements of S none of which is an element of A. The complement of A is written A' and it is represented by the shaded region of Figure 2.6. (Other notations used for the complement of A relative to S are $\bar{A}$, $\tilde{A}$, and $S - A$.) Referring

* Some authors prefer to define "mutually exclusive" in a different way, as is explained on page 39.

again to 5 flips of a coin, if A represents the event of getting 2 heads, then A' represents the event of getting 0, 1, 3, 4, or 5 heads, namely, the event of *not* getting 2 heads. Similarly, with reference to the 6 candidates, the complement of $\{A, C, D\}$, representing the event that the candidate who is elected is male, is $\{B, E, F\}$, representing the event that the candidate who is elected is female.

2.1.3 *The algebra of sets*

Two sets A and B are *equal* and we write $A = B$, if and only if each element of A is an element of B and each element of B is an element of A. Using this definition of the equality of sets, it is possible to state some of the concepts introduced earlier in a more concise fashion. For example, we can now say that two sets A and B are disjoint if and only if $A \cap B = \phi$. Similarly, we could have defined what we mean by the complement of a set by stating that A' is the complement of A relative to the sample space S if and only if *both* $A \cap A' = \phi$ and $A \cup A' = S$. The first of these equations specifies that A and A' have no elements in common and the second specifies that, between them, A and A' contain all the elements of S.

In the *Algebra of Sets*, or *Boolean Algebra*, the above two equations concerning A and A' are actually contained among the basic postulates. These postulates are listed below and although they can be interpreted more generally, we shall look upon A, B, C, D, etc., as subsets of some sample space S:

P_1 (*laws of closure*): for every pair of sets A and B there exist unique sets $A \cup B$ and $A \cap B$.

P_2 (*commutative laws*):
$$A \cup B = B \cup A$$
$$A \cap B = B \cap A$$

P_3 (*associative laws*):
$$(A \cup B) \cup C = A \cup (B \cup C)$$
$$(A \cap B) \cap C = A \cap (B \cap C)$$

P_4 (*distributive laws*):
$$A \cap (B \cup C) = (A \cap B) \cup (A \cap C)$$
$$A \cup (B \cap C) = (A \cup B) \cap (A \cup C)$$

P_5 (*identity laws*): there exist unique sets ϕ and S such that for each A, $A \cap S = A$ and $A \cup \phi = A$.

P_6 (*complementation law*) corresponding to each set A there exists a unique set A' such that both $A \cap A' = \phi$ and $A \cup A' = S$.

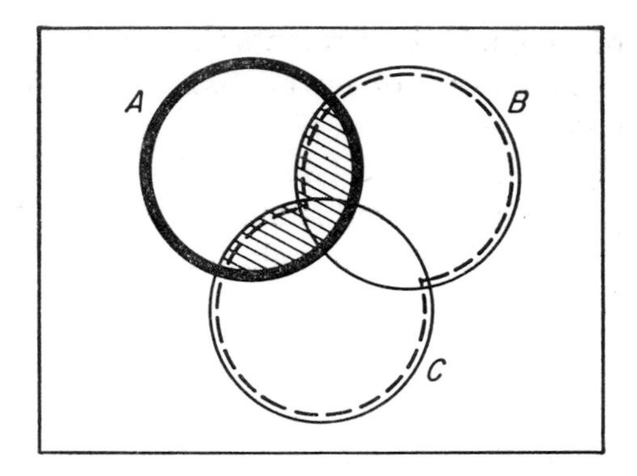

Figure 2.7

It is easy to verify that these postulates hold if we interpret sets intuitively as collections of points or other kinds of objects. We can do so either by checking whether the sets given on both sides of each equation contain the same elements or by verifying that they are represented by identical regions of Venn diagrams. For example, to verify the first distributive law, we have only to observe that the shaded region of Figure 2.7, representing $A \cap (B \cup C)$, equals the shaded region of Figure 2.8, representing $(A \cap B) \cup (A \cap C)$. In Figure 2.7, set A is indicated by means of the heavy line, $B \cup C$ by means of the dotted line, and the shaded region represents their intersection. In Figure 2.8, $A \cap B$ is indicated by means of the heavy line, $A \cap C$ by means of the dotted line, and the shaded region representing their union is identical with the shaded region of Figure 2.7.

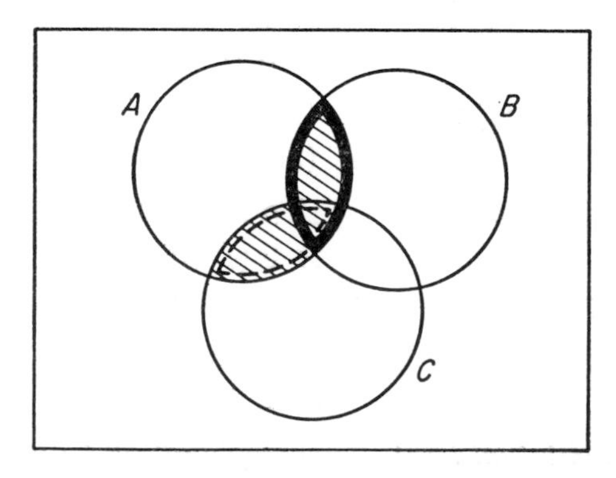

Figure 2.8

Using the basic postulates of the Algebra of Sets, it is possible to derive many further rules (theorems), among which the following are of particular importance:

1. $A \cup S = S$ and $A \cap \phi = \phi$ for all A
2. $A \cup A = A$ and $A \cap A = A$ for all A
3. $S' = \phi$ and $\phi' = S$
4. $(A')' = A$ for all A
5. $(A \cup B)' = A' \cap B'$ and $(A \cap B)' = A' \cup B'$
6. $A \cup (A \cap B) = A$ and $A \cap (A \cup B) = A$
7. $A \cap (B_1 \cup B_2 \cup \ldots \cup B_n)$
$$= (A \cap B_1) \cup (A \cap B_2) \cup \ldots \cup (A \cap B_n)$$

All these rules can readily be verified by means of Venn diagrams. To illustrate how one can actually be *derived*, the following is a proof of the first part of Rule 1:

	Justification
$A \cup S = (A \cup S) \cap S$	postulate P_5
$= (A \cup S) \cap (A \cup A')$	postulate P_6
$= A \cup (S \cap A')$	postulate P_4
$= A \cup A'$	postulate P_5
$= S$	postulate P_6

In the proofs that follow in this and in later chapters, we shall frequently have the occasion to refer to the above postulates and theorems. However, without going into detail, it will always be possible to justify whatever rules are needed by means of Venn diagrams.

EXERCISES

1. An urn contains four tags labeled 1, 2, 3, and 4. Using these numbers as coordinates for two successive draws, the first tag being replaced before the second is drawn, (2, 3), for instance, represents the outcome of first drawing tag 2 and then tag 3. Letting A represent the event that tag 1 is drawn at least once in two draws, B the event that the same tag is drawn twice, C the event that tags with even numbers are

drawn both times, and D the event that tags with odd numbers are drawn both times, list the elements of

(a) the whole sample space
(b) A
(c) B
(d) C
(e) D
(f) $A \cap B$
(g) $B \cup C$
(h) A'
(i) $A \cap C$
(j) $(A \cap C)'$
(k) $A \cap (B \cup D)$
(l) $(A \cap B) \cup (A \cap D)$

2. If in the experiment of Exercise 1 the first tag is not replaced before the second is drawn, list the 12 elements of the new sample space and the elements which now belong to sets A, B, C, and D.

3. Among 8 applicants for a teaching position Mr. Allen is 25 years old, single, a republican, and a bridge player, Mr. Burns is 30 years old, single, a democrat, and not a bridge player, Mr. Carlson is 35 years old, single, a republican, and not a bridge player, Mr. Davis is 40 years old, single, a democrat, and not a bridge player, Mr. Evans is 25 years old, married, a democrat, and not a bridge player, Mr. French is 30 years old, married, a republican, and not a bridge player, Mr. Green is 35 years old, married, a democrat, and not a bridge player, and Mr. Hughes is 40 years old, married, a republican, and a bridge player. One of these eight applicants is to get the teaching position and the event that the job is given to someone 25 years old may, thus, be represented by the set {Allen, Evans}. Indicate in a similar fashion sets representing the events that

(a) the position is given to a married man
(b) the position is given to a democrat
(c) the position is given to a bridge player
(d) the position is given to someone 35 or 40 years old.

4. Referring to Exercise 3, indicate

(e) the complement of the set of (a)
(f) the union of the sets of (b) and (c)
(g) the intersection of the sets of (c) and (d)
(h) the intersection of the sets of (f) and (g)

Also state in words what kind of persons are contained in these four sets.

5. Referring to Exercise 3, let X represent the event that the position if given to a married republican, Y the event that the position is given to a person 30 or 35 years old, and Z the event that the position is given to a married person who is not a bridge player. List the elements of each of the following sets:

(a) X (b) Y (c) Z

(d) $X \cup Y$ (e) $X \cap Z$ (f) $X \cup Z'$

(g) $X \cap (Y \cup Z)$ (h) $(X \cap Y) \cup (X \cap Z)$ (i) $(Y \cup Z)'$

6. An experiment consists of first rolling a die and then flipping a coin if and only if the die came up 2, 4, or 6. List the elements of the sample space of this experiment.

7. A given inspection procedure requires that tires are classified as 0, 1, or 2, to indicate that they are, respectively, perfect, slightly damaged, or damaged beyond repair. Using these numbers as coordinates, draw a two-dimensional figure representing the sample space for the inspection of two tires. Also list the elements of the subsets which represent the events that at least one of the tires is damaged beyond repair and that neither of the tires is slightly damaged.

8. Using Venn diagrams verify that

(a) $A \cup (B \cap C) = (A \cup B) \cap (A \cup C)$, the second of the distributive laws of postulate P_4

(b) $(A \cup B)' = A' \cap B'$, the first part of rule 5 on page 15

(c) $A = (A \cap B) \cup (A \cap B')$

(d) $A \cup B = (A \cap B) \cup (A \cap B') \cup (A' \cap B)$.

9. Using the postulates of the Algebra of Sets, *prove* that

(a) $A \cap \phi = \phi$, the second part of rule 1 on page 15

(b) $A \cup A = A$, the first part of rule 2 on page 15

(c) $A = (A \cap B_1) \cup (A \cap B_2) \cup (A \cap B_3)$, given that $B_1 \cup B_2 \cup B_3 = S$.

2.2 Some Combinatorial Theory

Many problems in probability and statistics require the counting, sometimes the enumeration, of the elements of given sets. For instance, if an experiment consists of first rolling a die and then flipping a coin, it may be of interest to know how many points there are in its sample space. The "tree" of Figure 2.9 shows that there are altogether 12 distinct outcomes; they are (1, 0), (1, 1), (2, 0), (2, 1), (3, 0), (3, 1), (4, 0), (4, 1), (5, 0), (5, 1), (6, 0), and (6, 1), where the first coordinate represents the result obtained with the die and the second coordinate is 0 or 1 depending on whether the coin comes up tail or head.

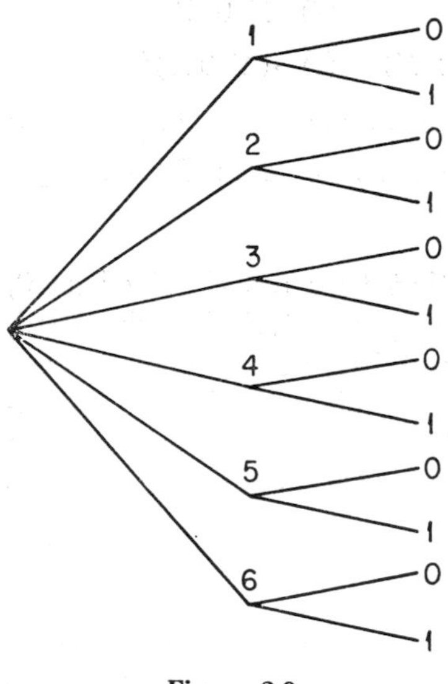

Figure 2.9

Although counting the elements of sets poses no difficulties when the number of elements of a set is small, it becomes very impractical to construct a tree like that of Figure 2.9 or otherwise count the elements of sets representing, say, all possible outcomes for 10 successive flips of a coin or 4 rolls of a die. (For 10 flips of a coin the number of distinct outcomes is 1024 and for 4 rolls of a die it is 1296.) Fortunately, there exist general methods for determining the number of elements of many sets arising in probability and statistics without having to go through actual counts. For instance, the following is a theorem which is applicable to the example mentioned above concerning the roll of a die and subsequent flip of a coin:

THEOREM 2.1:

*If sets A_1 and A_2 have n_1 and n_2 elements, respectively, there are $n_1 \cdot n_2$ ways in which one can first select an element of A_1 and then an element of A_2.**

In the die and coin example, A_1 is the sample space for one roll of a die, A_2 is the sample space for one flip of a coin, $n_1 = 6$, $n_2 = 2$, and there are altogether $n_1 \cdot n_2 = 6 \cdot 2 = 12$ possible outcomes for the entire experiment. To give another example, if a person has the choice of 5 routes driving from San Francisco to Chicago and 4 routes driving from Chicago to New York, he has $5 \cdot 4 = 20$ routes to choose from driving from San Francisco to New York via Chicago.

* Actually, this theorem, and also Theorem 2.2, hold when the order in which the selections are made is changed or unspecified. However, it is desirable to specify the order to make the theorems directly applicable to repeated selections from *one* set.

To justify Theorem 2.1 one could actually construct an array showing all possible pairs or visualize a "tree" with n_1 branches eminating from the starting point and then n_2 branches eminating from the end points of each of the first n_1. In the same fashion one can demonstrate more generally that

THEOREM 2.2:

If sets $A_1, A_2, \ldots,$ and A_k have, respectively, $n_1, n_2, \ldots,$ and n_k elements, there are $n_1 \cdot n_2 \cdot \ldots \cdot n_k$ ways in which one can first select an element of A_1, then an element of $A_2, \ldots,$ and finally an element of A_k.

This theorem can be used, for example, to determine the number of elements in the sample space for 10 successive flips of a coin; there are 2 possible outcomes for each flip, $n_1 = n_2 = \ldots = n_{10} = 2$, and the total number of elements in the sample space is $2^{10} = 1024$. Similarly, the number of distinct outcomes for 4 rolls of a die is $6 \cdot 6 \cdot 6 \cdot 6 = 1296$, and if a person has the choice of 15 sandwiches, 8 drinks, and 6 desserts, there are $15 \cdot 8 \cdot 6 = 720$ ways in which he can order a sandwich, a drink, and a dessert.

Although Theorem 2.2 finds wide application, it must be used with care. Consider, for example, the sample space for 5 flips of a coin and suppose that we want to find the number of elements in the subset which represents the event that throughout the series of flips heads is always ahead. It is clear that the first 2 flips must be heads, that the third can be head or tail, and that, therefore,

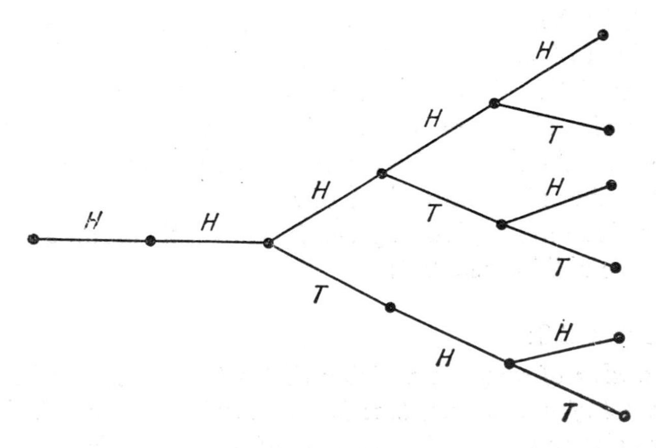

Figure 2.10

$n_1 = 1$, $n_2 = 1$, and $n_3 = 2$. However, the number of permissible outcomes for the fourth and fifth flips depend on what happened in the third, the general rule cannot be used, and we have no choice but to enumerate the elements of the subset, possibly with the aid of a "tree" like that of Figure 2.10. It can thus be seen that the subset under consideration has 6 elements.

2.2.1 *Permutations*

Theorem 2.2 applies to many problems in which several elements are selected from one and the same set and the order in which they are selected is of relevance. Suppose, for example, that a fraternity has 20 members and that one member is to be elected president, another is to be elected vice-president, and a third is to be elected secretary-treasurer. Here $n_1 = 20$, $n_2 = 19$, $n_3 = 18$, and the total number of ways in which these officers can be elected is $20 \cdot 19 \cdot 18 = 6840$. Although we cannot enumerate the elements of A_2 and A_3, the sets from which the second and third selections are made, we do know that $n_2 = 19$, since 19 members of the fraternity are eligible to become vice-president after the president has been elected and that $n_3 = 18$ since 18 members of the fraternity are eligible to become secretary-treasurer after the other two offices have been filled.

Defined

If the elements of a set are aligned in some fashion, that is, in a specific order, we refer to such an arrangement as a *permutation* of the elements of the set. Thus, 4 3 2 1 5 is a specific permutation of the first five positive integers, 5 1 3 4 2 is another, and $F\ E\ C\ B\ A\ D$ is a specific permutation of the first six letters of the alphabet. Also, *ab*, *ac*, *ad*, *bc*, *bd*, *cd*, *ba*, *ca*, *da*, *cb*, *db*, and *dc* are the 12 possible permutations of two distinct letters selected from among the first four letters of the alphabet. (A permutation of r elements selected from a set of n elements is also referred to sometimes as an *ordered r-tuple*; we shall consider these terms as synonymous.)

The number of permutations of r distinct elements selected from a set of n elements is given by the following theorem, an immediate consequence of Theorem 2.2:

THEOREM 2.3:

The number of ways in which r distinct elements can be selected from a set of n elements, that is, the number of permutations of r distinct elements selected from a set of n elements is

$$n(n-1)(n-2) \cdot \ldots \cdot (n-r+1).$$

With reference to Theorem 2.2, $n_1 = n$, $n_2 = n - 1$, $n_3 = n - 2, \ldots,$ and the rth selection is made from the $n - (r - 1) = n - r + 1$ elements which remain after the first $r - 1$ selections have been made. The number of permutations of r distinct elements selected from a set of n elements will be written $P(n, r)$; other notations are ${}_nP_r$ and ${}^nP_r$.

Using the factorial notation

$$n! = n(n-1)(n-2) \cdot \ldots \cdot 3 \cdot 2 \cdot 1$$

for positive integers n and letting, by definition, $0! = 1$, we can also write

$$P(n, r) = \frac{n(n-1)(n-2) \cdot \ldots \cdot (n-r+1) \cdot (n-r)!}{(n-r)!}$$

or

$$P(n, r) = \frac{n!}{(n-r)!} \tag{2.2.1}$$

for positive integers n and $r = 0, 1, 2, \ldots,$ or n. As a special case we find that for $r = n$

$$P(n, n) = n! \tag{2.2.2}$$

and the number of distinct ways in which all of the elements of a set of n elements can be arranged is, thus, $n!$.

As it is always assumed that the elements of a set are distinct, see page 11, formulas (2.2.1) and (2.2.2) must be used with some caution. For example, (2.2.2) cannot be used directly to determine the number of ways in which the letters in the word "cook" can be arranged. Distinguishing for the moment between the two o's by referring to them as o_1 and o_2, there are indeed $4! = 24$ permutations of the symbols c, o_1, o_2, and k. However, if we drop the subscripts, then co_1ko_2 and co_2ko_1, for example, yield the identical arrangement coko. Since each pair of permutations *with* subscripts yields but one arrangement *without* subscripts in this example, the total number of arrangements of the letters in "cook" is $\frac{24}{2} = 12$. Similarly, *with* subscripts there are $7!$ permutations of the letters in the word "receive", but interchanging the three e's there are always $3! = 6$ permutations *with* subscripts yielding the same arrangement *without* subscripts. Hence, there are $7!/3! = 840$ arrangements of the letters in "receive".

Using the same sort of reasoning, we can state more generally that the number of arrangements of n symbols of which r_1 are alike, r_2 others are alike, . . ., and r_k others are alike is

$$\frac{n!}{r_1!r_2! \cdot \ldots \cdot r_k!} \tag{2.2.3}$$

For instance, the number of distinct arrangements of the 7 letters in "success" is $7!/3!2! = 420$.

2.2.2 *Combinations*

When using formula (2.2.1) we are concerned with the *order* in which the elements of subsets of r elements are selected from a set of n. Thus, there are the following 24 permutations of three of the first four letters of the alphabet:

abc	*acb*	*bac*	*bca*	*cab*	*cba*
abd	*adb*	*bad*	*bda*	*dab*	*dba*
acd	*adc*	*cad*	*cda*	*dac*	*dca*
bcd	*bdc*	*cbd*	*cdb*	*dbc*	*dcb*

However, if we are interested only in the number of distinct subsets and not in the order in which their elements are arranged, it should be noted that among the above 24 permutations each row constitutes the permutations of the elements of *one* subset. The set $\{a, b, c, d\}$ thus has actually only four subsets each of which contains three elements, namely, $\{a, b, c\}$, $\{a, b, d\}$, $\{a, c, d\}$, and $\{b, c, d\}$.

In general, there are $r!$ permutations of the elements of a subset of r and the $P(n, r)$ permutations of r elements selected from a set of n contain, therefore, each subset $r!$ times. Dividing $P(n, r)$ by $r!$ we thus have

THEOREM 2.4:

The number of ways in which distinct subsets of r elements can be selected from a set of n elements is

$$\frac{n!}{(n - r)!r!}$$

where $r = 0, 1, \ldots,$ *or* n.

Symbolically, we write

$$\binom{n}{r} = \frac{n!}{(n - r)!r!}$$

The number of combinations of n elements of a set taken r at a time is the number of distinct subsets of size r which can be found from the n elements without regard for the order in which the elements are arranged.

referring to $\binom{n}{r}$ also as "the number of *combinations* of n objects taken r at a time". Alternate notations for $\binom{n}{r}$, that is, the number of ways in which distinct subsets of r elements can be selected from a set of n, are $C(n, r)$, ${}_nC_r$, and ${}^nC_r$. For reasons to be explained below, we shall refer to $\binom{n}{r}$ also as a *binomial coefficient.*

If a subset of r elements is selected from a set of n, this automatically leaves a subset of $n - r$ elements. Hence, we could say that $\binom{n}{r}$ stands for the number of ways in which a set of n elements can be *partitioned* into an ordered pair of subsets containing r and $n - r$ elements, respectively. (Specifying the order of the subsets is necessary to accommodate the case where $n = 2r$.) It should also be noted that $\binom{n}{0} = \binom{n}{n} = 1$, which agrees with our previous observation that the empty set ϕ and the set itself are included among the subsets of each set.

To consider a numerical example, suppose we want to know in how many distinct ways 8 tosses of a coin can yield 3 heads and 5 tails. This is equivalent to asking in how many ways one can select the three tosses on which heads is to occur, or in other words how many subsets of 3 elements can be selected from a set of 8. Applying Theorem 2.4 we find that the answer is

$$\frac{8!}{5!\,3!} = 56.$$

This result could also have been obtained by the rather tedious process of enumerating the 56 possible outcomes yielding 3 heads and 5 tails, namely, (0, 0, 0, 1, 1, 0, 0, 1), (1, 0, 0, 1, 0, 1, 0, 0), . . . , where 0 and 1 again stand for tail and head.

2.2.3 *Binomial coefficients*

Down play

If n is a positive integer and we multiply out $(1 + x)^n$ term by term, each term is the product of x's and 1's, one x or 1 coming from each of the n factors $(1 + x)$. Thus, the expansion of $(1 + x)^3$ yields

$$\begin{aligned}(1 + x)(1 + x)(1 + x) &= 1\cdot1\cdot1 + 1\cdot1\cdot x + 1\cdot x\cdot1 + x\cdot1\cdot1 \\ &\quad + 1\cdot x\cdot x + x\cdot1\cdot x + x\cdot x\cdot1 + x\cdot x\cdot x \\ &= 1 + 3x + 3x^2 + x^3\end{aligned}$$

It should be noted that the coefficient of x is 3, which means that there are 3 ways in which *one* x and *two* 1's can be selected, one from each of the three factors $(1 + x)$. Similarly, the coefficient of x^2 is 3 since there are 3 ways in which *two* x's and *one* 1 can be selected, one from each of the three factors $(1 + x)$, and the constant term and the coefficient of x^3 are 1 since there is only 1 way in which either *three* 1's or *three* x's can be selected, one from each of the factors $(1 + x)$.

More generally, if n is a positive integer and we multiply out $(1 + x)^n$ term by term, the coefficient of x^r equals the number of ways in which r factors x and $n - r$ factors 1 can be selected, one from each of the n factors $(1 + x)$. The coefficient of x^r thus equals the number of ways in which a subset of r elements can be selected from a set of n, namely, $\binom{n}{r}$. This explains why we previously referred to $\binom{n}{r}$ as a binomial coefficient. Making use of the fact that by definition $\binom{n}{0} = 1$, we can now state the following theorem, which is a special form of the *binomial theorem for positive integral exponents*:

THEOREM 2.5:
For positive integers n,

$$(1 + x)^n = \sum_{r=0}^{n} \binom{n}{r} x^r$$

(If the reader is not familiar with the Σ notation, he will find a brief explanation in the Appendix at the end of this book.)

The calculation of binomial coefficients can often be simplified by making use of the following two theorems:

THEOREM 2.6:

$$\binom{n}{r} = \binom{n}{n - r}$$ *for positive integers n and r* $= 0, 1, \ldots,$ *or n.*

THEOREM 2.7:

$$\binom{n}{r} = \binom{n - 1}{r} + \binom{n - 1}{r - 1}$$ *for positive integers n and r* $= 0, 1, \ldots,$ *or* $n - 1$.

To prove the first, we have only to refer to Theorem 2.4 and write

$$\binom{n}{r} = \frac{n!}{(n - r)!r!} = \frac{n!}{r!(n - r)!} = \binom{n}{n - r}$$

This implies that if we calculate the binomial coefficients for $r = 0, 1, \ldots, (n+2)/2$ when n is even and for $r = 0, 1, \ldots, (n+1)/2$ when n is odd, the remaining binomial coefficients can be obtained by symmetry. For example, if we are given

$$\binom{4}{0} = 1, \quad \binom{4}{1} = 4, \quad \text{and} \quad \binom{4}{2} = 6,$$

we can immediately write

$$\binom{4}{3} = \binom{4}{1} = 4 \quad \text{and} \quad \binom{4}{4} = \binom{4}{0} = 1$$

and if we are given

$$\binom{5}{0} = 1, \quad \binom{5}{1} = 5, \quad \text{and} \quad \binom{5}{2} = 10,$$

we can immediately write

$$\binom{5}{3} = \binom{5}{2} = 10, \quad \binom{5}{4} = \binom{5}{1} = 5, \quad \text{and} \quad \binom{5}{5} = \binom{5}{0} = 1$$

In exactly this fashion Theorem 2.6 is used in connection with Table VII on page 371, which contains the values of binomial coefficients for $n = 1$ to $n = 20$. For example, to find $\binom{20}{14}$ we make use of the fact that $\binom{20}{14} = \binom{20}{6}$ and look up $\binom{20}{6}$.

Theorem 2.7 can be proved by expressing the binomial coefficients on both sides of the equation in terms of factorials. Leaving this to the reader in Exercise 18 on page 30, let us illustrate an alternate, and often useful, method of proof. Writing

$$(1 + x)^n = (1 + x)(1 + x)^{n-1}$$

or

$$(1 + x)^n = (1 + x)^{n-1} + x(1 + x)^{n-1}$$

we can prove Theorem 2.7 by equating the coefficients of x^r on both sides of this last equation. On the lefthand side the coefficient of x^r is $\binom{n}{r}$, and on the righthand side it is the *sum* of the coefficients of x^r in $(1 + x)^{n-1}$ and in $x(1 + x)^{n-1}$. Since the coefficient of x^r in $(1 + x)^{n-1}$ is $\binom{n-1}{r}$ and the coefficient of x^r in $x(1 + x)^{n-1}$ equals the coefficient of x^{r-1} in $(1 + x)^{n-1}$, namely, $\binom{n-1}{r-1}$, we obtain

$$\binom{n}{r} = \binom{n-1}{r} + \binom{n-1}{r-1}$$

and this completes the proof of Theorem 2.7.

Using Theorem 2.7, binomial coefficients are often calculated by constructing the following pattern, known as *Pascal's triangle*:

$$
\begin{array}{ccccccccccc}
 & & & & & 1 & & & & & \\
 & & & & 1 & & 1 & & & & \\
 & & & 1 & & 2 & & 1 & & & \\
 & & 1 & & 3 & & 3 & & 1 & & \\
 & 1 & & 4 & & 6 & & 4 & & 1 & \\
1 & & 5 & & 10 & & 10 & & 5 & & 1 \\
\cdot & & \cdot & & \cdot & & \cdot & & \cdot & & \cdot
\end{array}
$$

Each row begins and ends with a 1 since $\binom{n}{0} = \binom{n}{n} = 1$, and each other number is the sum of the two nearest numbers in the line immediately above. To complete the picture of the triangle we wrote a 1 on top, letting, thus, by definition $\binom{0}{0} = 1$.

Referring back to Theorem 2.5, it is possible to prove, in one step, the following theorem in the theory of sets:

THEOREM 2.8:

A set of n elements has 2^n subsets.

Useful

Substituting $x = 1$ in the binomial expansion of Theorem 2.5, we find that

$$\sum_{r=0}^{n} \binom{n}{r} = (1 + 1)^n = 2^n$$

The lefthand member of this equation gives the total number of subsets since $\binom{n}{0}$ is the number of subsets with 0 elements, $\binom{n}{1}$ is the number of subsets with 1 element, $\binom{n}{2}$ is the number of subsets with 2 elements, ..., and $\binom{n}{n}$ is the number of subsets with n elements.

To prove another theorem involving binomial coefficients, let us make the following definition:

$$\binom{n}{r} = 0 \qquad \text{for} \quad r > n.$$

This has less obvious combinatorial meaning, but it makes it possible to write certain formulas involving binomial coefficients in a general form. (It is also useful, at times, to make the definition that $\binom{n}{r} = 0$ when r is a negative integer.)

THEOREM 2.9:

$$\sum_{r=0}^{k} \binom{m}{r}\binom{n}{k-r} = \binom{m+n}{k}$$

Using the same method of proof as on page 25, let us prove this theorem by equating the coefficients of x^k on both sides of

$$(1+x)^{m+n} = (1+x)^m(1+x)^n$$

The coefficient of x^k in $(1+x)^{m+n}$ is $\binom{m+n}{k}$, and the coefficient of x^k in

$$(1+x)^m(1+x)^n = \left\{\binom{m}{0} + \binom{m}{1}x + \ldots + \binom{m}{m}x^m\right\}$$
$$\times \left\{\binom{n}{0} + \binom{n}{1}x + \ldots + \binom{n}{n}x^n\right\}$$

is the *sum* of the terms which we obtain by multiplying the constant term of the first factor by the coefficient of x^k in the second factor, the coefficient of x in the first factor by the coefficient of x^{k-1} in the second factor, the coefficient of x^2 in the first factor by the coefficient of x^{k-2} in the second factor, and so forth. The coefficient of x^k in $(1+x)^m(1+x)^n$ is thus

$$\binom{m}{0}\binom{n}{k} + \binom{m}{1}\binom{n}{k-1} + \binom{m}{2}\binom{n}{k-2} + \ldots + \binom{m}{k}\binom{n}{0}$$

and since this equals $\binom{m+n}{k}$, the coefficient of x^k in $(1+x)^{m+n}$, we have completed the proof of Theorem 2.9. This particular relationship among binomial coefficients will be of use later in Section 4.3.2.

It should be noted that in Theorem 2.9 it is not necessary that m and n are greater than k. For example, for $m = 2$, $n = 3$, and $k = 4$ we obtain

$$\binom{2}{0}\binom{3}{4} + \binom{2}{1}\binom{3}{3} + \binom{2}{2}\binom{3}{2} + \binom{2}{3}\binom{3}{1} + \binom{2}{4}\binom{3}{0} = \binom{5}{4}$$

and since $\binom{3}{4} = \binom{2}{3} = \binom{2}{4} = 0$ according to the definition on page 26, this reduces to

$$\binom{2}{1}\binom{3}{3} + \binom{2}{2}\binom{3}{2} = \binom{5}{4}$$

It can easily be verified that both sides of this equation are equal to 5.

Problem Set 2 PS. 7 {1, 2, 4, 5, 6, 7, 8, 11, 14, 16, 18, 20, 21, 22, 23, 26, 30}

EXERCISES

1. Given that 4 airlines provide service between Los Angeles and Phoenix, in how many distinct ways can a person select airlines for a trip from Los Angeles to Phoenix and back if

(a) he must travel both ways by the same airline

(b) he can but need not travel both ways by the same airline

(c) he cannot travel both ways by the same airline.

2. A building contractor offers 2-, 3-, and 4-bedroom houses, which may be had in 6 different exterior finishes and with or without garage. How many distinct choices can be made?

3. If license plates are to have 3 letters followed by 3 digits, the first of which cannot be 0, how many distinct plates can be made?

4. Construct a tree similar to the one of Figure 2.10 to determine the number of ways in which a coin can be flipped 5 times in succession so that throughout this series of flips there are never fewer heads than tails.

5. (*Matching*) Given four boxes labeled 1, 2, 3, 4 and four tags marked 1, 2, 3, 4, construct a tree or otherwise enumerate the number of ways in which one tag can be placed into each box so that no tag goes into a box having the same number as the tag. This is a simple example of the general problem of matching treated in detail in the books by Feller and Munroe listed in the Bibliography on page 60. Generalizing the problem to n boxes and n tags, it can be shown that the number of ways in which one tag can be placed into each box so that no tag goes into a box having the same number as the tag is

$$n!\left(\frac{1}{2!} - \frac{1}{3!} + \frac{1}{4!} - \cdots \pm \frac{1}{n!}\right)$$

Use this formula to verify the result obtained above for $n = 4$.

6. In how many ways can 8 persons be seated in a row?

7. In how many ways can 8 persons be seated around a circular table, taking into account only who sits to each person's left and right.

8. In how many ways can 8 persons be seated in a row of 12 seats?

9. The membership of a club consists of 12 boys and 8 girls. In how many ways can they elect a president, a vice-president, a secretary, and a treasurer if

   (a) the president and secretary must be boys and the vice-president and treasurer must be girls

   (b) two of the officers must be boys and two must be girls?

10. How many 11-man football teams can be chosen from a squad of 20, if one disregards the positions played by the members of the squad.

11. If the football squad of Exercise 10 contains 13 linemen and 7 backs, how many teams can be chosen containing 7 linemen and 4 backs?

12. How many distinct bridge hands of 13 cards can be dealt from an ordinary deck of 52 playing cards? Also find the number of bridge hands of 13 cards which contain all 4 aces.

13. A shipment of 50 transistors contains 40 that are perfect and 10 defectives. In how many ways can 5 of these transistors be selected so that 3 are perfect and 2 are defective?

14. A magician has a repertoire of 7 tricks of which he performs 2 on each show. In how many ways can he plan his program for three successive shows if

   (a) he does not want to perform the same trick on any two successive shows

   (b) he wants to use the same trick for the opening number of each show

   (c) he does not want to use any one trick on all three shows?

15. Construct a tree or otherwise enumerate the number of ways in which 5 (indistinguishable) apples can be distributed among 3 children, if there is no restriction as to the number of apples any one child can receive. What would be the answer if each child had to receive at least one apple?

16. (*Occupancy theory*) Exercise 15 deals with a simple problem of *occupancy theory* arising in physics, namely, the problem of determining the number of ways in which r indistinguishable particles can be distributed among n cells, with no restriction as to the number of particles permitted in any one cell. Show that the answer to this general question is $\binom{n+r-1}{r}$ and use this result to verify the answer obtained in Exercise 15. (*Hint*: considering the special case where $r = 5$ and $n = 3$ and using bars to separate the particles in the various cells, $p|pp|pp$, for example, is an arrangement where the first cell

contains 1 particle while the second and third contain 2. Considering all such arrangements of p's and bars, the result follows immediately.)

17. (*Occupancy theory*) Find (a) the number of ways in which r distinguishable particles can be distributed among n cells with no restriction as to the number of particles allowed in any one cell, and (b) the number of ways in which r indistinguishable particles can be distributed among n cells with at least 1 particle in each cell. [For part (b) assume that $r \geq n$.]

18. Prove Theorem 2.7 on page 24 by expressing all the binomial coefficients in terms of factorials.

19. Expressing both sides of the equation in terms of factorials, verify that

$$n\binom{n}{r-1} = r\binom{n}{r} + (r-1)\binom{n}{r-1}$$

20. Prove that

$$\sum_{i=1}^{r+1} \binom{n-i}{r-i+1} = \binom{n}{r}$$

(*Hint*: Use Theorem 2.7 repeatedly)

21. Prove that

$$\sum_{i=0}^{n} (-1)^i \binom{n}{i} = 0$$

22. Show that

(a) $\displaystyle\sum_{i=0}^{n} \binom{n}{i}^2 = \binom{2n}{n}$

(b) $\displaystyle\sum_{x=0}^{n} \binom{n}{x}(a-1)^x = a^n$

23. (*Stirling's formula*) When n is large, $n!$ can be approximated by means of Stirling's formula, namely,

$$n! \approx (n/e)^n \sqrt{2\pi n}$$

where e, the base of natural logarithms, is 2.71828 . . . . A derivation of Stirling's formula may be found in the books by Feller and Munroe in the Bibliography on page 60.

(a) Use Stirling's formula to obtain an approximation for 10!. Also show that compared with the exact value of 10!, namely, 3,628,800, the relative error is less than 1 per cent.

(b) Use Stirling's formula to obtain an approximation for the number of bridge hands of 13 cards that can be dealt with an ordinary deck of 52 playing cards. Compare your result with the answer obtained in Exercise 12 and find the relative error.

(c) Use Stirling's formula to show that

$$\frac{\binom{2n}{n}\sqrt{\pi n}}{2^{2n}} \approx 1$$

24. (*Binomial expansions with negative or non-integral exponents*) If n is not a positive integer or zero, the binomial expansion of $(1 + x)^n$ yields, for $-1 < x < 1$, the infinite series

$$1 + \binom{n}{1}x + \binom{n}{2}x^2 + \binom{n}{3}x^3 + \ldots + \binom{n}{r}x^r + \ldots$$

where

$$\binom{n}{r} = \frac{n(n-1)\cdot\ldots\cdot(n-r+1)}{r!} \quad \text{for} \quad r = 1, 2, 3, \ldots.$$

Using this *generalized definition* of the symbol $\binom{n}{r}$ which, incidentally, reduces to the definition on page 22 for positive integral values of n,

(a) evaluate $\binom{1/2}{3}$ and $\binom{-2}{5}$

(b) show that $\binom{-1}{r} = (-1)^r$

(c) show that $\binom{-n}{r} = (-1)^r\binom{n+r-1}{r}$ for $n > 0$

25. (*Multinomial coefficients*) As we pointed out on page 23, $\binom{n}{r}$ gives the number of ways in which a set of n elements can be partitioned into an ordered pair of subsets having r and $n - r$ elements, respectively. To consider a more general problem, let us now find the number of ways in which a set of n elements can be partitioned into an ordered set of k subsets having r_1, r_2, ..., and r_k elements, respectively. Of course, $\Sigma_{i=1}^{k} r_i = n$. Since the first subset can be selected from the entire set in $\binom{n}{r_1}$ ways, the second subset can subsequently be selected from the remaining $n - r_1$ elements in $\binom{n-r_1}{r_2}$ ways, the third subset can then be selected from the remaining $n - r_1 - r_2$ elements in $\binom{n-r_1-r_2}{r_3}$ ways, the desired number of partitions is

$$\binom{n}{r_1}\binom{n - r_1}{r_2}\binom{n - r_1 - r_2}{r_3} \cdots \binom{r_k}{r_k} = \frac{n!}{r_1!r_2!r_3! \cdot \ldots \cdot r_k!}$$

Symbolically, we write this number of partitions as

$$\binom{n}{r_1, r_2, r_3, \ldots, r_k}$$

and call it a *multinomial coefficient* as it is the coefficient of

$$x_1^{r_1}x_2^{r_2} \cdot \ldots \cdot x_k^{r_k}$$

in the expansion of $(x_1 + x_2 + \ldots + x_k)^n$. Using the above formula for multinomial coefficients find

(a) the number of ways in which 8 rolls of a die can yield 2 *ones*, 1 *three*, 2 *fours*, 3 *fives*, and 0 *twos* or *sixes*

(b) the number of ways in which two A's, three B's, four C's, and one F can be given to 10 students taking a course in statistics

(c) the number of ways in which 6 salesmen can be assigned to 3 hotel rooms each having 2 beds.

2.3 Probability

A *function* may be defined as a correspondence between the elements of two sets X and Y which coordinates a unique element of Y to each element of X and at least one element of X to each element of Y. The sets X and Y are referred to, respectively, as the *domain* and the *range* of the function.

Whenever possible, such correspondences are expressed in terms of mathematical equations such as $y = x^2$, $y = 1/x$, $y = \cos x$, where in each case x is an element of an appropriate domain X and y is an element of the corresponding range Y. However, this is not always possible or practicable; there are situations where we actually list the element of Y that is coordinated to each element of X. For instance, if the domain X consists of the integers from 1 through 31, representing the 31 days of January, and the range Y consists of the integers from 1 through 7, representing Monday,

Tuesday, ..., and Sunday, the correspondence, or pairing, for January 1961 is

Elements of X	*Elements of Y*
1	7
2	1
3	2
4	3
.	.
.	.
29	7
30	1
31	2

Although the reader may be familiar mostly with functions where the elements of the domain and range are numbers, there is no reason why they cannot be other kinds of mathematical objects. In what follows, we shall be interested, particularly, in the case where the elements of the domain are *sets* while the elements of the range are real numbers. If this is the case, we refer to the function as a *set function*. Moreover, if set A is an element of the domain of a set function, we shall use the customary functional notation of writing the corresponding element of the range as $f(A)$, $\phi(A)$, $N(A)$, $P(A)$, etc.

A simple example of a set function is the one which assigns to each subset A of a given sample space *the number of elements in* A, written $N(A)$. Thus, referring to the sample space for 3 flips of a coin (see Figure 2.1), we have

A	$N(A)$
$\{(0, 0, 0)\}$	1
$\{(1, 0, 0), (1, 1, 1)\}$	2
ϕ	0
$\{(1, 1, 0), (1, 0, 1), (0, 1, 1)\}$	3
$\{(1, 1, 1)\}$	1
. . . . . .	. .

To complete this list we would have to give the value of $N(A)$ for each of the $2^8 = 256$ subsets of S including $N(S) = 8$.

An alternate set function that can be defined on the sample space for 3 flips of a coin is the one which coordinates to each element of S *the number of heads*, $H(A)$. The resulting correspondence is

A	$H(A)$
$\{(0, 0, 0)\}$	0
$\{(1, 0, 0)\}$	1
$\{(0, 1, 0)\}$	1
$\{(0, 0, 1)\}$	1
$\{(1, 1, 0)\}$	2
$\{(1, 0, 1)\}$	2
$\{(0, 1, 1)\}$	2
$\{(1, 1, 1)\}$	3

It should be noted that the domain of the set function now consists of the individual elements of S, whereas in the preceding example it consisted of all subsets of S.

An interesting and important property of the set function which assigns to each subset the number of elements it contains is that it is *additive*. This is meant to imply that if subsets A and B are disjoint,

$$N(A \cup B) = N(A) + N(B).$$

2.3.1 *The postulates of probability*

Using the concept of set function, let us now define what we mean by the *probability of an event*. Referring to a discrete sample space S, we shall write $P(A)$ for a real number assigned to a subset A and call it the "probability of the event represented by A", provided the set function **P** is such that

POSTULATE 1:
$0 \leq P(A) \leq 1$ *for each subset* A *of* S

POSTULATE 2:
$P(S) = 1$

POSTULATE 3:
If $A_1, A_2, \ldots,$ *is a finite or infinite sequence of disjoint subsets of* S, *then*

$$P(A_1 \cup A_2 \cup \ldots) = P(A_1) + P(A_2) + \ldots$$

To talk about probabilities in the discrete case, we thus need a discrete sample space S and a set function, also called a *probability measure*, which assigns a real number to each subset of S and satisfies Postulates 1, 2, and 3. As will be shown in Theorem 2.10, a probability measure can be specified without having to give $P(A)$ for each subset A of the sample space S; it is sufficient to specify the probabilities of the sets which represent the individual outcomes, that is, the individual elements of S.

As was indicated in the Introduction, there is general agreement about the postulates of probability, but considerable disagreement and controversy about questions of interpretation and meaning. To demonstrate that the three postulates are consistent with the frequency interpretation, let us point out that the proportion of the time an event occurs cannot be negative or exceed 1 and that, each time, one outcome or another must occur. To justify Postulate 3 in the simplest case, if A_1 and A_2 represent mutually exclusive events, the proportion of the time that either one or the other occurs is the *sum* of the proportions of the time with which they occur. Thus, if the proportion of customers ordering tea at a certain restaurant is 0.25, the proportion ordering coffee is 0.60, then the proportion ordering either tea or coffee is $0.25 + 0.60 = 0.85$.

To give some examples of probability functions, let us consider an experiment which has 4 possible and mutually exclusive outcomes represented by A, B, C, and D. The following are 3 arbitrary, though permissible, ways in which probabilities can be assigned:

$$(1)\quad P(A) = \tfrac{4}{10},\quad P(B) = \tfrac{3}{10},\quad P(C) = \tfrac{2}{10},\quad P(D) = \tfrac{1}{10}$$

$$(2)\quad P(A) = \tfrac{1}{4},\quad P(B) = \tfrac{1}{4},\quad P(C) = \tfrac{1}{4},\quad P(D) = \tfrac{1}{4}$$

$$(3)\quad P(A) = 0.13,\ P(B) = 0.65,\ P(C) = 0.05,\ P(D) = 0.17$$

On the other hand,

$$(4)\quad P(A) = 0.02,\ P(B) = 1.05,\ P(C) = 0.08,\ P(D) = -0.15$$

$$(5)\quad P(A) = 0.35,\ P(B) = 0.60,\ P(C) = 0.15,\ P(D) = 0.20$$

are *not* permissible: in the first case $P(B) = 1.05$ and $P(D) = -0.15$, which violates Postulate 1, and in the second case the sum of the probabilities is 1.30, which violates Postulate 2. *These examples serve to emphasize the point that the three postulates do not tell us how to assign probabilities, they merely restrict the ways in which it can be done. In practice, probability measures are assigned on the basis of assumptions, on the basis of an analysis of the experimental conditions, and on the basis of estimates obtained from past experience.*

2.3.2 *Some elementary theorems of probability*

Since a sample space of n elements has 2^n subsets (over a million for $n = 20$), the problem of specifying a probability measure is greatly simplified by making use of the following theorem:

THEOREM 2.10:

If A is a subset of a discrete sample space S, then $P(A)$ equals the sum of the probabilities of the sets which represent the individual outcomes contained in A. In particular, $P(\phi) = 0$.

To prove this theorem, let $E_1, E_2, E_3, \ldots$, be a finite or infinite sequence of subsets of S, representing the individual outcomes contained in A. Thus

$$A = E_1 \cup E_2 \cup E_3 \cup \ldots$$

and since the E's are by definition disjoint (they represent mutually exclusive outcomes), Postulate 3 yields

$$P(A) = P(E_1) + P(E_2) + P(E_3) + \ldots$$

To show that $P(\phi) = 0$, let us make use of the fact that $S \cup \phi = S$, that S and ϕ are disjoint, and write

$$P(S \cup \phi) = P(S)$$

$$P(S) + P(\phi) = P(S)$$

$$P(\phi) = 0$$

This proves that in any probability measure the probability assigned to ϕ must be 0. On the other hand, if $P(A) = 0$ for some set A, it does not necessarily follow that $A = \phi$. In practice, we often assign a probability of 0 to an event which in colloquial terms would not happen in ten million years. For instance, if a monkey is left alone to play with a typewriter, it is not impossible that he might type Plato's *Republic* word for word without a mistake, but we would certainly be justified in assigning a probability of 0 to this event. An interesting discussion of what kinds of events may be assigned 0 probabilities from the human perspective, terrestial perspective, cosmic perspective, and super-cosmic perspective is given in the book by Borel referred to in the Bibliography on page 60. As we shall see later, the fact that $P(A) = 0$ does not imply $A = \phi$ is of relevance, particularly, in the continuous case.

To illustrate the use of Theorem 2.10, let us refer to the sample space of Figure 1.5, the one which represents the outcomes for a roll of a pair of dice. If each of the 36 possible outcomes is assigned a probability of $\frac{1}{36}$, the probability of rolling a 7 is the *sum* of the probabilities of the six outcomes inside the dotted line, namely, $\frac{6}{36}$.

As was pointed out on page 36, the use of Theorem 2.10 greatly simplifies the task of specifying a probability measure. As a consequence of this theorem, it is sufficient to specify the probabilities of the individual outcomes and if S is *finite* the probabilities can be assigned by actually listing the outcomes and the corresponding probabilities. If S is discrete but *infinite*, it will have to be done by means of some mathematical rule. For instance, letting E_1, E_2, E_3, ..., represent the infinitely many individual outcomes of an experiment, their probabilities might be specified by the rule:

$$P(E_i) = (1/2)^i \quad \text{for} \quad i = 1, 2, 3, \ldots$$

There are many important theorems which can be proved on the basis of the postulates of probability. A very elementary one is

THEOREM 2.11:

Proof

$$P(A') = 1 - P(A)$$

Using the fact that $A \cup A' = S$, see page 13, and that A and A' are disjoint, we have

$$P(A \cup A') = P(S)$$

$$P(A) + P(A') = 1$$

$$P(A') = 1 - P(A)$$

Thus, if the probability that it will rain is 0.30, the probability that it will not rain is $1 - 0.30 = 0.70$; if the probability that a housewife who enters a supermarket will buy some kind of soap is 0.83, the probability that she will not buy any soap is $1 - 0.83 = 0.17$.

If A and B represent events which are mutually exclusive, the formula $P(A \cup B) = P(A) + P(B)$, often called the *Special Rule of Addition*, is merely a special case of Postulate 3. The fact that this formula does not necessarily apply when A and B represent events which are *not* mutually exclusive is apparent from the following example: if A represents the event that a person who enters a given store will buy a shirt, B represents the event that he will buy a tie, $P(A) = 0.80$, and $P(B) = 0.60$, then the probability that he will buy a shirt, a tie, or both, is *not* $0.80 + 0.60 = 1.40$. Arriving at this figure we made the mistake of adding in *twice* the probability that the person will buy a shirt as well as a tie, and to compensate for this we should have used the following theorem, often called the *General Rule of Addition*:

THEOREM 2.12:
$$P(A \cup B) = P(A) + P(B) - P(A \cap B)$$

To prove this theorem, let us write

$$A \cup B = (A \cap B') \cup (A \cap B) \cup (A' \cap B)$$

which was proved in part (d) of Exercise 8 on page 17, and which can be verified with reference to the Venn diagram of Figure 2.11. Since, furthermore, $A \cap B'$, $A \cap B$, and $A' \cap B$ are disjoint we have

$$P(A \cup B) = P(A \cap B') + P(A \cap B) + P(A' \cap B)$$

and, adding and subtracting $P(A \cap B)$, this becomes

$$P(A \cup B) = [P(A \cap B') + P(A \cap B)] + [P(A \cap B) + P(A' \cap B)] - P(A \cap B)$$

As was proved in part (c) of Exercise 8 on page 17 and as can also be seen from Figure 2.11,

$$A = (A \cap B') \cup (A \cap B)$$

$$B = (A \cap B) \cup (A' \cap B)$$

and it follows that $P(A \cup B) = P(A) + P(B) - P(A \cap B)$.

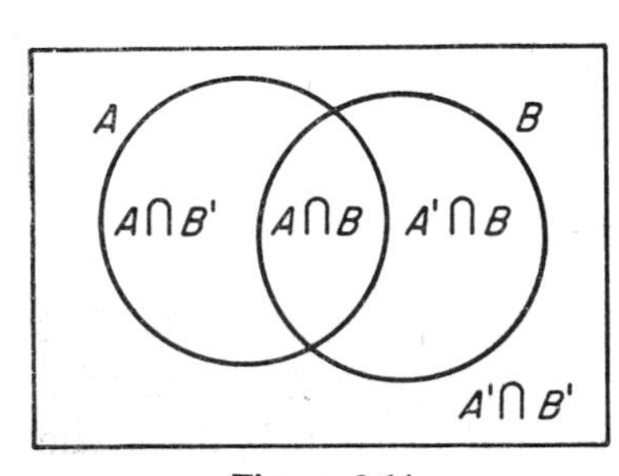

Figure 2.11

If the probability that a person buys a shirt as well as a tie is 0.50

in the illustration used above, that is, $P(A \cap B) = 0.50$, we now find that the probability that a person entering the store will buy a shirt, a tie, or both is $0.80 + 0.60 - 0.50 = 0.90$. To consider another example, suppose that A represents the event that a student passes a final examination in mathematics, B represents the event that he passes a final examination in physics, $P(A) = 0.80$, $P(B) = 0.75$, and $P(A \cap B) = 0.60$. Then, the probability that he will pass at least one of these final examinations is

$$P(A \cup B) = 0.80 + 0.75 - 0.60 = 0.95.$$

Generalizations of Theorem 2.12 are given in Exercises 7 and 9 on page 41. It should be noted, incidentally, that the General Rule of Addition reduces to the Special Rule given on page 38 when A and B represent mutually exclusive events. In that case $A \cap B = \phi$ and $P(A \cap B) = 0$.*

If $B_1, B_2, B_3, \ldots$ is a sequence of disjoint subsets of S and among them they contain all the elements of S, that is, $B_1 \cup B_2 \cup B_3 \cup \ldots = S$, these subsets are referred to as a *partition* of S. For instance, the sets which represent the individual outcomes of an experiment constitute a partition of the sample space and so do any subset A and its complement A'. Another example of a partition of a sample space are the subsets representing the events of getting 0, 1, 2, and 3 heads, respectively, in 3 flips of a coin.

Using the notion of a partition of a sample space, let us now prove the following theorem, which is of special importance in problems relating to games of chance:

THEOREM 2.13:

If $B_1, B_2, \ldots$, and B_n constitute a partition of a sample space and $P(B_1) = P(B_2) = \ldots = P(B_n)$, then if A is the union of s of these sets $P(A) = s/n$.

Making use of the fact that the B's constitute a partition of S, we have

$$P(B_1 \cup B_2 \cup \ldots \cup B_n) = P(S) = 1$$

and

$$P(B_1) + P(B_2) + \ldots + P(B_n) = 1$$

* Some authors prefer to define "mutually exclusive" by stating that A and B represent mutually exclusive events if and only if $P(A \cap B) = 0$. With this alternate definition the General Rule of Addition reduces to the Special Rule of Addition *if and only if* A and B represent mutually exclusive events. The "only if" part of this does not hold with the definition of "mutually exclusive" which we gave on page 12.

Since the B's have, furthermore, equal probabilities, it follows that

$$P(B_i) = \frac{1}{n} \quad \text{for } i = 1, 2, 3, \ldots, n,$$

and Postulate 3 yields

$$P(A) = \underbrace{\frac{1}{n} + \ldots + \frac{1}{n}}_{s \text{ terms}} = \frac{s}{n}$$

Theorem 2.13 is often given as a "definition" of probability in elementary texts, claiming that *if an experiment has n equally likely outcomes among which s are labeled "success," the probability of a "success" is s/n*. We advisedly wrote the word "definition" in quotes in view of the obvious circularity of defining probability in terms of equally likely, that is, equiprobable events.

As we have mentioned earlier, Theorem 2.13 has many useful applications in problems relating to games of chance, where it is assumed, for example, that each card has an equal chance of being drawn, heads has the same probability as tails, 1, 2, 3, 4, 5, and 6 are equiprobable outcomes for a symmetrical die, and so forth. Thus, the probability of drawing a king from an ordinary deck of playing cards is $\frac{4}{52}$ since there are 4 kings and $s = 4$ and $n = 52$; the probability of rolling 2 or 4 with a symmetrical die is $2/6$ since $s = 2$ and $n = 6$.

EXERCISES

1. An experiment has five possible (mutually exclusive) outcomes represented by A, B, C, D, and E. State for each of the following why it is *not* a permissible probability measure for the sample space of this experiment

   (a) $P(A) = 0.13$, $P(B) = 0.27$, $P(C) = 0.19$, $P(D) = 0.16$, $P(E) = 0.18$

   (b) $P(A) = 0.10$, $P(B) = 0.40$, $P(C) = 0.30$, $P(C \cup D) = 0.20$, $P(E) = 0.18$

   (c) $P(A) = 0.2$, $P(B) = 0.2$, $P(C) = 0.1$, $P(D) = 0.4$, $P(D \cap E) = 0.1$

   (d) $P(A) = 0.37$, $P(B) = 0.27$, $P(C) = 0.24$, $P(D) = 0.25$, $P(E) = -0.13$

   (e) $P(A) = 0.05$, $P(B) = 0.01$, $P(C) = 1.07$, $P(D) = 0.08$, $P(E) = 0.12$.

2. If A and B represent mutually exclusive events, $P(A) = 0.25$, and $P(B) = 0.40$, find each of the following probabilities:

(a) $P(A')$ (c) $P(A \cup B)$ (e) $P(A' \cap B')$
(b) $P(B')$ (d) $P(A \cap B)$

3. Given $P(A) = 0.50$, $P(B) = 0.30$, and $P(A \cap B) = 0.10$, find

(a) $P(A \cup B)$ (c) $P(A' \cap B)$
(b) $P(A \cap B')$ (d) $P(A' \cup B')$

4. If A represents the event that a person selected from a certain group is healthy and B represents the event that he is wealthy, state in words what probabilities are given by each of the following:

(a) $1 - P(A)$ (c) $P(A \cap B)$
(b) $P(A \cup B)$ (d) $P(A' \cap B)$

5. An experiment has three possible mutually exclusive outcomes represented by A, B, and C. If $P(A) = 0.60$, $P(B) = 0.30$, and $P(C) = 0.10$, find the probabilities of the other *five* subsets of the sample space of this experiment.

6. Show that (a) $P(A) \geq P(A \cap B)$ and (b) $P(A) \leq P(A \cup B)$. (*Hint*: refer to parts (c) and (d) of Exercise 8 on page 17.)

7. Using a Venn diagram, verify that

$$P(A \cup B \cup C) = P(A) + P(B) + P(C) - P(A \cap B) - P(A \cap C) - P(B \cap C) + P(A \cap B \cap C)$$

8. If a person takes an afternoon's ride in the desert near Phoenix, Arizona, the probability that he will see a roadrunner is 0.12, the probability that he will see a gambel quail is 0.10, the probability that he will see a cactus wren is 0.14, the probability that he will see a roadrunner and a gambel quail is 0.03, the probability that he will see a roadrunner and a cactus wren is 0.05, the probability that he will see a gambel quail and a cactus wren is 0.04, and the probability that he will see all three is 0.01. What is the probability that he will see at least one of these birds?

9. Writing $P(A \cup B \cup C \cup D)$ as $P[(A \cup B) \cup (C \cup D)]$, and repeatedly applying Theorem 2.12, show that

$$\begin{aligned} P(A \cup B \cup C \cup D) &= P(A) + P(B) + P(C) + P(D) - P(A \cap B) \\ &\quad - P(A \cap C) - P(A \cap D) - P(B \cap C) - P(B \cap D) \\ &\quad - P(C \cap D) + P(A \cap B \cap C) + P(A \cap B \cap D) \\ &\quad + P(A \cap C \cap D) + P(B \cap C \cap D) - P(A \cap B \cap C \cap D) \end{aligned}$$

The formulas of this exercise and Exercise 7 suggest a possible form for a general formula for the probability of the union of n sets. What is it?

10. (*The set function* **N** *which assigns to each set the number of elements that it contains*) It can easily be verified that Theorem 2.12 as well as the formulas of Exercises 7 and 9 hold if we substitute $N(A)$ for $P(A)$, with $N(A)$ as defined on page 33. Using this analogy, solve each of the following problems:

(a) A market research organization claims that among 100 housewives interviewed 62 regularly buy Product X, 53 regularly buy Product Y, 18 regularly buy both of these products, and 13 do not buy these products at all. Should the results of this survey be questioned?

(b) In a group of 250 college students 77 are enrolled in a course in Philosophy, 109 are enrolled in a course in Literature, 74 are enrolled in a course in French, 28 are enrolled in Philosophy as well as Literature, 22 are enrolled in Philosophy as well as French, 30 are enrolled in Literature as well as French, and 12 are enrolled in all three subjects. How many of the 250 students are not taking any of these subjects?

11. Assuming that each of the 52 cards of an ordinary deck of playing cards has a probability of $\frac{1}{52}$ of being drawn, what is the probability of drawing

(a) a red queen
(b) a black card
(c) an 8, 9, or 10
(d) a red jack or a black king
(e) a card which is either a spade or a red 10.

12. If the numbers from 1 through 100 are written on slips of paper which are mixed in a goldfish bowl and each slip of paper has an equal chance of being drawn, what is the probability of drawing a number that is divisible by 13?

13. What is the probability of rolling 1, 2, 3, or 4 with a balanced die? Referring to the sample space of Figure 1.5, also find the probability of rolling 7 or 11 with a pair of dice.

14. An urn contains 90 black marbles and 10 white marbles. If each marble has an equal chance of being drawn, what is the probability of drawing a black marble. Also, if 50 of the black marbles have imperfections while 3 of the white ones have imperfections, what is the probability of drawing a marble without imperfections and what is the probability of drawing a marble that is black, imperfect, or both.

15. If the 8 possible outcomes for three flips of a coin have equal probabilities of $\frac{1}{8}$, what is the probability of getting 1 head and 2 tails (not necessarily in that order). See Figure 2.1 on page 8.

2.4 Conditional Probability

As we saw in the previous section, it is meaningful to talk about the probability of an event *only* if we specify a sample space in which the event is represented by a subset and if we, furthermore, specify an appropriate probability measure. To ask for the probability that a college professor has a salary of $9000 or more is *meaningless* unless we specify whether we are referring to the entire United States, a given state, a particular college or university, etc., and unless we specify how the selection is to be made.

Since there are many problems in which we are interested in probabilities relative to *different* sample spaces, let us introduce the symbol $P(A \mid S)$ and call it the "*conditional* probability of A relative to S". *Every probability is thus a conditional probability although, whenever possible, we use the simplified notation $P(A)$ with the tacit understanding that we are referring to some specific sample space S.*

To illustrate this idea, let us consider the following problem: suppose that there are 100 applicants for a teaching position, each of which has a probability of 0.01 of being selected; some of these applicants hold Ph.D. degrees and some do not, some are married and some are single, some are male and some are female, the exact breakdown being

	married	*single*
male	3	12
female	10	5

without Ph.D.

	married	*single*
male	40	10
female	10	10

with Ph.D.

If we let F, M, and D represent the events that the candidate who is elected is female, married, and the holder of a Ph.D. degree, Theorem

2.13 yields

$$P(F) = \frac{10 + 5 + 10 + 10}{100} = 0.35$$

$$P(M) = \frac{3 + 10 + 40 + 10}{100} = 0.63$$

$$P(D) = \frac{40 + 10 + 10 + 10}{100} = 0.70$$

and $P(F') = 1 - 0.35 = 0.65$, $P(M') = 1 - 0.63 = 0.37$, and $P(D') = 1 - 0.70 = 0.30$. It must be understood, of course, that these probabilities are relative to the sample space for all 100 candidates; we could have indicated this by writing the probabilities as $P(F \mid S)$, $P(M \mid S)$, and so forth.

Suppose now that we want to know the probability that the person selected is married *given that he (or she) must have a Ph.D. degree* and the probability that the person selected is male *given that he (or she) is married.* In the first case we are interested in the *reduced* sample space of applicants with Ph.D. degrees, for which the breakdown is

	married	*single*
male	40	10
female	10	10

Assuming that each of these 70 candidates has a probability of $\frac{1}{70}$ of being selected, we find that

$$P(M \mid D) = \frac{40 + 10}{70} = \frac{5}{7}$$

which differs from the previously obtained result $P(M) = 0.63$. In the second case we are interested in the *reduced* sample space of married applicants, for which the breakdown is

	without Ph.D.	*with Ph.D.*
male	3	40
female	10	10

Assuming that each of these 63 applicants has a probability of $\frac{1}{63}$ of being selected, we get

$$P(F' \mid M) = \frac{3 + 40}{63} = \frac{43}{63}$$

which differs from the previously obtained result $P(F') = 0.65$. Using the two tables above, the reader can readily verify that also $P(F \mid D) = \frac{2}{7}$, $P(F' \mid D) = \frac{5}{7}$, $P(M' \mid D) = \frac{2}{7}$, $P(F \mid M) = \frac{20}{63}$, $P(D' \mid M) = \frac{13}{63}$, and $P(D \mid M) = \frac{50}{63}$.

This illustration shows that events can have different probabilities when considered relative to different sample spaces and that the probabilities assigned to individual outcomes may have to be modified when the sample space is changed. For the entire sample space each candidate's selection was assigned a probability of $\frac{1}{100}$, for the sample space for candidates with Ph.D. degrees each candidate's selection was assigned a probability of $\frac{1}{70}$, and for the sample space for married candidates each candidate's selection was assigned a probability of $\frac{1}{63}$.

Assuming equal probabilities for the individual outcomes within the reduced sample spaces, the two conditional probabilities asked for on page 44 were readily obtained. As a matter of fact, they could have been written

$$P(M \mid D) = \frac{N(M \cap D)}{N(D)} \qquad \text{and} \qquad P(F' \mid M) = \frac{N(F' \cap M)}{N(M)}$$

where **N** is the set function which coordinates to each set the number of elements which it contains. $P(M \mid D)$ is thus the *ratio* of the number (or proportion) of the elements of the entire sample space that are in $M \cap D$ to the number (or proportion) of the elements of the entire sample space that are in D. Using this argument as an intuitive justification, let us now make the following definition: *if A and B are subsets of a discrete sample space and $P(B) \neq 0$, the conditional probability of A relative to B, written $P(A \mid B)$, is*

$$P(A \mid B) = \frac{P(A \cap B)}{P(B)} \tag{2.4.1}$$

This definition is general inasmuch as it does not depend on assumptions about equal probabilities as it did in our example. *It amounts to the fact that the original probability of each element of the reduced sample space is multiplied by the constant* $1/P(B)$, *so that the sum of the conditional probabilities* $P(A \mid B)$, *added over the reduced sample space* B, *is equal to* 1.

To illustrate this definition of conditional probability, suppose that for a certain football game the probability that the home team will be ahead at half-time is 0.60 and the probability that the home team will be ahead at half-time as well as at the final gun is 0.45. What we would like to know is the probability that the home team will win this game *given that it is ahead at the half*. Letting W represent the home team's winning the game and H its being ahead at the half, we have $P(H) = 0.60$, $P(W \cap H) = 0.45$, and hence

$$P(W \mid H) = \frac{0.45}{0.60} = 0.75$$

Note that we were able to find this probability without being given the probability measure for the entire sample space, whose four possible outcomes are represented by the sets $W \cap H$, $W \cap H'$, $W' \cap H$, $W' \cap H'$. The given information is not sufficient, however, to determine the probability $P(W \mid H')$, namely the probability that the home team wins the game given that it is not ahead at the half.

Multiplying $P(A \mid B)$ by $P(B)$, we find that the first part of the theorem which follows, often called the *General Rule of Multiplication,* is an immediate consequence of our definition of conditional probabilities:

THEOREM 2.14:*

$$P(A \cap B) = P(B) \cdot P(A \mid B)$$
$$P(A \cap B) = P(A) \cdot P(B \mid A)$$

The second part of the theorem is proved by interchanging A and B in (2.4.1) and multiplying $P(B \mid A)$ by $P(A)$. In words, this theorem states that the probability that the events represented by A and B *both* occur is the product of the probability that one of them will occur and the probability that the other will occur given that the first has occurred, occurs, or will occur. For instance, the probability of drawing two aces in succession from an ordinary deck of 52

* Note that by definition $P(A \mid B)$ assumes that $P(B) \neq 0$; hence, the two parts of the theorem hold only if $P(B) \neq 0$ and $P(A) \neq 0$, respectively.

playing cards, the first card not being replaced before the second is drawn, is

$$\frac{4}{52} \cdot \frac{3}{51} = \frac{1}{221},$$

where $\frac{4}{52}$ is the probability that the first card drawn is an ace and $\frac{3}{51}$ is the probability that the second card drawn is an ace given that the first card drawn is an ace. In this example there is a definite *temporal order* between the events of getting aces in the two successive draws; *however, when writing* $P(A \mid B)$ *or* $P(B \mid A)$, *this does not necessarily imply any temporal ordering between the events represented by* A *and* B. For instance, in the example above we *could* ask for the probability that the first card drawn is an ace given that the second card drawn is an ace: the answer is $\frac{3}{51}$.

To give another illustration of Theorem 2.14, let us refer again to the example on page 43. Having found that $P(D) = \frac{7}{10}$ and $P(M \mid D) = \frac{5}{7}$, it follows immediately that $P(M \cap D) = P(D) \cdot P(M \mid D) = \frac{1}{2}$, namely, that the probability that the candidate who is selected holds the Ph.D. degree and is married is $\frac{1}{2}$. This result could also have been obtained directly with the use of Theorem 2.13, noting that 50 of the candidates are married and hold Ph.D. degrees.

Informally speaking, two events are considered to be *independent* if the probability of the occurrence of either is not affected by the occurrence or nonoccurrence of the other. We thus assume that getting heads in the second flip of a coin is independent of what happened in the first, but that getting an ace in the second draw from a deck of cards is not independent of what card was drawn first, assuming that the first card drawn was not replaced. Symbolically, the independence of A and B implies, among other things, that $P(A) = P(A \mid B)$, and substituting $P(A)$ for $P(A \mid B)$ into the first equation of Theorem 2.14 yields $P(A \cap B) = P(A) \cdot P(B)$. Using the latter equation as a definition for reasons to be explained below, let us state formally that

A and B are independent if and only if $P(A \cap B) = P(A) \cdot P(B)$.

(Note that the term "independent" is used with reference to events as well as the corresponding sets.) Applying this definition, if two successive rolls of a balanced die are independent, the probability of getting two 6's is $\frac{1}{6}\cdot\frac{1}{6} = \frac{1}{36}$. This result could also have been obtained from Figure 1.5, if each of the 36 elements of the sample space is assigned a probability of $\frac{1}{36}$.

The following theorem is an immediate consequence of our definition of independence:

THEOREM 2.15:
If A and B are independent and $P(B) \neq 0$, then $P(A) = P(A \mid B)$.

To prove this theorem we have only to refer to the definition of independence and Theorem 2.14, getting

$$P(A \cap B) = P(B)\cdot P(A \mid B) = P(A)\cdot P(B)$$

Dividing by $P(B)$, which by assumption cannot equal 0, we get $P(A) = P(A \mid B)$.

We used the above definition of independence primarily because of its *symmetry*: had we used $P(A) = P(A \mid B)$ to define what is meant by A being independent of B, it would not have been immediately apparent that $P(B) = P(B \mid A)$, namely, that B is necessarily also independent of A. The following is an even stronger result:

THEOREM 2.16:
If A and B are independent, then (1) A and B' are independent, (2) A' and B are independent, and (3) A' and B' are independent.

The following is a proof of part (1) of this theorem; the reader will be asked to prove the other two parts in Exercise 8 on page 52: If $P(A) = 0$, then $P(A \cap B') = 0$ since $A \cap B'$ is a subset of A, and $P(A \cap B') = P(A)\cdot P(B')$; if $P(A) \neq 0$, we can write

$$\begin{aligned} P(A \cap B') &= P(A)\cdot P(B' \mid A) \\ &= P(A)[1 - P(B \mid A)] \\ &= P(A)[1 - P(B)] \\ &= P(A)\cdot P(B') \end{aligned}$$

using in succession Theorems 2.14, 2.11, 2.15, and again 2.11.

To illustrate the concept of independence as well as Theorems 2.15 and 2.16, suppose that the probability that a person examined for military service in a certain city has bad eyes and flat feet is 0.05, the probability that he has bad eyes but not flat feet is 0.15, the probability that he has good eyes and flat feet is 0.20, and the probability that he has good eyes and not flat feet is 0.60. Letting E and F, respectively, represent the events that one of these persons has bad eyes and flat feet, let us examine first whether E and F are independent. Since $P(E) = 0.05 + 0.15 = 0.20$, $P(F) = 0.05 + 0.20 = 0.25$, and $P(E \cap F) = 0.05$, we find that

$$P(E) \cdot P(F) = (0.20)(0.25) = 0.05 = P(E \cap F)$$

and, hence, that E and F are independent. Furthermore, $P(E) = P(E \mid F) = P(E \mid F')$ since

$$P(E) = 0.20$$

$$P(E \mid F) = \frac{P(E \cap F)}{P(F)} = \frac{0.05}{0.25} = 0.20$$

$$P(E \mid F') = \frac{P(E \cap F')}{P(F')} = \frac{0.15}{0.75} = 0.20$$

It will be left to the reader to verify in Exercise 7 on page 52 that also $P(F) = P(F \mid E) = P(F \mid E') = 0.25$.

In order to extend the concept of independence to more than two events and the corresponding sets, let us now make the following definition:

> *$A_1, A_2, \ldots,$ and A_r are independent if and only if the probability of the intersection of any $2, 3, \ldots,$ or r of these sets equals the product of their respective probabilities.*

Three sets A, B, and C are, thus, independent if and only if $P(A \cap B) = P(A) \cdot P(B)$, $P(A \cap C) = P(A) \cdot P(C)$, $P(B \cap C) = P(B) \cdot P(C)$, and $P(A \cap B \cap C) = P(A) \cdot P(B) \cdot P(C)$.

It is of interest to note that if three or more events are *pairwise independent,* they are not necessarily independent. This is illustrated by Figure 2.12 representing the sample space of an experiment which has 100 equally likely outcomes; the numbers indicate the number of distinct outcomes contained in the respective subsets of the sample space. It can thus be seen that $P(A) = P(B) = P(C) = \frac{1}{2}$, $P(A \cap B) = P(A \cap C) = P(B \cap C) = \frac{1}{4}$, and that the events represented by A, B, and C are pairwise independent, namely, $P(A \cap B) = P(A) \cdot P(B)$, $P(A \cap C) = P(A) \cdot P(C)$, and

$P(B \cap C) = P(B) \cdot P(C)$. However, $P(A \cap B \cap C) = \frac{7}{100}$, which does *not* equal the product of $P(A)$, $P(B)$, and $P(C)$, and A, B, and C are, therefore, not independent.

It is also of interest to note that if $P(A \cap B \cap C) = P(A) \cdot P(B) \cdot P(C)$, this does not necessary imply that A, B, and C are

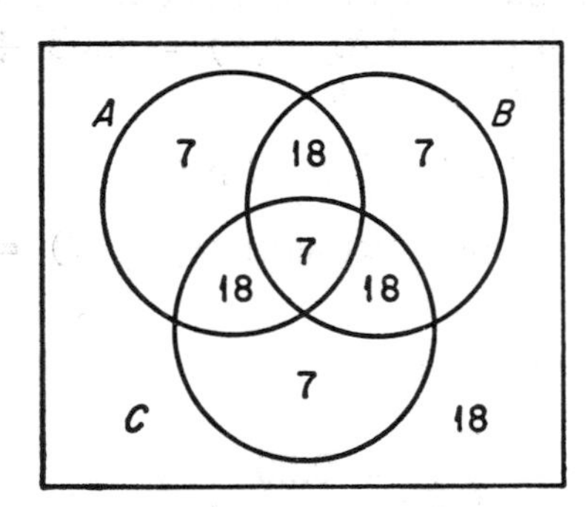

Figure 2.12

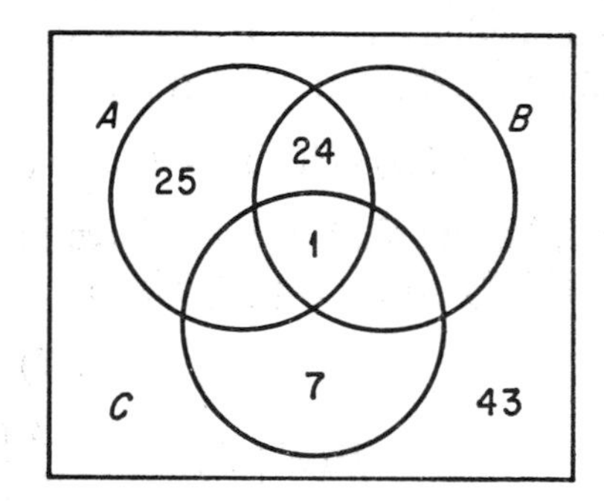

Figure 2.13

independent. This is illustrated by Figure 2.13, representing the sample space of an experiment which has 100 equally likely outcomes; as in Figure 2.12, the numbers indicate the number of distinct outcomes contained in the respective subsets of the sample space. It can thus be seen that $P(A) = \frac{50}{100} = \frac{1}{2}$, $P(B) = \frac{25}{100} = \frac{1}{4}$, $P(C) = \frac{8}{100}$, $P(A \cap B \cap C) = \frac{1}{100}$, and that

$$P(A) \cdot P(B) \cdot P(C) = \frac{1}{2} \cdot \frac{1}{4} \cdot \frac{8}{100} = \frac{1}{100} = P(A \cap B \cap C)$$

However, $P(A \cap B) = \frac{25}{100} = \frac{1}{4}$, $P(A \cap C) = \frac{1}{100}$, $P(B \cap C) = \frac{1}{100}$, and $P(A \cap B) \neq P(A) \cdot P(B)$, $P(A \cap C) \neq P(A) \cdot P(C)$, and $P(B \cap C) \neq P(B) \cdot P(C)$.

Given three or more events, it is possible to derive formulas analogous to that of Theorem 2.14. For instance,

$$\begin{aligned} P(A \cap B \cap C) &= P(A \cap B) \cdot P(C \mid A \cap B) \\ &= P(A) \cdot P(B \mid A) \cdot P(C \mid A \cap B) \end{aligned} \tag{2.4.2}$$

and

$$\begin{aligned} P(A \cap B \cap C \cap D) &= P(A \cap B \cap C) \cdot P(D \mid A \cap B \cap C) \\ &= P(A) \cdot P(B \mid A) \cdot P(C \mid A \cap B) \\ &\quad \cdot P(D \mid A \cap B \cap C) \end{aligned} \tag{2.4.3}$$

To illustrate the first of these formulas, suppose we want to find the probability of getting three kings in succession, drawing three cards without replacement from an ordinary deck of 52 playing cards. The probability of getting a king in the first draw is $\frac{4}{52}$, the probability of getting a king in the second draw given that the first draw yielded a king is $\frac{3}{51}$, and the probability of getting a king in the third draw given that the first two draws both yielded kings is $\frac{2}{50}$. Multiplying these three quantities, we find that the probability of getting three kings in succession is

$$\frac{4}{52}\cdot\frac{3}{51}\cdot\frac{2}{50} = \frac{1}{5525}.$$

EXERCISES

1. One of the members of a club of male business executives is to be elected president of the club. If A represents the event that the person elected is a college graduate, B represents the event that the person elected is wealthy, and C the event that he has ulcers, state in words what probability is expressed by each of the following:

(a) $P(C \mid B)$ (c) $P(B \mid A' \cap C')$

(b) $P(A \cap B \mid C)$ (d) $P(B' \cap C \mid A)$

2. Referring to the example on page 43, find

(a) $P(M \mid F)$ (c) $P(D' \mid F')$

(b) $P(M \mid D')$ (d) $P(M \mid F \cap D)$

3. If A and B represent mutually exclusive events, $P(A) = 0.28$, and $P(B) = 0.46$, find

(a) $P(A \cup B)$ (c) $P(B \mid A)$

(b) $P(A \cap B)$ (d) $P(A' \cap B')$

4. If the probability that a married man will vote in a given election is 0.50, the probability that a married woman will vote in the election is 0.60, and the probability that a woman will vote in the election given that her husband votes is 0.90, find

(a) the probability that a husband and wife will both vote in the election

(b) the probability that a man will vote in the election given that his wife will vote

(c) the probability that at least one of a married couple will vote.

5. If A and B are independent, $P(A) = 0.20$, and $P(B) = 0.45$, find

   (a) $P(A \mid B)$ (c) $P(A \cup B)$

   (b) $P(A \cap B)$ (d) $P(A' \cap B')$

6. If possible, give one example each from real life (perhaps, a game of chance) of two events which are

   (a) mutually exclusive and independent

   (b) mutually exclusive but not independent

   (c) not mutually exclusive but independent

   (d) not mutually exclusive and not independent

7. Verify for the example on page 49 that

$$P(F) = P(F \mid E) = P(F \mid E') = 0.25.$$

8. Prove parts (2) and (3) of Theorem 2.16.

9. Given $P(A \cap B' \cap C') = \frac{1}{4}$, $P(A' \cap B \cap C') = \frac{1}{4}$, $P(A' \cap B' \cap C) = \frac{1}{4}$, and $P(A \cap B \cap C) = \frac{1}{4}$, check (a) whether A, B, and C are pairwise independent, and (b) whether A, B, and C are independent. (*Hint*: refer to an appropriate Venn diagram.)

10. In a certain course in statistics the students are given 3 tests. The probability that a student will get an A in the first test is 0.20, the probability that he will get an A in the second test given that he received an A in the first test is 0.75, and the probability that he will get an A in the third test given that he received A's in both previous tests is 0.90. What is the probability that a student will receive A's in all three of these tests?

2.5 Some Further Theorems of Probability

There are many problems in which the ultimate outcome of an experiment depends on what happens in various intermediate stages. Suppose, for instance, that we are concerned with the construction of a new highway and that the approval or disapproval of the project is deferred until after the election of a new Highway Commissioner. Suppose, furthermore, that Mr. Brown and Mr. Jones are running for this office, the probabilities that they will be elected are, respectively, 0.60 and 0.40, and that the probability for the project's approval is 0.35 if Brown is elected, 0.85 if Jones is elected. What is the probability that the project will be approved?

Letting A represent the project's approval and B Mr. Brown's election, we can use the result of part (c) of Exercise 8 on page 17 and write

$$A = (A \cap B) \cup (A \cap B')$$

$$P(A) = P(A \cap B) + P(A \cap B')$$

$$= P(B) \cdot P(A \mid B) + P(B') \cdot P(A \mid B')$$

Substituting the given probabilities into this last equation we get the desired probability for the project's approval, namely,

$$P(A) = (0.60)(0.35) + (0.40)(0.85) = 0.55.$$

An immediate generalization in which the intermediate stage permits more than two alternatives is taken care of by the following theorem, sometimes called the *Rule of Elimination*:

THEOREM 2.17:
If $B_1, B_2, \ldots,$ and B_n constitute a partition of the sample space and $P(B_i) \neq 0$ for $i = 1, 2, \ldots,$ and n, then for any A

$$P(A) = \sum_{i=1}^{n} P(B_i) \cdot P(A \mid B_i) \tag{2.5.1}$$

The proof of this theorem consists, essentially, of the same steps which we used above for the special case where $n = 2$; it will be left to the reader in Exercise 1 on page 58.

Generalizing the illustration which we gave earlier in this section, suppose that there are four candidates for the office of State Highway Commissioner, the respective probabilities that they will be elected are 0.30, 0.20, 0.40, 0.10, and the probabilities for the project's approval are 0.35, 0.85, 0.45, and 0.15, depending on which of the four candidates is elected. Letting A represent the project's approval and B_1, B_2, B_3, and B_4 the election of the respective candidates, we have $P(B_1) = 0.30$, $P(B_2) = 0.20$, $P(B_3) = 0.40$, $P(B_4) = 0.10$, $P(A \mid B_1) = 0.35$, $P(A \mid B_2) = 0.85$, $P(A \mid B_3) = 0.45$, $P(A \mid B_4) = 0.15$, and substitution into the formula of Theorem 2.17 yields

$$P(A) = (0.30)(0.35) + (0.20)(0.85) + (0.40)(0.45)$$
$$+ (0.10)(0.15)$$
$$= 0.47$$

This result may also be visualized by means of the "tree" diagram of Figure 2.14; note that it does not show the branches for all possible outcomes, only those leading to A. The probability for each branch is obtained by multiplying the probabilities of the two stages and, finally, $P(A)$ is given by the sum of the probabilities of the various branches leading to A.

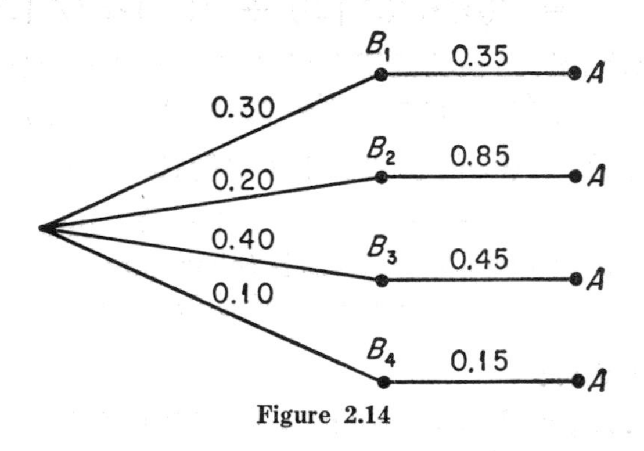

Figure 2.14

Theorem 2.17 can easily be generalized to situations involving several intermediate stages. For instance, it will be left to the reader to show in Exercise 4 on page 58 that if $B_1, B_2, \ldots, B_n$ and $C_1, C_2, \ldots, C_m$ are two partitions of the sample space, $P(B_i) \neq 0$ for $i = 1, 2, \ldots, n$ and $P(B_i \cap C_j) \neq 0$ for $i = 1, 2, \ldots, n$ and $j = 1, 2, \ldots, m$, then

$$P(A) = \sum_{i=1}^{n} \sum_{j=1}^{m} P(B_i)P(C_j \mid B_i)P(A \mid B_i \cap C_j) \qquad (2.5.2)$$

To illustrate this formula with an example from quality control inspection, suppose that B_1, B_2, and B_3 represent a certain missile component's being perfect, good, and inferior, that C_1 and C_2 represent its being properly and improperly installed, and that A represents its performing acceptably when fired. If the various probabilities are as shown in Figure 2.15, the probability that the missile will perform acceptably when fired is

$$\begin{aligned} P(A) = {} & (0.90)(0.95)(0.65) + (0.90)(0.05)(0.35) \\ & + (0.08)(0.95)(0.60) + (0.08)(0.05)(0.20) \\ & + (0.02)(0.95)(0.05) + (0.02)(0.05)(0.01) \\ = {} & 0.62 \text{ (approximately)} \end{aligned}$$

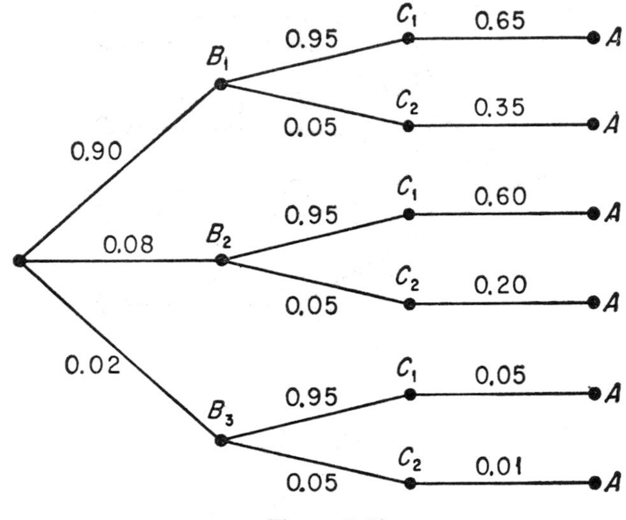

Figure 2.15

To introduce another important theorem of probability theory, suppose that a factory has four machines used in the manufacture of a certain product and that the number of pieces produced by these machines each day are 1000, 1200, 1800, and 2000, respectively. Suppose, furthermore, that the first machine is known to produce on the average 1 per cent defectives, the second $\frac{1}{2}$ per cent defectives, the third $\frac{1}{2}$ per cent defectives, and the fourth again 1 per cent defectives. If one piece is selected at random from a day's production (each piece produced that day has an equal chance of being selected) and found to be defective, *what is the probability that this piece came from the fourth machine*?

Letting B_1, B_2, B_3, and B_4 represent the events that the piece is produced by the respective machines, D the event that the piece selected is defective, the information with which we are supplied is

$$P(B_1) = \frac{1000}{1000 + 1200 + 1800 + 2000} = \frac{1}{6}$$

$P(B_2) = \frac{1}{5}$, $P(B_3) = \frac{3}{10}$, $P(B_4) = \frac{1}{3}$, $P(D \mid B_1) = 0.01$, $P(D \mid B_2) = 0.005$, $P(D \mid B_3) = 0.005$, and $P(D \mid B_4) = 0.01$. Analyzing this problem by means of the "tree" of Figure 2.16, we find that it is similar to the problems discussed earlier in this section; however, we are now interested in $P(B_4 \mid D)$ and not merely $P(D)$.

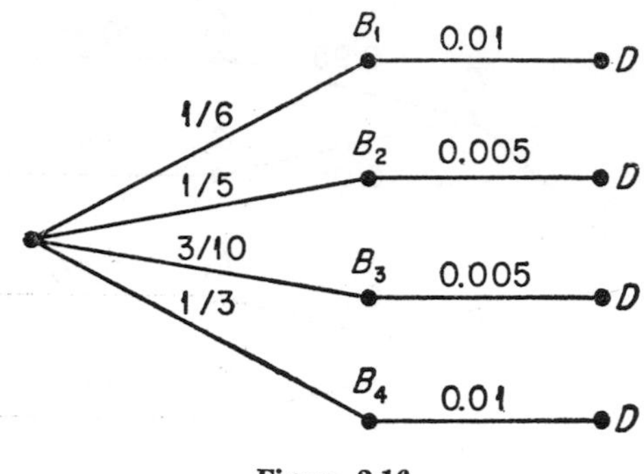

Figure 2.16

Using the definition of conditional probabilities, we have

$$P(B_4 \mid D) = \frac{P(B_4 \cap D)}{P(D)}$$

and according to Theorems 2.14 and 2.17 the numerator and denominator on the righthand side can be written

$$P(B_4) \cdot P(D \mid B_4) \qquad \text{and} \qquad \sum_{i=1}^{4} P(B_i) \cdot P(D \mid B_i)$$

We thus obtain the formula

$$P(B_4 \mid D) = \frac{P(B_4) \cdot P(D \mid B_4)}{\sum_{i=1}^{4} P(B_i) \cdot P(D \mid B_i)}$$

and substituting the given probabilities we get

$$P(B_4 \mid D) = \frac{\frac{1}{3}(0.01)}{\frac{1}{6}(0.01) + \frac{1}{5}(0.005) + \frac{3}{10}(0.005) + \frac{1}{3}(0.01)} = \frac{4}{9}.$$

It should be noted that this result is the *ratio* of the probability of reaching D along the branch passing through B_4 to the sum of the probabilities of reaching D through all four branches of the "tree" diagram of Figure 2.16. It will be left to the reader, see Exercise 6 on page 59, to find the respective probabilities that it came from the first, second, or third machine.

The formula which we derived to solve this problem is a special case of the famous *Rule of Bayes-Laplace*, of which the following is a more general formulation:

THEOREM 2.18:

If B_1, B_2, . . ., and B_n constitute a partition of the sample space, $P(B_i) \neq 0$ for $i = 1, 2, \ldots, n$, and $P(A) \neq 0$, then

$$P(B_r \mid A) = \frac{P(B_r) \cdot P(A \mid B_r)}{\sum_{i=1}^{n} P(B_i) \cdot P(A \mid B_i)}$$

for $r = 1, 2, \ldots,$ or n.

The proof of Theorem 2.18 is for all practical purposes identical with the one which we gave for the special case. Using the definition of conditional probabilities we have

$$P(B_r \mid A) = \frac{P(B_r \cap A)}{P(A)}$$

and according to Theorems 2.14 and 2.17 the numerator and denominator on the righthand side can be written

$$P(B_r) \cdot P(A \mid B_r) \quad \text{and} \quad \sum_{i=1}^{n} P(B_i) \cdot P(A \mid B_i)$$

This completes the proof of Theorem 2.18.

Although this theorem follows quite readily from the postulates of probability, it has been the subject of extensive controversy. There is no question about the validity of the theorem, but considerable argument about the interpretation of the probabilities $P(B_i)$. In his original formulation, Bayes assumed that the probabilities $P(B_i)$, sometimes called the "prior" or "a priori" probabilities, are all equal and, thus, cancel out in the formula for $P(B_r \mid A)$. This, of course, limits the applicability of the theorem and exposes it to criticism.

A good deal of the mysticism surrounding the Rule of Bayes-Laplace is due to the fact that it entails a "backward" or "inverse" sort of reasoning, that is, reasoning from effect to cause. In our numerical example, a defective piece was observed and we asked for the probability that it was "caused" by the fourth machine. To illustrate this further, let us consider the following example:*

> "Mr. Smith's gardener is not dependable; the probability that he will forget to water the rosebush during Smith's absence is $\frac{2}{3}$. The rosebush is in a questionable condition, anyhow; if watered, the probability for its withering is $\frac{1}{2}$; if it is not watered, the probability for its withering is $\frac{3}{4}$. Upon returning, Smith finds that the rosebush has withered. *What is the probability that the gardener did not water the rosebush*?"

Letting W represent the event that the rosebush is watered and D the event that it withers, we are asked to find $P(W' \mid D)$. According to Theorem 2.18 we have

$$P(W' \mid D) = \frac{(2/3)(3/4)}{(1/3)(1/2) + (2/3)(3/4)} = 0.75$$

EXERCISES

1. Prove Theorem 2.17 using, *without proof*, a generalization of the result obtained in part (c) of Exercise 9 on page 17.

2. The probability that a person who enters a certain university drops out before graduation is 0.38, the probability that he graduates *cum laude* is 0.04, and the probability that he graduates without this special distinction is 0.58. The probability that a person who entered this university as a freshman in 1950 has an income in excess of $10,000 in 1962 is 0.75 if he graduated *cum laude*, 0.50 if he graduated without this special distinction, and 0.24 if he dropped out before graduation. What is the probability that a person who entered this university as a freshman in 1950 has an income in excess of $10,000 in 1962?

3. Playing five-card draw poker, Mr. Jones is dealt a pair and decides to flip a coin—heads he keeps the pair and draws 3 cards, tails he keeps the pair and a "kicker" to bluff his opponents and draws only 2 cards. If he draws 3 cards, the probability of Mr. Jones' improving his hand is 0.287; if he draws only 2 cards the probability is 0.260. What is the probability that Mr. Jones will improve his hand?

4. Prove formula (2.5.2) on page 54.

* This example is taken from Reichenbach, H., *The Theory of Probability*, Berkeley, Calif., University of California Press, 1949.

5. A restaurant offers its patrons a choice of steak, chicken, and ham; if so desired, red wine or white wine may be ordered with the main course. It is known from experience that the probabilities that a customer will order steak, chicken, or ham are, respectively, 0.60, 0.30, and 0.10. Also, the probabilities that a customer will order red wine, white wine or no wine after he has selected steak are 0.40, 0.10, and 0.50, and the corresponding probabilities after having selected chicken are 0.05, 0.25, 0.70, and after having selected ham they are 0.15, 0.20, 0.65. Finally, the probability that a customer leaves a good tip is 0.80 if he had steak and red wine, 0.30 if he had steak and white wine, 0.60 if he had steak and no wine, 0.40 if he had chicken and red wine, 0.80 if he had chicken and white wine, 0.70 if he had chicken and no wine, 0.70 if he had ham and red wine, 0.70 if he had ham and white wine, and 0.50 if he had ham and no wine. What is the probability that a customer will leave a good tip?

6. Referring to the illustration on page 55, find the probabilities that the defective piece came from the first, second, and third machines.

7. Suppose that if a person with tuberculosis is given a chest X-ray the probability that his condition will be detected is 0.95 and that if a person without tuberculosis is given a chest X-ray the probability that he will be diagnosed incorrectly as having tuberculosis is 0.002. Suppose, furthermore, that 0.1 per cent of the adult residents of a certain city have tuberculosis. If one of these persons (selected at random, that is, with equal probabilities) is diagnosed as having tuberculosis on the basis of a chest X-ray, what is the probability that he actually has tuberculosis?

8. Playing five-card draw poker, Mr. "Poker-face" Smith draws 1 card and wins the game with a full house. His opponents would like to know whether he drew to two pair or whether he kept three of a kind and a "kicker". If a person is dealt either two pair or three of a kind, the probability that it is two pair is 0.696; if a person draws 1 card to two pair, the probability that he gets a full house is 0.085, if he draws 1 card to three of a kind and a "kicker", the probability that he gets a full house is 0.064. What is the probability that Mr. Smith originally held two pair?

9. Suppose that among three indistinguishable boxes one contains 2 pennies, one contains a penny and a dime, and one contains 2 dimes. Selecting one of the boxes at random (each box has a probability of $\frac{1}{3}$), one coin is taken out (each coin has a probability of $\frac{1}{2}$) without looking at the other. If the coin that is taken out is a penny, what is the probability that the other coin in this box is also a penny?

BIBLIOGRAPHY

Elementary, though more detailed, treatments of the material covered in this chapter may be found in

Goldberg, S., *Probability—An Introduction*, Englewood Cliffs, N. J.: Prentice-Hall, Inc., 1960.

Mosteller, F., R. E. K. Rourke, and G. B. Thomas, *Probability and Statistics*, Reading, Mass.: Addison-Wesley Publishing Co. Inc., 1961.

Some of the most widely used texts on probability theory are

Cramer, H., *The Elements of Probability Theory*, New York: John Wiley & Sons, Inc., 1955.

Feller, W., *An Introduction to Probability Theory and its Applications*, Vol. I, 2nd ed., New York: John Wiley & Sons, Inc., 1957.

Munroe, M. E., *Theory of Probability*, New York: McGraw-Hill Book Co., Inc., 1951.

Parzen, E., *Modern Probability Theory and its Applications*, New York: John Wiley & Sons, Inc., 1960.

Uspensky, J. V., *Introduction to Mathematical Probability*, New York: McGraw-Hill Book Co., Inc., 1937.

An interesting discussion of various philosophical views on objective, subjective, and logical probabilities may be found in

Nagel, E., *Principles of the Theory of Probability*, Chicago: University of Chicago Press, 1939.

The question as to what probabilities are negligible or practically equal to one is treated in

Borel, E., *Éléments de la Théorie des Probabilités*, Paris: Editions Albin Michel, 1950.

Chapter 3

Probability Distributions

3.1 Random Variables

In most problems of probability and statistics we are interested only in a particular aspect (or particular aspects) of the outcome of an experiment. When rolling a pair of dice we are usually interested only in the total, not in the outcome for each die; when interviewing a randomly selected housewife we may be interested in her I.Q. and the size of her family, not in her age or weight; repeatedly flipping a coin we may be interested only in the total number of heads, not in the order in which they were obtained; and in describing the winner of a lottery we may be interested only in his annual income, not in anything else.

In each of these examples we are interested in a number which is associated with the outcome of a chance experiment, that is, the value which is assumed by what is called a *random variable*. In the language of statistics, the total rolled with a pair of dice is a random variable, the I.Q. and the size of the family of a randomly selected housewife are random variables, and so are the number of heads obtained in repeated flips of a coin and the annual income of the winner of a lottery. To be more specific, let us consider Figure 3.1 which represents the sample space of an experiment consisting of three flips of a coin, with each outcome having a probability of $\frac{1}{8}$. (As in Figure 2.1, the three coordinates represent the successive flips and 0 and 1 stand again for *tail* and *head*.) Note that in this figure we have also associated a number with each point: we as-

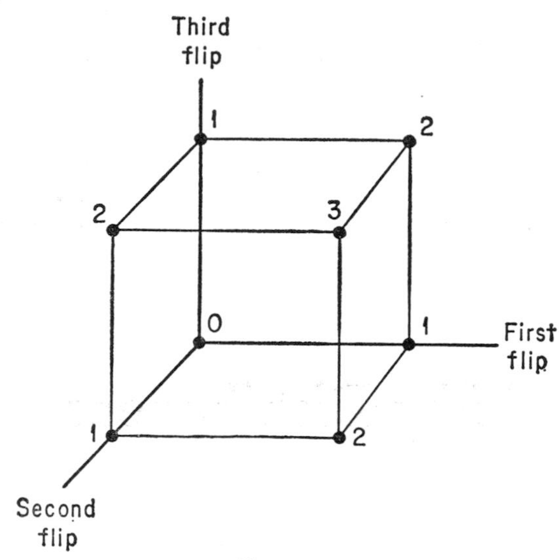

Figure 3.1

sociated the number 0 with the point (0, 0, 0), the number 1 with the points (1, 0, 0), (0, 1, 0), (0, 0, 1), the number 2 with the points (1, 1, 0), (1, 0, 1), (0, 1, 1), and the number 3 with the point (1, 1, 1). In other words, we associated with each point the value of the random variable *the total number of heads.*

Since "Associate numbers with the points (elements) of the sample space" is merely another way of saying "Define a function over the points of the sample space," let us now make the following definition:

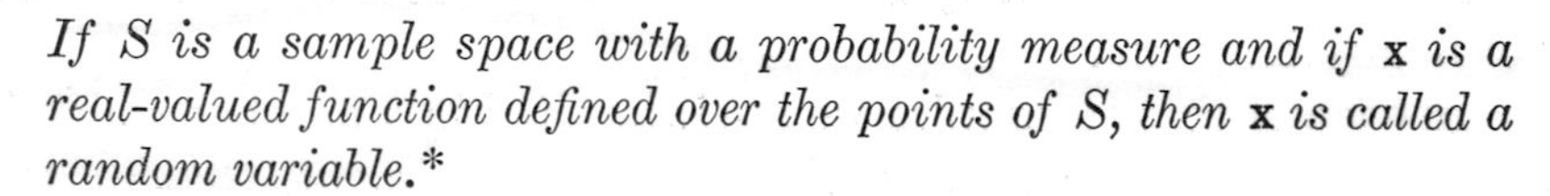

If S is a sample space with a probability measure and if **x** *is a real-valued function defined over the points of S, then* **x** *is called a random variable.**

In this book we shall consistently write random variables symbolically in boldface type. This practice is relatively new and not universally accepted, but we shall see later that it has many advantages. (It has been the custom for a long time to use capital letters to indicate random variables.) When taking notes or writing on a blackboard, the reader may find it convenient to indicate random variables by underlining the respective symbols, perhaps with wiggly lines, the usual type-setting symbol for boldface type.

* Instead of "random variable," the terms "chance variable," "stochastic variable," and "variate" are also widely used.

The fact that we limited our definition to real-valued functions does not impose any undue restrictions. If the numbers which we want to assign to the outcome of an experiment are complex, we can always look upon the real and imaginary parts separately as values assumed by *two* random variables. Also, if we want to describe the outcome of an experiment, say, by giving the color of a person's hair, we can arbitrarily make this random variable real-valued by *coding* the various colors, for example, representing them with the numbers 1, 2, 3, etc.

Note that for the time being we have to limit ourselves to functions defined over *discrete* sample spaces S; the continuous case will be treated later in Chapter 5. If the range of a random variable is discrete, namely, if the set of values a random variable can assume is finite or countably infinite (see page 8), the random variable, itself, is referred to as *discrete.* In view of our definition of functions on page 32, it follows immediately that random variables defined over discrete sample spaces must necessarily be discrete.

Perhaps the most pertinent feature of discrete random variables is that the probabilities specified for the elements of S, the discrete sample space over which a random variable is defined, *automatically* provide the probabilities that the random variable assumes any set of values within its range. For instance, having specified probabilities of $\frac{1}{8}$ for the elements of the sample space of Figure 3.1, it follows immediately that the probabilities with which the random variable *the total number of heads* assumes the values 0, 1, 2, and 3 are, respectively, $\frac{1}{8}$, $\frac{3}{8}$, $\frac{3}{8}$, and $\frac{1}{8}$. The probability that it assumes the value 1 is the *sum* of the probabilities of the points to which we attached the number 1 in Figure 3.1.

If x is a real number within the range of a discrete random variable $\mathbf{x}$, the probability that the random variable will assume this value will be written $f_{\mathbf{x}}(x)$ or simply $f(x)$.* It is customary to refer to the probabilities $f(x)$, specified for all values within the range of $\mathbf{x}$, as values of the *probability distribution* or the *probability function* of $\mathbf{x}$. In order to distinguish between the probability distributions of different random variables, we also use the symbols $g(x)$, $h(x)$, $f_1(x)$, $\phi(x)$, and so forth.

* It is common practice to write the probability that the random variable $\mathbf{x}$ assumes the value x as $P(\mathbf{x} = x)$. This notation fails to distinguish between the *random variable,* a function, and the *value of a random variable,* the corresponding dependent variable.

Symbolic definition of ~~cumulative~~ probability distribution is:

~~$F(x) = P(X \leq x)$~~ $f(x) = P(X = x)$

Whenever possible, we try to represent probability distributions by means of equations which enable us to calculate the various probabilities by substituting appropriate values of x. Thus, for the total number of heads obtained in three flips of a coin (see Figure 3.1) we could write

$$f(x) = \frac{\binom{3}{x}}{8} \qquad \text{for } x = 0, 1, 2, 3$$

It can easily be verified that, as before, $f(0) = \frac{1}{8}$, $f(1) = \frac{3}{8}$, $f(2) = \frac{3}{8}$, and $f(3) = \frac{1}{8}$.

Since there are many problems in which it is of interest to know the probability that the value of a random variable is less than or equal to some real number x, let us write the probability that the value of $\mathbf{x}$ is less than or equal to x as

$$F(x) = \sum_{t \leq x} f(t) \qquad \text{for} \quad -\infty \leq x \leq \infty \tag{3.1.1}$$

where the summation extends over all values within the range of $\mathbf{x}$ that are less than or equal to x. It is customary to refer to the probabilities $F(x)$, specified for $-\infty \leq x \leq \infty$, as values of the *distribution function* or the *cumulative distribution* of the random variable $\mathbf{x}$. Note that in (3.1.1) the domain of the distribution function is the set of all real numbers, not only those within the range of $\mathbf{x}$.

Referring again to Figure 3.1 and the total number of heads obtained in three flips of a coin, it can be seen that the distribution function of this random variable is given by

$$F(x) = \begin{cases} 0 & \text{for} \quad x < 0 \\ \frac{1}{8} & \text{for} \quad 0 \leq x < 1 \\ \frac{4}{8} & \text{for} \quad 1 \leq x < 2 \\ \frac{7}{8} & \text{for} \quad 2 \leq x < 3 \\ 1 & \text{for} \quad 3 \leq x \end{cases}$$

Cumulative Distribution

$F(x) = P(X \leq x)$

The graph of this distribution function is shown in Figure 3.2. Note that at all points of discontinuity this *step-function* assumes the greater of the two values.

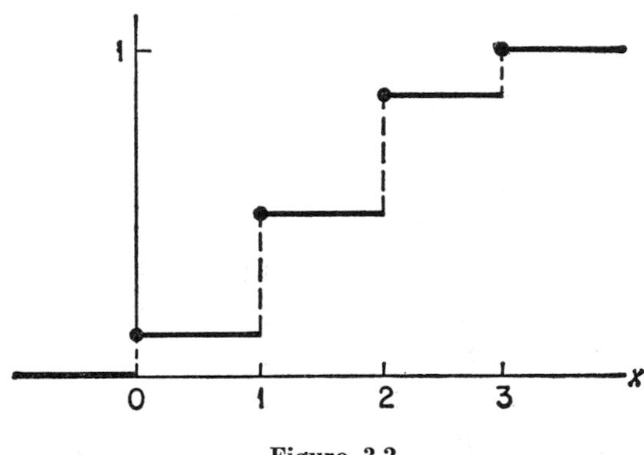

Figure 3.2

EXERCISES

1. Referring to the sample space of Figure 3.1 and assigning a probability of $\frac{1}{8}$ to each point, indicate what number is assigned to each point of this sample space by the random variable $\mathbf{y}$, *the number of heads minus the number of tails.* Also find the probability distribution of this random variable, that is, find $f(y)$ for $y = -3, -1, 1$, and 3.

2. Referring to the sample space of Figure 1.5 and assigning a probability of $\frac{1}{36}$ to each point, indicate what number is assigned to each point by random variable $\mathbf{x}$, *the total rolled with the two dice.* Also find the probability distribution of this random variable, that is, find $f(x)$ for $x = 2, 3, \ldots, 11$, and 12, and draw the graph of its distribution function.

3. An experiment consists of flipping a coin, then flipping it again if and only if the first flip yielded *head*, and then flipping it again if and only if the second flip yielded *head*. Draw a "tree" diagram showing the possible outcomes of this experiment and attach a probability to each outcome, assuming that the successive flips are independent and the probability of heads is $\frac{1}{2}$ for each flip. Then indicate what number is assigned to each outcome by the random variable $\mathbf{x}$, *the total number of heads,* and find its probability distribution and its distribution function.

4. Taking the four 2's and the four 3's of an ordinary deck of playing cards, two cards are drawn in succession (without replacement) from this set of eight cards. If the cards remaining for each draw have equal probabilities of being selected, find the probability distribution of the random

variable **x**, *the total of the numbers obtained in the two draws.* Also find the distribution function of this random variable.

5. If $F(x)$ is, as before, the probability that the value of a random variable **x** is less than or equal to x, show that

   (a) $F(-\infty) = 0$ and $F(\infty) = 1$

   (b) $F(a) \leq F(b)$ if $a < b$.

3.2 Special Probability Distributions

In this section we shall study several probability distributions which are of special importance. Three of them, the *binomial distribution*, the *hypergeometric distribution*, and the *Poisson distribution*, are given in the text; three others, the *discrete uniform distribution*, the *geometric distribution*, and the *negative binomial distribution* are introduced in the exercises on pages 76 and 77. Various applications of these probability distributions are indicated in the exercises of Section 3.2.4 and some of their mathematical properties will be discussed in Chapter 4.

3.2.1 *The binomial distribution*

The probability distribution which, undoubtedly, is more widely used than any other is the *binomial distribution*; it applies to situations often referred to as "repeated trials." If we want to know the probabilities that 12 flips of a balanced coin will yield 5 heads and 7 tails, that 3 of 10 persons will respond to a given mail questionnaire, that 16 of 25 persons will recover from a certain disease, that among 15 children born on a given day there are 6 boys and 9 girls, we are in each case interested in the probability of getting a certain number of "successes" in a given number of "trials."*

The assumptions which underly the binomial distribution are that (1) *the probability of a success is the same for each trial,* and (2) *the trials are independent.* Of course, there are situations dealing with

* This usage of "success," "failure," and "trials" is a holdover from the days when probability theory was considered only in connection with games of chance. Thus, the term "success" is not meant to imply that the outcome must necessarily be advantageous or desirable; if a doctor wants to know the probability that 3 of 40 pneumonia patients will not recover, he is concerned with the probability of "3 successes in 40 trials." Similarly, the term "failure" may be applied to the event that a ball bearing is *not* defective or that a person interviewed does not have red hair.

x successes in n trials where these assumptions cannot be met, but this simply means that the binomial distribution does not apply. It cannot be used, for example, to find the probability that it will rain at a resort on 30 of 120 consecutive days; clearly, the probability that it will rain does not remain constant over such a long period of time and, furthermore, the occurrence of rain on successive days can hardly be looked upon as independent events.

To derive the formula for the binomial distribution, let us represent each possible outcome by a point whose kth coordinate, representing the kth trial, is 0 or 1, with 0 standing for failure and 1 for success. Thus, the event of getting *success, success, failure, success, . . . , success, failure* is represented by the point $(1, 1, 0, 1, \ldots, 1, 0)$. If the trials are independent and the constant probabilities for success and failure are θ and $1 - \theta$, the probability of any point $(1, 0, 1, 0, \ldots, 1, 1)$, representing x successes and $n - x$ failures *in a specified order*, is $\theta^x(1 - \theta)^{n-x}$. There is one factor θ for each success, one factor $1 - \theta$ for each failure, and they are all multiplied together in view of the assumption that the trials are independent. Note that this probability does not depend on the order in which the x successes and $n - x$ failures are obtained.

To find the probability for x successes and $n - x$ failures *in any order*, we now have to add the probabilities of all points, each of which represents x successes and $n - x$ failures in some specific order. Since there are $\binom{n}{x}$ ways in which the x successes can be distributed among the n trials, there are $\binom{n}{x}$ such points having the same probability $\theta^x(1 - \theta)^{n-x}$. Hence, the probability for x successes and $n - x$ failures in any order is

$$b(x; n, \theta) = \binom{n}{x}\theta^x(1 - \theta)^{n-x} \qquad \text{for } x = 0, 1, 2, \ldots, n \qquad (3.2.1)$$

This probability distribution, which gives the probabilities for x successes in n trials when θ, the probability for success, is constant from trial to trial and the n trials are independent, is called the *binomial distribution*. We used the notation $b(x; n, \theta)$ instead of simply $f(x)$ or $b(x)$ to indicate that the distribution depends on the two *parameters* n and θ. The term "parameter" is used here as in other branches of mathematics; n and θ are *constants* when referring to a specific binomial distribution, but they can, of course, assume different values for different binomial distributions. Incidentally, the name "binomial distribution" derives from the fact that the expressions yielded by (3.2.1) for $x = 0, 1, 2, \ldots,$ and n are the corresponding terms of the binomial expansion of $[(1 - \theta) + \theta]^n$.

To illustrate the use of (3.2.1), let us calculate two of the four probabilities asked for in the first paragraph of this section. For the probability of getting 5 heads and 7 tails in 12 flips of a balanced coin, we substitute $x = 5, n = 12, \theta = \frac{1}{2}, \binom{12}{5} = 792$ (see Table VII), and get

$$b(5; 12, \tfrac{1}{2}) = 792(\tfrac{1}{2})^5(\tfrac{1}{2})^7 = \tfrac{99}{512}$$

or approximately 0.19. Similarly, to find the probability of getting 3 responses to 10 mail questionnaires, let us suppose that the probability of any one person's answering the questionnaire is $\frac{1}{5}$. Then, substituting $x = 3$, $n = 10$, $\theta = \frac{1}{5}$, and $\binom{10}{3} = 120$ (see Table VII), we get

$$b(3; 10, \tfrac{1}{5}) = 120(\tfrac{1}{5})^3(\tfrac{4}{5})^7 = \tfrac{393216}{1953125}$$

or approximately 0.20.

Figures 3.3 and 3.4 show graphical presentations of the binomial distribution with $n = 10$ and $\theta = 0.25$. The first is called a *histogram* and it is the most widely used form of presenting probability distributions in graphical form. Letting 0 be represented by the interval from $-\frac{1}{2}$ to $\frac{1}{2}$, 1 by the interval from $\frac{1}{2}$ to $1\frac{1}{2}$, 2 by the interval from $1\frac{1}{2}$ to $2\frac{1}{2}$, . . . , we are thus "spreading" the discrete variable over a continuous scale. This will help later to visualize how binomial distributions (and other probability distributions) can be approximated with continuous curves. The graph of Figure 3.4 is called a *bar chart*; each probability is represented by the height of the corresponding bar.

In practice, binomial probabilities are rarely calculated directly with (3.2.1); these probabilities have been tabulated for $n = 2$ to $n = 49$ by the National Bureau of Standards and for $n = 50$ to $n = 100$ by H. G. Romig (see Bibliography on page 89). In this book, Table I on page 355 gives the values of $b(x; n, \theta)$ for $n = 1$ to $n = 20$ and $\theta = 0.05, 0.10, 0.15, 0.20, \ldots$, and 0.50. For values of θ greater than 0.50 we can make use of Table I using the identity $b(x; n, \theta) = b(n - x; n, 1 - \theta)$, see Exercise 5 on page 75.

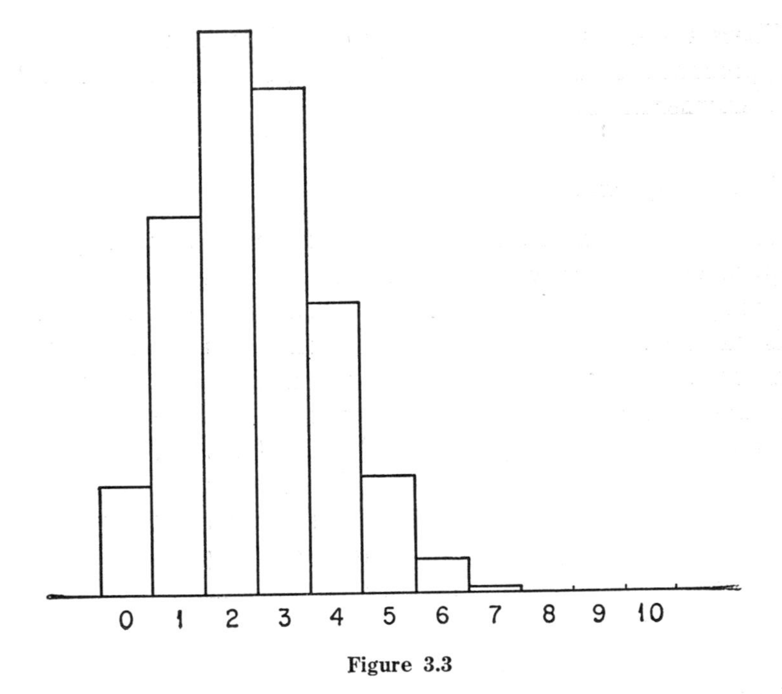

Figure 3.3

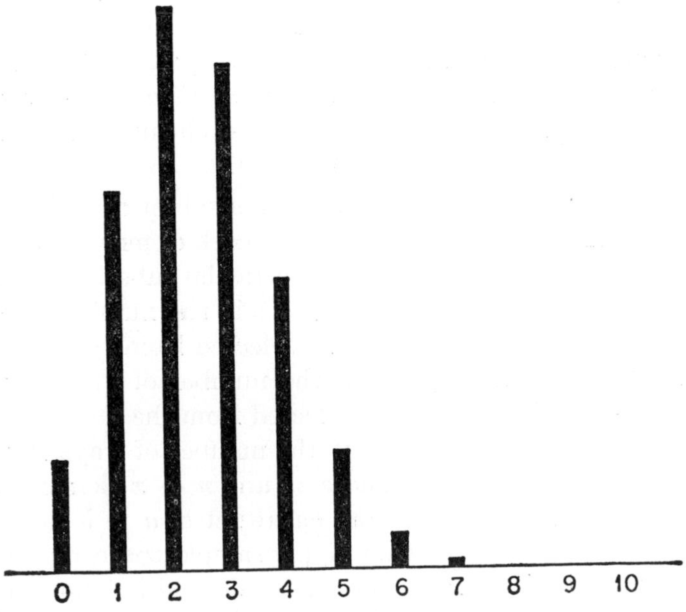

Figure 3.4

There are also several ways in which binomial probabilities can be approximated when n is large. One of these is discussed in Section 3.2.3, another in Section 6.4.3.

3.2.2 *The hypergeometric distribution*

The binomial distribution is often referred to as applying to *sampling with replacement.* If we are interested in the probability of obtaining 3 kings in 5 draws from a standard deck of 52 playing cards, the binomial distribution applies only if each card is replaced (and the deck is reshuffled) before the next one is drawn. If the cards are not replaced, obtaining kings on successive draws are not independent events and the binomial distribution does not apply. Similarly, if we are interested in the probability that 5 of 10 persons interviewed are in favor of a certain piece of legislation, the binomial distribution applies only if we sample with replacement, that is, if a person who has been interviewed once may conceivably be interviewed again.

To develop a formula analogous to that of the binomial distribution which applies to *sampling without replacement,* suppose that a set has $a + b$ elements of which a are labeled "success" and b are labeled "failure." As before, we are interested in the probability of getting x successes in n trials or, better, *the probability of obtaining a subset containing x elements labeled "success" and $n - x$ elements labeled "failure."* It will be assumed that each subset of n elements has an equal probability of being selected.

Since there are $\binom{a+b}{n}$ ways in which a subset of n elements can be selected from a set of $a + b$ elements, each element of the sample space (representing the selection of a particular subset of n elements) has a probability of $1/\binom{a+b}{n}$. Also $\binom{a}{x}$ is the number of ways in which a subset of x elements can be selected from the set of a elements labeled "success," $\binom{b}{n-x}$ is the number of ways in which a subset of $n - x$ elements can be selected from the set of b elements labeled "failure," and $\binom{a}{x}\binom{b}{n-x}$ is the number of ways in which a subset of x elements labeled "success" and $n - x$ elements labeled "failure" can be selected from the entire set of $a + b$ elements. In other words, $\binom{a}{x}\binom{b}{n-x}$ elements of the sample space represent the selection of x successes and $n - x$ failures, and it follows that the probability of obtaining a subset containing x elements labeled "success" and $n - x$ elements labeled "failure" is

$$h(x; n, a, b) = \frac{\binom{a}{x}\binom{b}{n-x}}{\binom{a+b}{n}} \quad \text{for} \quad x = 0, 1, 2, \ldots, n \qquad (3.2.2)$$

This probability distribution is called the *hypergeometric distribution*; we used the notation $h(x; n, a, b)$ to indicate that it depends on the three parameters n, a, and b.

To illustrate the use of (3.2.2), let us calculate the two probabilities asked for in the beginning of this section. For the probability of getting 3 kings in 5 draws (without replacement) from a standard deck of 52 playing cards, we substitute $x = 3$, $n = 5$, $a = 4$, $b = 48$, and get

$$h(3; 5, 4, 48) = \frac{\binom{4}{3}\binom{48}{2}}{\binom{52}{5}} = \frac{94}{54145}$$

or approximately 0.002.

To find the probability that 5 of 10 persons interviewed are in favor of the given piece of legislation, let us suppose that this sample is taken from 100 persons among whom 60 are for the legislation and 40 are against it. Furthermore, it is assumed that each subset of 10 persons has an equal chance of being selected. Substituting $x = 5$, $n = 10$, $a = 60$, and $b = 40$ into (3.2.2), we get

$$h(5; 10, 60, 40) = \frac{\binom{60}{5}\binom{40}{5}}{\binom{100}{10}}$$

and rather tedious calculation yield the result that this probability is approximately 0.208. We obtained the values of the required binomial coefficients by using a table of the logarithms of factorials, which can be found in most handbooks of mathematical tables.

Had we made the *mistake* of using the binomial distribution with $\theta = 60/(60 + 40) = 0.6$ in the last example, we would have obtained

$$b(5; 10, 0.6) = \binom{10}{5}(0.6)^5(0.4)^5 = 0.201$$

which is very close to the correct value of 0.208. Indeed, the binomial distribution is very often used to approximate the hypergeometric distribution, letting $\theta = a/(a + b)$. This is justifiable when n is small compared to $a + b$.

3.2.3 *The Poisson distribution*

In this section we shall introduce another important probability distribution, the *Poisson distribution,* as a limiting form of the binomial distribution when $\theta \to 0$, $n \to \infty$, and $n\theta$ remains constant. It will thus be used to approximate the binomial distribution when θ is close to 0 and n is very large. As is illustrated in Exericse 12 on page 76, the Poisson distribution can also be derived *without reference to the binomial distribution* and it has many applications in its own rights; in other words, it has many applications where the binomial distribution does not apply. Some of these applications are referred to in the exercises on pages 78 and 79.

To derive the Poisson distribution as a limiting case of the binomial distribution when $\theta \to 0$, $n \to \infty$, and $n\theta = \lambda$ remains constant, let us first write the formula for the binomial distribution as

$$\frac{n(n-1)(n-2)\cdot \ldots \cdot(n-x+1)}{x!}\theta^x(1-\theta)^{n-x}$$

Eliminating θ by using the equation $n\theta = \lambda$, that is, substituting $\theta = \lambda/n$, we get

$$\frac{n(n-1)(n-2)\cdot \ldots \cdot(n-x+1)}{x!}\left(\frac{\lambda}{n}\right)^x\left(1-\frac{\lambda}{n}\right)^{n-x}$$

Then, dividing one of the x factors n into each factor of

$$n(n-1)(n-2)\cdot \ldots \cdot(n-x+1)$$

and writing

$$\left(1 - \frac{\lambda}{n}\right)^{n-x}$$

as

$$\left[\left(1 - \frac{\lambda}{n}\right)^{-n/\lambda}\right]^{-\lambda}\left(1 - \frac{\lambda}{n}\right)^{-x},$$

we obtain

$$\frac{1\left(1 - \frac{1}{n}\right)\left(1 - \frac{2}{n}\right) \cdot \ldots \cdot \left(1 - \frac{x-1}{n}\right)}{x!} \times (\lambda)^x\left[\left(1 - \frac{\lambda}{n}\right)^{-n/\lambda}\right]^{-\lambda}\left(1 - \frac{\lambda}{n}\right)^{-x}$$

If we now let $n \to \infty$ while x and λ remain fixed,

$$1\left(1 - \frac{1}{n}\right)\left(1 - \frac{2}{n}\right) \cdot \ldots \cdot \left(1 - \frac{x-1}{n}\right) \to 1$$

$$\left(1 - \frac{\lambda}{n}\right)^{-x} \to 1$$

$$\left(1 - \frac{\lambda}{n}\right)^{-n/\lambda} \to e$$

and the limiting distribution becomes

$$f(x; \lambda) = \frac{\lambda^x e^{-\lambda}}{x!} \quad \text{for} \quad x = 0, 1, 2, \ldots \tag{3.2.3}$$

This probability distribution is called the *Poisson distribution*, named after the French mathematician S. Poisson (1781–1840); we used the notation $f(x; \lambda)$ to indicate that it depends on the one parameter λ. The significance of this parameter will be discussed in Section 4.3.3.

It is easy to verify that (3.2.3) is, indeed, a probability distribution for $\lambda > 0$; $f(x; \lambda)$ is positive for each x and

$$\sum_{x=0}^{\infty} \frac{\lambda^x e^{-\lambda}}{x!} = e^{-\lambda} \sum_{x=0}^{\infty} \frac{\lambda^x}{x!} = e^{-\lambda}e^{\lambda} = 1$$

since

$$1 + \lambda + \frac{\lambda^2}{2!} + \frac{\lambda^3}{3!} + \cdots$$

converges to e^λ for all real λ.

To illustrate how the Poisson distribution is used to approximate the binomial distribution, let us calculate $b(x; n, \theta)$ for $n = 49$, $\theta = 0.04$, and $x = 0, 1, 2, \ldots$, and compare it with the corresponding probabilities of a Poisson distribution having $\lambda = 49(0.04) = 1.96$. Omitting probabilities less than 0.001, we get

x	*Binomial probabilities*	*Poisson probabilities*
0	0.135	0.141
1	0.276	0.276
2	0.276	0.270
3	0.180	0.176
4	0.086	0.086
5	0.032	0.034
6	0.010	0.011
7	0.003	0.003
8	0.001	0.001
. . .	. . .	. . .

and it is apparent that the approximation is very close. The binomial probabilities of this table were obtained from the National Bureau of Standards Table referred to in the Bibliography on page 89; the Poisson probabilities *could* have been obtained with (3.2.3) and $\lambda = 1.96$. Actually, we calculated $f(0; 1.96)$ with (3.2.3) and then used the recursion formula

$$\frac{f(x+1; \lambda)}{f(x; \lambda)} = \frac{(\lambda^{x+1}e^{-\lambda})/(x+1)!}{(\lambda^x e^{-\lambda})/x!} = \frac{\lambda}{x+1}$$

which can also be written

$$f(x+1; \lambda) = \frac{\lambda}{x+1} f(x; \lambda) \tag{3.2.4}$$

Thus, after having found that $f(0; 1.96) = 0.141$, we obtained

$$f(1; 1.96) = \frac{1.96}{1}(0.141) = 0.276$$

$$f(2; 1.96) = \frac{1.96}{2}(0.276) = 0.270$$

and so forth. Similar recursion formulas for the binomial and hypergeometric distributions are given in Exercises 6 and 10 below.

Table II on pages 360 through 365 contains Poisson probabilities for selected values of λ; more extensive tables are referred to in the Bibliography on page 89.

EXERCISES

1. Using the formula for the binomial distribution, find (a) the probability of rolling 2 sixes in 5 rolls of a balanced die, and (b) the probability of rolling at most 2 sixes in 5 rolls of a balanced die.

2. Using (3.2.1) find the probabilities of getting (a) 6 heads in 8 flips of a balanced coin, and (b) at least 6 heads in 8 flips of a balanced coin.

3. A multiple choice test consists of 10 questions and 4 answers to each question. If each question is answered by shuffling 4 tags labeled 1, 2, 3, and 4, drawing one, and marking the alternative whose number is drawn, find the probability of getting 3 of these questions answered correctly.

4. The probability that Mr. Jones, a rifleman, will hit a target is 0.80. Use (3.2.1) to find the probability that he will hit the target in 3 out of 4 shots.

5. Show that $b(x; n, \theta) = b(n - x; n, 1 - \theta)$.

6. The calculation of binomial probabilities is often simplified by first calculating $b(0; n, \theta)$ with (3.2.1) and then obtaining the other probabilities with the use of the recursion formula

$$b(x + 1; n, \theta) = \frac{\theta(n - x)}{(x + 1)(1 - \theta)} b(x; n, \theta)$$

   Derive this formula and then use it to calculate the binomial probabilities for $n = 6$ and $\theta = 0.20$. Verify your results by referring to Table I.

7. Use the recursion formula of Exercise 6 to show that for $\theta = 0.50$ the binomial distribution has a maximum at $x = n/2$ when n is even, and at $x = (n - 1)/2$ as well as $x = (n + 1)/2$ when n is odd.

8. If 5 cards are dealt (without replacement) from a standard deck of 52 playing cards, what are the probabilities that (a) exactly 1 of them will be an ace, and (b) at least one of them will be an ace?

9. A club has 20 members of which 12 are boys and 8 are girls. If a committee of 5 is to be selected by drawing lots, what are the probabilities that (a) the committee will consist of 3 boys and 2 girls, (b)

the committee will contain at least 3 boys, and (c) the members of the committee will all be of the same sex?

10. The calculation of hypergeometric probabilities is often simplified by first calculating $h(0; n, a, b)$ with (3.2.2) and then using the recursion formula

$$h(x+1; n, a, b) = \frac{(n-x)(a-x)}{(x+1)(b-n+x+1)} h(x; n, a, b)$$

Derive this formula and then use it to calculate the hypergeometric probabilities for $n = 5$, $a = 8$, and $b = 12$.

11. Approximate the binomial probability for $x = 2$, $n = 100$, and $\theta = 0.10$ using a Poisson distribution and compare your result with the exact value obtained with (3.2.1). (*Hint*: use logarithms to find the binomial probability and refer to Table II to find the corresponding Poisson probability.)

12. The following is one way of introducing the Poisson distribution without reference to the binomial distribution. Suppose that $f(x, t)$ is the probability of getting x successes during a time interval of length t when (1) the probability of a success during a *very small* time interval from t to $t + \Delta t$ is $\alpha \cdot \Delta t$, (2) the probability of more than one success occurring during such a time interval is negligible, and (3) the probability of a success during such a time interval does not depend on what happened prior to time t. Show that:

$$f(x, t + \Delta t) = f(x, t)[1 - \alpha\,\Delta t] + f(x-1, t)\alpha\,\Delta t$$

and hence

$$\frac{d[f(x, t)]}{dt} = \alpha[f(x-1, t) - f(x, t)]$$

Also show by direct substitution that a solution of this infinite system of differential equations (there is one for each value of x) is given by the Poisson distribution with $\lambda = \alpha t$. It is assumed that α and t are both non-negative. (For applications where the above assumptions are met see Exercises 7 through 9 on page 79.)

13. (*Discrete uniform distribution*) If each value within the range of a random variable $\mathbf{x}$ has an equal probability, the probability distribution of $\mathbf{x}$ is referred to as a *discrete uniform distribution*. Thus if the range of $\mathbf{x}$ is $\{x_1, x_2, \ldots, x_n\}$, the formula for the discrete uniform distribution is

$$f(x) = \frac{1}{n} \quad \text{for} \quad x = x_1, x_2, \ldots, x_n$$

Taking the special case where:

$$f(x) = \frac{1}{12} \qquad \text{for} \quad x = 5, 6, \ldots, 16$$

find the probabilities that (a) the value of a random variable having this distribution is greater than 8, (b) the value of a random variable having this distribution is greater than 6 but less than or equal to 14, and (c) the value of a random variable having this distribution is greater than or equal to 10.

14. (*Geometric distribution*) Suppose an experiment meets the assumptions underlying the binomial distribution, except that n is not fixed. If $\mathbf{x}$ is the number of the trial on which the first success occurs, show that the probability distribution of this random variable is given by:

$$g(x; \theta) = \theta(1 - \theta)^{x-1} \qquad \text{for} \quad x = 1, 2, 3, \ldots$$

This distribution is called the *geometric distribution* in view of the fact that its successive terms constitute a geometric progression. To apply the geometric distribution, consider the game of billiards, where a player's turn continues until he misses a shot. If the probability that Mr. Brown misses any one shot is 0.20 and the outcomes for successive shots are independent, what is the probability that (a) his turn lasts exactly 5 plays, and (b) his turn lasts at least 5 plays?

15. (*Negative binomial distribution*) Suppose that an experiment meets the assumptions underlying the binomial distribution, except that n is not fixed. If $\mathbf{x}$ is the number of the trial on which the kth success occurs, show that the probability distribution of this random variable is given by:

$$f(x; k, \theta) = \binom{x-1}{k-1}\theta^k(1 - \theta)^{x-k}$$

$$\text{for} \quad x = k, k + 1, k + 2, \ldots$$

This distribution is called the *negative binomial distribution* in view of the fact that the expressions obtained for $x = k, k + 1, k + 2, \ldots,$ are the successive terms of the binomial expansion of

$$\left(\frac{1}{\theta} - \frac{1 - \theta}{\theta}\right)^{-k}.$$

Use the formula for the negative binomial distribution to find the probability that a person flipping a balanced coin gets the 4th head on the 10th flip.

3.2.4 *Some applications*

In the preceding sections we have illustrated the various probability distributions primarily with examples from games of chance; in the set of exercises which follows they are applied to more general problems of statistics. In the first four exercises it will be assumed that the conditions underlying the binomial distribution can be met; they are numerical problems which should be solved with the use of Table I. Exercises 7 through 10 are applications of the Poisson distribution and they should be worked with the use of Table II. In the other exercises it will be left to the reader to decide which of the probability distributions we have introduced provides the appropriate *model.*

EXERCISES

1. It is known that on the average 40 per cent of certain bulbs will bloom. If Mrs. Jones plants 12 of these bulbs, find (a) the probability that exactly 7 of the bulbs will bloom, (b) the probability that at least 8 of them will bloom, and (c) the probability that fewer than 4 will bloom.

2. A manufacturer of TV tubes claims that only 5 per cent of his tubes have any sort of imperfection. To investigate this claim, a testing service decides to test 20 of these tubes and then accept the claim if only 0 or 1 have imperfections, reject it if 2 or more have imperfections. What is the probability that the testing service will thus reject the manufacturer's claim even though it is correct, that is, even though the probability that any one tube has an imperfection is 0.05? Also find the probability that the testing service will accept the manufacturer's claim even though 10 per cent of his tubes have imperfections. (Assume that the number of tubes produced is so large that for all practical purposes the assumptions underlying the binomial distribution can be met.)

3. A physician knows that the probability that a patient will recover from a certain rare disease is 0.25. To test the effectiveness of a new drug he gives it to 10 patients having this disease and he decides, beforehand, to discredit the drug unless at least 4 of the 10 patients recover. What is the probability that he will discredit the new drug on the basis of this experiment even though it raises the recovery rate (the probability that any one patient will recover) to 0.35? What is the probability that he will fail to discredit the new drug on the basis of this experiment even though the new drug is totally ineffective, that is, the recovery rate is still 0.25?

4. A market research organization wants to test the claim that 60 per cent of all housewives in a certain area prefer Brand A cleanser to all competing brands. It is decided to take a sample of 18 housewives and reject the claim if fewer than 9 of them prefer Brand A to all competing brands. What is the probability that the market research organization will, thus, make the error of rejecting the claim even though it is correct?

5. Certain electronic components are shipped in lots of 100. At their destination a quality control engineer inspects a sample of 5 from each lot and accepts the lot if none of the 5 are defective; if 1 or more are defective, the lot is inspected 100 per cent. What is the probability that a lot will get by without 100 per cent inspection if, actually, it contains 5 defectives?

6. When buying a dozen eggs, Mrs. Murphy has the practice of inspecting 3 eggs for cracks; if one or more of these eggs has a crack, she does not buy the carton. Assuming that each subset of 3 eggs has an equal probability of being selected, what is the probability that Mrs. Murphy will buy a carton which has 5 eggs with cracks?

7. In the inspection of paper produced in continuous rolls, the probability of spotting a defect in a very small interval of time Δt is $(0.1)\,\Delta t$, time being measured in minutes. What are the probabilities of spotting, respectively, 0, 1, and 2 defects in 10 minutes?

8. The probability that an office with a very large switchboard will have an incoming call during a small time interval Δt is $\frac{7}{120}\,\Delta t$, time being measured in seconds. Find (a) the probability that during one minute there will be exactly 4 incoming calls, and (b) the probability that during 2 minutes there will be at least 5 incoming calls.

9. If a person fishes at a certain spot on the East Verde river, the probability of catching a trout in a very small time interval Δt is $\frac{3}{5}\,\Delta t$, with time being measured in hours. What is the probability that a person fishing at this spot for 2 hours does not catch a single trout? Also find the probability that in 4 hours he will catch at least 4 trout.

10. The number of tornadoes hitting a certain area each year is a random variable whose probability distribution can be approximated closely with a Poisson distribution having the parameter $\lambda = 8$. Find (a) the probability that in a given year fewer than 6 tornadoes will hit this area, and (b) the probability that in a given year 7, 8, or 9 tornadoes will hit the area.

11. The tanks which were manufactured by a certain factory during August, 1943, were given the serial numbers from 5010 to 5640, inclusive. What is the probability that if one of these tanks is captured it will have a serial number whose first two digits are, respectively, 5 and 4?

12. Suppose that the number of times a person has to take a test before he gets his driver's license is a random variable whose probability distribution can be approximated closely with a geometric distribution having the parameter $\theta = 0.8$. Find (a) the probability that a person gets his license on the first try, (b) the probability that a person gets his license on the third try, and (c) the probability that a person fails to get his license on the first four tries.

13. In a "torture test" a mattress is pounded until it becomes defective. If the probability that the mattress becomes defective on any one pounding is 0.001 and the poundings are, furthermore, independent, what is the probability that the mattress will become defective *after* it has been pounded 1000 times. (*Hint*: use the formula for the sum of the terms of a geometric progression and logarithms.)

14. The probability that a person who is exposed to a certain contageous disease will catch it is 0.20. Find the probability that the 20*th* person exposed to this disease is the 5th one to catch it.

15. The manager of a supermarket puts 5 packages of wild rice on a shelf in the gourmet department and another 5 packages on a shelf in the cereal department. If a customer comes into the store to buy wild rice, the probability that he will get it from the gourmet department is 0.60. What is the probability that there will be 3 packages of wild rice left in the cereal department the moment a customer takes the 5th and last package of wild rice of the shelf in the gourmet department?

16. (*Random walk*) Suppose that a point moves along the x-axis in jumps of one unit each, starting from the origin. Each jump may be to the right or to the left with respective probabilities of θ and $1 - \theta$. Furthermore, each jump is assumed to be independent of all others. If $\mathbf{x}$ is the coordinate of the point after n jumps, show that

$$f(x) = \binom{n}{\frac{x+n}{2}}[\theta(1-\theta)]^{n/2}\left(\frac{\theta}{1-\theta}\right)^{x/2}$$

for $x = \ldots, -2, -1, 0, 1, 2, \ldots$. Note that $\binom{n}{r} = 0$ if r is not an integer.

3.3 Multivariate Probability Distributions

In the preceding sections we considered experiments in which we were interested in *one* particular aspect, that is, the value assumed by *one* random variable. However, we also saw that given a discrete sample space with a probability measure, we can define over this sample space *more than one* random variable. Referring again to the sample space of Figure 3.1 we considered in the text the random variable **x**, the total number of heads, and in Exercise 1 on page 65 the random variable **y**, the number of heads minus the number of tails. Similarly, we could define over this sample space the random variable **z**, three times the number of heads plus five times the number of tails, the random variable **u**, the square of the number of heads times the third power of the number of tails, and so forth.

Given a discrete sample space with a probability measure over which we define two random variables **x** and **y**, the probability that the value of **x** is x *and* the value of **y** is y will be written $f(x, y)$. Specified for all pairs of values within the range of **x** and **y**, the probabilities $f(x, y)$ are referred to as values of the *joint distribution* or the *joint probability distribution* of the random variables **x** and **y**.

To give an example, let us consider an experiment which consists of 2 rolls of a balanced die. The sample space of this experiment consists of 36 points (see Figure 3.5), each of which will be assigned a probability of $\frac{1}{36}$. If the two random variables in which we are

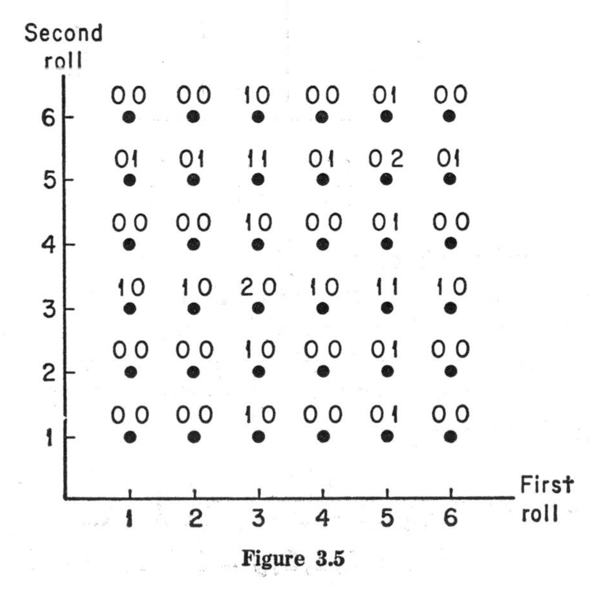

Figure 3.5

interested are **x**, the number of threes, and **y**, the number of fives obtained in the two rolls of the die, each element of the sample space is assigned two numbers as indicated in Figure 3.5. The first number is the value of **x** at that point and the second number is the value of **y**.

To obtain $f(x, y)$ for any pair of values x and y, we have only to add the probabilities of those elements of the sample space to which these particular values are assigned. For instance, $f(1, 0) = \frac{8}{36}$ in our example since eight of the points, each with a probability of $\frac{1}{36}$, were assigned the ordered pair of numbers 1 and 0. Proceeding in this way, it is easy to verify that the values of the joint distribution of the given random variables **x** and **y** are as shown inside the following table:

		x = 0	x = 1	x = 2	
y	0	$\frac{16}{36}$	$\frac{8}{36}$	$\frac{1}{36}$	$\frac{25}{36}$
	1	$\frac{8}{36}$	$\frac{2}{36}$		$\frac{10}{36}$
	2	$\frac{1}{36}$			$\frac{1}{36}$
		$\frac{25}{36}$	$\frac{10}{36}$	$\frac{1}{36}$	

As in the *univariate* case, that is, in the case of one random variable, it is desirable to express joint distributions of 2 random variables by means of formulas which enable us to calculate the various probabilities by substituting appropriate values for x and y. As will be shown in Section 3.3.1, we can thus write for the *bivariate* distribution of our example

$$f(x, y) = \frac{2!}{x!y!(2-x-y)!}\left(\frac{1}{6}\right)^{x+y}\left(\frac{4}{6}\right)^{2-x-y}$$

$$\text{for } x = 0, 1, 2; y = 0, 1, 2; \quad \text{and } x + y \leq 2$$

For instance, substituting $x = 1$ and $y = 1$, we obtain

$$f(1, 1) = \frac{2!}{1!1!0!}\left(\frac{1}{6}\right)^2\left(\frac{4}{6}\right)^0 = \frac{2}{36}$$

which agrees with the value shown in the above table.

It is of interest to note that the numbers given in the *bottom margin* of the table for the probabilities $f(x, y)$, *the totals of the respective columns,* are in fact the probabilities that the random variable **x** will assume the values 0, 1, and 2. In other words, the column totals give the values of the probability distribution of the random variable **x**; by the same token the row totals, the values given in the *righthand margin* of the table, give the values of the probability distribution of the random variable **y**.

In general, given the joint probabilities $f(x, y)$, the probability distribution of the random variable **x** alone is given by

$$f(x) = \sum_y f(x, y) \tag{3.3.1}$$

with the summation extending over all values within the range of **y** for which $f(x, y)$ exists, and the probability distribution of the random variable **y** alone is given by

$$g(y) = \sum_x f(x, y) \tag{3.3.2}$$

with the summation extending over all values within the range of **x** for which $f(x, y)$ exists. Obtaining the probability distributions of **x** and **y**, thus, from their joint distribution, it is customary to refer to them, respectively, as the *marginal distribution* of **x** and the *marginal distribution* of **y**.

When dealing with two random variables it may also be of interest to know the probability that **x** assumes the value x *given* that the value of **y** is y. Writing this probability as $f_1(x \mid y)$, we have

$$f_1(x \mid y) = \frac{f(x, y)}{g(y)} \qquad g(y) \neq 0 \tag{3.3.3}$$

in accordance with the definition on page 45. It is customary to refer to the conditional probabilities $f_1(x \mid y)$ as values of the *conditional distribution* of **x** given that the value of **y** is y. By the same token, the *conditional distribution* of **y** given that the value of **x** is x is given by

$$f_2(y \mid x) = \frac{f(x, y)}{f(x)} \qquad f(x) \neq 0 \tag{3.3.4}$$

Referring to our numerical example, we find that the probability of getting 1 three given that there are no fives is

$$f_1(1 \mid 0) = \frac{f(1, 0)}{g(0)} = \frac{8/36}{25/36} = \frac{8}{25}$$

and that the probability of getting 1 five given that there is 1 three is

$$f_2(1 \mid 1) = \frac{f(1, 1)}{f(1)} = \frac{2/36}{10/36} = \frac{2}{10}$$

The concept of a joint distribution is not limited to two random variables. Given a discrete sample space with a probability measure over which we define n random variables $\mathbf{x}_1$, $\mathbf{x}_2$, . . ., and $\mathbf{x}_n$, the probability that $\mathbf{x}_1$ assumes the value x_1, $\mathbf{x}_2$ assumes the value x_2, . . ., and $\mathbf{x}_n$ assumes the value x_n, will be written $f(x_1, x_2, \ldots, x_n)$. Specified for all n-tuples of values within the range of these random variables, the probabilities $f(x_1, x_2, \ldots, x_n)$ are referred to as values of their *joint probability distribution.*

To give an example, consider n flips of a balanced coin and let $\mathbf{x}_1$ be the number of heads obtained on the first flip, $\mathbf{x}_2$ the number of heads obtained on the second flip, . . . , and $\mathbf{x}_n$ the number of heads obtained on the nth flip. Assuming that each point of the sample space has the same probability, the joint distribution of these random variables is given by

$$f(x_1, x_2, \ldots, x_n) = (\tfrac{1}{2})^n \quad \text{for} \quad x_1 = 0 \text{ or } 1,\ x_2 = 0, \text{ or } 1, \ldots, \text{ and } \quad x_n = 0 \text{ or } 1$$

When dealing with more than two random variables, we can also speak of marginal distributions, joint marginal distributions, conditional distributions, and joint conditional distributions. For instance, in the *trivariate* case, the *marginal distribution* of x_3 is given by

$$f(x_3) = \sum_{x_1} \sum_{x_2} f(x_1, x_2, x_3)$$

with the summation extending over all pairs of values within the ranges of $\mathbf{x}_1$ and $\mathbf{x}_2$ for which $f(x_1, x_2, x_3)$ is defined. The *joint marginal distribution* of x_1 and x_2 is given by

$$h(x_1, x_2) = \sum_{x_3} f(x_1, x_2, x_3)$$

with the summation extending over all values within the range of $\mathbf{x}_3$ for which $f(x_1, x_2, x_3)$ is defined. Also,

$$\phi_3(x_3 \mid x_1, x_2) = \frac{f(x_1, x_2, x_3)}{h(x_1, x_2)} \qquad h(x_1, x_2) \neq 0$$

gives the conditional distribution of $\mathbf{x}_3$ given that $\mathbf{x}_1$ and $\mathbf{x}_2$ assume the values x_1 and x_2, and

$$p_{12}(x_1, x_2 \mid x_3) = \frac{f(x_1, x_2, x_3)}{f(x_3)} \qquad f(x_3) \neq 0$$

gives the joint conditional distribution of $\mathbf{x}_1$ and $\mathbf{x}_2$ given that $\mathbf{x}_3$ assumes the value x_3. Another concept, that of a distribution function, is generalized to two or more random variables in Exercise 2 on page 88.

Questions of *independence* are also of special importance in connection with the distribution of n random variables. We shall say that, by definition, *the random variables* $\mathbf{x}_1, \mathbf{x}_2, \ldots,$ *and* $\mathbf{x}_n$ *are independent if and only if*

$$f(x_1, x_2, \ldots, x_n) = \prod_{i=1}^{n} f_i(x_i) \tag{3.3.5}$$

for all values within the ranges of these random variables for which $f(x_1, x_2, \ldots, x_n)$ *is defined.* Here $f(x_1, x_2, \ldots, x_n)$ and $f_i(x_i)$ are, respectively, values of the joint distribution of the n random variables and values of the marginal distribution of $\mathbf{x}_i$.

Referring again to the example on page 82, it is easy to show that the two random variables are *not independent.* For instance, $f(1, 1) = \frac{2}{36}$, and this does not equal the product of $f(1) = \frac{10}{36}$ and $g(1) = \frac{10}{36}$.

3.3.1 *The multinomial distribution*

An immediate generalization of the binomial distribution arises if we let each trial have more than two possible outcomes. Thus, in a public opinion poll a person may be for a candidate, against him, or undecided, the grade a student gets in a certain course may be an A, B, C, D, or F, and a card dealt from a standard deck of 52 playing cards may be one of four different suits.

Let us, thus, consider the case where each trial permits k mutually exclusive outcomes, the probability for the ith outcome is θ_i so that

$$\sum_{i=1}^{k} \theta_i = 1,$$

and there are n independent trials. The n-dimensional sample space of this experiment consists of k^n points, since each of the n coordinates (representing the successive trials) can assume one of k values (representing the k outcomes.) The random variables in which we shall be interested are $\mathbf{x}_1$, $\mathbf{x}_2$, . . . , and $\mathbf{x}_k$, where $\mathbf{x}_i$ is the number of times the ith outcome occurs in n trials. Proceeding as on page 67, let us first find the probability of getting x_1 outcomes of the first kind, x_2 outcomes of the second kind, . . . , and x_k outcomes of the kth kind in some *specified* order. As there is one factor θ_1 for each outcome of the first kind, one factor θ_2 for each outcome of the second kind, and so forth, this probability is

$$\theta_1^{x_1}\theta_2^{x_2} \cdot \ldots \cdot \theta_k^{x_k}$$

with

$$\sum_{i=1}^{k} x_i = n$$

In other words, the above probability is assigned to each point of the sample space which represents *in a specified order* x_1 outcomes of the first kind, x_2 outcomes of the second kind, etc. To find the probability of getting x_1 outcomes of the first kind, x_2 outcomes of the second kind, etc., *in any order*, we have only to multiply

$$\theta_1^{x_1}\theta_2^{x_2} \cdot \ldots \cdot \theta_k^{x_k}$$

by

$$\frac{n!}{x_1!\,x_2! \cdot \ldots \cdot x_k!}$$

the number of ways in which n trials can consist of x_1 outcomes of the first kind, x_2 outcomes of the second kind, . . . , and x_k outcomes of the kth kind. [See (2.2.3) on page 22 and also Exercise 25 on page 31.] Hence, the joint distribution of the random variables $\mathbf{x}_1, \mathbf{x}_2, \ldots,$ and $\mathbf{x}_k$ is given by

$$f(x_1, x_2, \ldots, x_k) = \frac{n!}{x_1!x_2! \cdot \ldots \cdot x_k!} \theta_1^{x_1}\theta_2^{x_2} \cdot \ldots \cdot \theta_k^{x_k} \tag{3.3.6}$$

for $x_i = 0, 1, \ldots, n$ for each i, subject to the restriction that

$$\sum_{i=1}^{k} x_i = n$$

This joint distribution is called the *multinomial distribution*; it owes its name to the fact that for various values of the x_i we obtain terms of the multinomial expansion of $(\theta_1 + \theta_2 + \ldots + \theta_k)^n$.

Note that k random variables having a multinomial distribution cannot be independent; in fact, given the values of any $k - 1$, that of the kth random variable is automatically determined since

$$\sum_{i=1}^{k} x_i = n$$

This is why for $k = 2$ the multinomial distribution reduces to the binomial distribution, where we ignore the second random variable, *the number of failures*.

To give an illustration, suppose that the probability that a rifleman hits the bulls-eye is 0.30, the probability that he hits the target but not the bulls-eye is 0.60, and the probability that he misses the target altogether is 0.10. What we would like to know is the probability that in 5 shots he will hit the bulls-eye twice, the target but not the bulls-eye twice, and miss the target altogether once. Substituting $x_1 = 2$, $x_2 = 2$, $x_3 = 1$, $n = 5$, $\theta_1 = 0.3$, $\theta_2 = 0.6$, and $\theta_3 = 0.1$ into (3.3.6), we get

$$f(2, 2, 1) = \frac{5!}{2!2!1!} (0.3)^2(0.6)^2(0.1)^1$$

which is approximately equal to 0.10. Also note that the joint distribution on page 82 is a multinomial distribution with $n = 2$, $\theta_1 = \frac{1}{6}$, $\theta_2 = \frac{1}{6}$, and $\theta_3 = \frac{4}{6}$. We ignored the third random variable since its value is automatically determined by the other two.

EXERCISES

1. Given a joint probability distribution whose values $f(x, y)$ are

$f(1, 1) = 5/27 \quad f(1, 2) = 1/27 \quad f(1, 3) = 3/27$

$f(2, 1) = 4/27 \quad f(2, 2) = 3/27 \quad f(2, 3) = 4/27$

$f(3, 1) = 2/27 \quad f(3, 2) = 3/27 \quad f(3, 3) = 2/27$

find

(a) the marginal distribution of $\mathbf{x}$

(b) the marginal distribution of $\mathbf{y}$

(c) the conditional distribution of $\mathbf{x}$ given that the value of $\mathbf{y}$ is 2

(d) the conditional distribution of $\mathbf{y}$ given that the value of $\mathbf{x}$ is 1

2. Given the random variables $\mathbf{x}_1$, $\mathbf{x}_2$, ..., and $\mathbf{x}_n$, the probability that $\mathbf{x}_1$ assumes a value less than or equal to x_1, $\mathbf{x}_2$ assumes a value less than or equal to x_2, ..., and $\mathbf{x}_n$ assumes a value less than or equal to x_n, is written $F(x_1, x_2, \ldots, x_n)$. Specified for all real values of the x's, the probabilities $F(x_1, x_2, \ldots, x_n)$ are referred to as values of the *joint distribution function* of the n random variables. Referring to the illustration on page 82, find

(a) $F(-1, 1)$ (c) $F(1, 2)$ (e) $F(0, 10)$

(b) $F(0, \frac{3}{5})$ (d) $F(\frac{2}{5}, \frac{7}{5})$ (f) $F(6, 6)$

3. Referring to the joint probability distribution of Exercise 1, find

(a) $F(0, 1)$ (c) $F(2, 3)$ (e) $F(4, 1)$

(b) $F(\frac{3}{5}, \frac{5}{2})$ (d) $F(\frac{1}{3}, \frac{7}{3})$ (f) $F(8, 10)$

4. Check whether the two random variables of Exercise 1 are independent.

5. Drawing (with replacement) 8 cards from a standard deck of 52 playing cards, what is the probability of getting 2 cards in each of the four suits?

6. Find the probability of getting 2 ones, 0 twos, 3 threes, 1 four, 1 five, and 3 sixes in 10 rolls of a balanced die.

7. According to the Mendelian theory of heredity, if plants with round yellow seeds are crossbred with plants with wrinkled green seeds, the probability of getting a plant with round yellow seeds is $\frac{9}{16}$, the probability of getting a plant with wrinkled yellow seeds is $\frac{3}{16}$, the probability of getting a plant with round green seeds is $\frac{3}{16}$, and the probability of getting a plant with wrinkled green seeds is $\frac{1}{16}$. Find the probability that among 10 plants thus obtained there are 4 with round yellow seeds, 3 with wrinkled yellow seeds, 2 with round green seeds, and 1 with wrinkled green seeds.

8. The probability that a car driven from Denver to Chicago meets with a serious accident is 0.02, the probability that it meets with a minor accident is 0.05, and hence the probability that it does not meet with an accident is 0.93. What is the probability that among 6 cars driven from Denver to Chicago 5 arrive without an accident while 1 has a minor accident?

9. (*Extension of hypergeometric distribution*) Consider a set of N elements among which a_1 are labeled 1, a_2 are labeled 2, . . . , a_k are labeled k, and

$$\sum_{i=1}^{k} a_i = N$$

If each subset of n elements has an equal probability of being selected, find the probability that such a subset will contain x_1 elements labeled 1, x_2 elements labeled 2, . . ., and x_k elements labeled k.

10. A library shelf contains 10 detective stories, 5 novels, and 8 biographies. If each subset of 4 of these 23 books has an equal chance of being selected, what is the probability that such a subset contains 2 detective stories, 1 novel, and 1 biography?

11. If the random variables $\mathbf{x}_1, \mathbf{x}_2, \ldots, \mathbf{x}_k$ have the multinomial distribution (3.3.6), show that the marginal distribution of $\mathbf{x}_i$ is a binomial distribution with the parameters n and θ_i, with $i = 1, 2, \ldots,$ or k.

BIBLIOGRAPHY

Binomial probabilities for $n = 2$ to $n = 49$ may be found in

Tables of the *Binomial Probability Distribution.* National Bureau of Standards Applied Mathematics Series No. 6. Washington, D. C.: U.S. Government Printing Office, 1950.

and for $n = 50$ to $n = 100$ in

Romig, H. G., *50–100 Binomial Tables,* New York: John Wiley & Sons, Inc., 1953.

Both of these tables also contain values of $\sum_{i=x}^{n} b(i; n, \theta)$.

The most widely used table of Poisson probabilities is

Molina, E. C., *Poisson's Exponential Binomial Limit,* New York: D. Van Nostrand Company, Inc., 1943.

Chapter 4

Mathematical Expectation: Discrete Random Variables

4.1 Mathematical Expectation

If someone buys a ticket in a lottery which promises to pay \$1000 to the holder of one of 10,000 tickets issued, his *expectation* is \$0.10, namely, the product of the amount he stands to win and the probability of winning it. Of course, a person who buys such a lottery ticket does not really "expect" to win \$0.10; he wins \$1000 or nothing and he does not "expect" \$0.10 in the sense of wishful thinking or for other subjective reasons. Instead, his expectation of \$0.10 must be interpreted in the sense of an *average*, that is, persons buying such tickets will on the average win \$0.10.

To consider a slightly more complicated example, suppose that another lottery, which also issues 10,000 tickets, awards three prizes: a first prize of \$1000, a second prize of \$500, and a third prize of \$100. If we divided the total of \$1600 among the holders of the 10,000 tickets, this would give \$0.16 per ticket or, in other words, a *mathematical expectation* of \$0.16 per ticket. Note that this result could also have been obtained by multiplying each amount by the probability that it will be won by the holder of any given ticket, namely,

$$1000(0.0001) + 500(0.0001) + 100(0.0001) + 0(0.9997) = 0.16$$

where 0.9997 is the probability that the ticket will not win anything at all.

The amount a person wins in a lottery is a random variable, and as we indicated, the mathematical expectation of such a random variable is the sum obtained by multiplying each value within its range by the corresponding probability. More generally, *if* $\{x_1, x_2, x_3, \ldots\}$ *is the range of a random variable which assumes the value* x_i *with the probability* $f(x_i)$, *then the mathematical expectation of* **x** *or the expected value of* **x** *is*

$$E(\mathbf{x}) = \sum_i x_i f(x_i) \tag{4.1.1}$$

The summation extends from $i = 1$ to $i = n$ or ∞, depending on whether the range of **x** has n elements or whether it consists of an infinite sequence. When the range of **x** is infinite,

$$\sum_{i=1}^{\infty} x_i f(x_i)$$

may converge or diverge; if it diverges, the corresponding mathematical expectation *does not exist.*

For instance, if **x** is the result obtained in one roll of a balanced die, the range of this random variable is $\{1, 2, 3, 4, 5, 6\}$, the probabilities are all equal to $\frac{1}{6}$ and the expected value of **x** is

$$E(\mathbf{x}) = 1\left(\frac{1}{6}\right) + 2\left(\frac{1}{6}\right) + 3\left(\frac{1}{6}\right) + 4\left(\frac{1}{6}\right) + 5\left(\frac{1}{6}\right) + 6\left(\frac{1}{6}\right) = \frac{7}{2}$$

This means that a person rolling a balanced die will on the average get $3\frac{1}{2}$. (Note that on any one roll he cannot possibly get this amount and it is in this sense that we say that female graduates of a certain university can *expect* to have 1.43 children or that in a certain area a person can *expect* 2.78 colds a year.)

There are many problems in statistics in which we are interested not only in the expected value of a random variable **x**, but also in the expected values of random variables *related to* **x**. By this we mean the following: *given a random variable* **x**, $g(\mathbf{x})$ *is a random variable whose value is equal to* $g(x)$ *whenever* **x** *assumes the value* x. Thus, if for a given point of the sample space the value of **x** is 3, then the value of $\mathbf{x}^2$ is 9, the value of $2\mathbf{x} + 1$ is 7, and in general the value of $g(\mathbf{x})$ is $g(3)$. [Note that $g(x)$ must be single valued; otherwise $g(\mathbf{x})$ cannot be a random variable.] Since the probability that the value of $\mathbf{x}$ is x_i equals the probability that the value of $g(\mathbf{x})$ is $g(x_i)$, it follows from (4.1.1) that

$$E[g(\mathbf{x})] = \sum_i g(x_i)f(x_i) \tag{4.1.2}$$

To illustrate, if $\mathbf{x}$ is again the result obtained in one roll of a balanced die, then

$$E(\mathbf{x}^2) = 1\left(\frac{1}{6}\right) + 4\left(\frac{1}{6}\right) + 9\left(\frac{1}{6}\right) + 16\left(\frac{1}{6}\right) + 25\left(\frac{1}{6}\right) + 36\left(\frac{1}{6}\right)$$

$$= \frac{91}{6}$$

This means that if a person receives (in dollars) the square of the amount he rolls with one die, he will get on the average \$15$\frac{1}{6}$. It will be left to the reader to show that for this same example $E(e^{\mathbf{x}})$ is approximately 106.1.

The calculation of mathematical expectations is often simplified by using the following theorems, which are immediate consequences of (4.1.2):

THEOREM 4.1:*
If c is a constant, $E(\mathbf{c}) = c$.

THEOREM 4.2:
If c is a constant, $E[c \cdot g(\mathbf{x})] = c \cdot E[g(\mathbf{x})]$.

THEOREM 4.3:

$$E\left[\sum_{j=1}^{k} g_j(\mathbf{x})\right] = \sum_{j=1}^{k} E[g_j(\mathbf{x})]$$

To prove these theorems we have only to refer to (4.1.2) and the rules for summations given in the Appendix on page 351. The details will be left to the reader, see Exercise 4 below.

The following is another useful theorem concerning mathematical expectations; its proof utilizes Theorems 4.1, 4.2, as well as 4.3:

THEOREM 4.4: Prove
If a and b are constants, $E(a\mathbf{x} + b) = a \cdot E(\mathbf{x}) + b$.

* Note that we have to use boldface type for the constant function $\mathbf{c}$, which assigns the constant c to each value within its domain.

The proof of this theorem will also be left to the reader, see Exercise 5 below.

The concept of mathematical expectation can easily be extended to apply to problems involving more than one random variable. Given two random variables **x** and **y**, whose joint distribution is given by the probabilities $f(x_i, y_j)$, we define

$$E[g(\mathbf{x}, \mathbf{y})] = \sum_i \sum_j g(x_i, y_j) f(x_i, y_j) \qquad (4.1.3)$$

with the summation extending over all pairs (x_i, y_j) within the respective domains of **x** and **y**. (As before, $g(x_i, y_j)$ must be single valued.) Introducing an appropriate notation, (4.1.3) can readily be extended to define the mathematical expectation of a function of more than two random variables.

To illustrate (4.1.3), let us refer to the bivariate distribution on page 82 and calculate $E(\mathbf{x}\cdot\mathbf{y})$. Omitting all terms where the value of either random variable is 0, we get

$$E(\mathbf{x}\cdot\mathbf{y}) = 1\cdot 1\cdot\left(\frac{2}{36}\right) = \frac{1}{18}$$

This means that if we multiply the number of threes obtained when rolling a pair of dice by the number of fives, we will on the average get $\frac{1}{18}$.

EXERCISES

1. If someone gives us \$8.00 each time that we roll a 1 with a balanced die, how much should we pay him when we roll a 2, 3, 4, 5, or 6 to make the game *equitable*? (A game is said to be equitable if the expected value of the amount we receive or pay is 0. If the amount we receive is taken to be positive, the amount we pay must be negative.)

2. If two teams are evenly matched, the probabilities that a World Series will end in 4, 5, 6, or 7 games are, respectively, $\frac{1}{8}$, $\frac{1}{4}$, $\frac{5}{16}$, and $\frac{5}{16}$. What is the expected length of a World Series for two teams that are evenly matched?

3. The probabilities that there will be 1, 2, 3, 4, 5, or 6 persons in a car traveling over the Apache Trail are 0.05, 0.43, 0.27, 0.12, 0.09, and 0.04, respectively. What is the expected number of persons per car?

4. (a) Prove Theorem 4.1, (b) Prove Theorem 4.2, (c) Prove Theorem 4.3.

5. Prove Theorem 4.4.

6. Referring to the random variables whose joint distribution is given in Exercise 1 on page 88, find (a) $E(\mathbf{x}^2)$, (b) $E(2\mathbf{x} - 3\mathbf{y})$, and (c) $E(\mathbf{xy})$.

7. (*Gambler's ruin*) Mr. Adams and Mr. Brown are betting on repeated flips of a balanced coin. At the start of the game Mr. Adams has a dollars, Mr. Brown has b dollars, at each flip the loser pays the winner one dollar, and the game is continued until either player has lost all the money with which he began. Show that the probability that Mr. Adams will win Mr. Brown's b dollars before he loses his a dollars is $p = a/(a + b)$. (*Hint*: make use of the fact that in an equitable game each player's expectation is zero.)

4.2 Moments

If $g(\mathbf{x}) = \mathbf{x}^r$, formula (4.1.2) yields what is called the *rth moment about the origin* of the distribution of $\mathbf{x}$. Using the symbol μ_r' we thus write

$$\mu_r' = E(\mathbf{x}^r) = \sum_i x_i^r \cdot f(x_i) \qquad (4.2.1)$$

for $r = 0, 1, 2, \ldots$. It should be noted that the term "moment" as it is used here is borrowed from the field of Physics. If the quantities $f(x_i)$ were point masses acting perpendicular to the x-axis at distances x_i from the origin, μ_1' would give the center of gravity, that is, the first moment divided by

$$\sum_i f(x_i) = 1.$$

Similarly, μ_2' would give the moment of inertia. This also explains why the moments μ_r' are called moments about the origin; in the analogy from Physics, the lever arm is in each case the distance from the origin.

For $r = 0$ we get $\mu_0' = 1$, since this is merely the sum of the probabilities $f(x_i)$. For $r = 1$ we get the expected value of the random variable $\mathbf{x}$, itself, and since this is of special importance in statistics we shall write it simply as μ. Thus, $\mu = \mu_1' = E(\mathbf{x})$ and we refer to it as the *mean* of the distribution of $\mathbf{x}$. Informally, the mean is what in everyday language is referred to as an average. We shall see later that for $n = 100$ and $\theta = \frac{1}{2}$ the mean of the binomial distribution is $\mu = 50$; flipping a balanced coin 100 times we can, thus, expect (on the average) 50 heads.

If $g(\mathbf{x}) = (\mathbf{x} - \mu)^r$, formula (4.1.2) yields what is called the *rth moment about the mean* of the distribution of **x**. Using the symbol μ_r we thus write

$$\mu_r = E[(\mathbf{x} - \mu)^r] = \sum_i (x_i - \mu)^r f(x_i) \tag{4.2.2}$$

for $r = 0, 1, 2, \ldots$. It is easy to verify that $\mu_0 = 1$ and $\mu_1 = 0$; the first of these quantities is simply the sum of the probabilities $f(x_i)$, and for the second we can write

$$\mu_1 = E(\mathbf{x} - \mu) = E(\mathbf{x}) - E(\mathbf{u}) = \mu - \mu = 0$$

using Theorems 4.1 and 4.3.

Moments about the mean are of special importance in statistics since they can be used to describe the *shape* of a probability distribution. The second moment about the mean tells us something about the *spread* or *dispersion* of a distribution; that is, it tells us how close one can expect the value of a random variable to be to the mean. A brief discussion of how the third moment about the mean is used to describe another important feature of probability distributions, their *symmetry* or *skewness*, is given in Exercise 8 on page 98.

In view of its importance in statistics, μ_2 is given a special name and a special symbol. It is called the *variance* of the distribution of **x** and it is written σ^2. Alternate symbols used for the variance of the distribution of **x** are $V(\mathbf{x})$ and $var(\mathbf{x})$. Thus,

$$\sigma^2 = \mu_2 = E[(\mathbf{x} - \mu)^2] \tag{4.2.3}$$

and σ, the positive square root of μ_2, is called the *standard deviation* of the distribution.

In many instances moments about the mean are obtained by first calculating moments about the origin and then expressing the μ_r in terms of the μ'_r. Using the binomial expansion and Theorems 4.1 through 4.3, it can readily be shown that

THEOREM 4.5:

$$\mu_r = \mu'_r - \binom{r}{1}\mu'_{r-1}\mu + \ldots + (-1)^i\binom{r}{i}\mu'_{r-i}\mu^i + \ldots + (-1)^{r-1}(r-1)\mu^r$$

for $r = 1, 2, 3, \ldots$.

Leaving the general proof to the reader in Exercise 7 on page 98, let us prove it here for the important special case where $r = 2$. We thus get

$$\begin{aligned} \mu_2 &= E[(\mathbf{x} - \mu)^2] \\ &= E(\mathbf{x}^2 - 2\mathbf{x}\mu + \mu^2) \\ &= E(\mathbf{x}^2) - 2\mu E(\mathbf{x}) + E(\mu^2) \\ &= \mu_2' - 2\mu^2 + \mu^2 \\ &= \mu_2' - \mu^2 \end{aligned}$$

In view of the importance of the variance, $\sigma^2 = \mu_2' - \mu^2$ is one of the most widely used formulas of mathematical statistics.

4.2.1 *Chebyshev's theorem*

To see how close one can expect the value of a random variable to be to the mean of its distribution, let us now prove the following theorem, called *Chebyshev's Theorem*, or *Chebyshev's Inequality*, after the Russian mathematician P. L. Chebyshev (1821–1894):

THEOREM 4.6:
If $\mathbf{x}$ *is a discrete random variable whose distribution has the mean* μ *and the standard deviation* σ, *then for any positive constant* k *the probability that* $\mathbf{x}$ *assumes a value less than* $\mu - k\sigma$ *or greater than* $\mu + k\sigma$ *is less than* $1/k^2$.*

Before we prove this theorem, let us stress its significance by means of an example. Considering an experiment which consists of 100 flips of a balanced coin, it will be shown in Exercise 2 on page 104 that the mean and the standard deviation of the distribution of the total number of heads are $\mu = 50$ and $\sigma = 5$. Using Theorem 4.6 with $k = 3$, we can then assert that the probability of getting more than 65 heads or fewer than 35 is less than $\frac{1}{9}$. Similarly, for $k = 5$ we can assert that the probability of getting more than 75 heads or fewer than 25 is less than 0.04.

* Using the notation referred to in the footnote to page 63, the result of this theorem can be written as

$$P(|\mathbf{x} - \mu| > k\sigma) < 1/k^2.$$

As will be seen later, Theorem 4.6 holds also when $\mathbf{x}$ is a continuous random variable.

another form is:

$$P(|X-u| > c) \leq \sigma^2/c^2$$

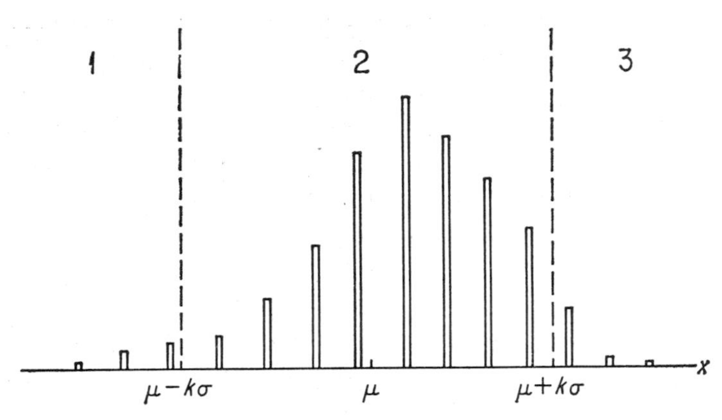

Figure 4.1

To prove Theorem 4.6, let us write as before

$$\sigma^2 = \sum_i (x_i - \mu)^2 f(x_i)$$

with the summation extending over all x_i within the range of **x**. Dividing this sum into three parts as indicated in Figure 4.1, we get

$$\sigma^2 = \sum_1 (x_i - \mu)^2 f(x_i) + \sum_2 (x_i - \mu)^2 f(x_i) + \sum_3 (x_i - \mu)^2 f(x_i)$$

where $\sum_1$ is summed over all x_i less than $\mu - k\sigma$, $\sum_2$ is summed over all x_i greater than or equal to $\mu - k\sigma$ but less than or equal to $\mu + k\sigma$, and $\sum_3$ is summed over all x_i greater than $\mu + k\sigma$. Since the quantities $(x_i - \mu)^2 f(x_i)$ are non-negative, we have

$$\sigma^2 \geq \sum_1 (x_i - \mu)^2 f(x_i) + \sum_3 (x_i - \mu)^2 f(x_i)$$

and since, furthermore, the absolute difference between x_i and μ exceeds $k\sigma$ for the lefthand and righthand parts of Figure 4.1, that is, for $\sum_1$ and $\sum_3$, it follows that

$$\sigma^2 > \sum_1 k^2\sigma^2 f(x_i) + \sum_3 k^2\sigma^2 f(x_i)$$

and that

$$\frac{1}{k^2} > \sum_1 f(x_i) + \sum_3 f(x_i)$$

assuming that $\sigma \neq 0$. Since the righthand side of this last inequality stands for the probability that the value of **x** is less than $\mu - k\sigma$ or greater than $\mu + k\sigma$, this completes the proof of Theorem 4.6.

As an immediate consequence of Theorem 4.6 we find that values of **x** falling on the interval from $\mu - k\sigma$ to $\mu + k\sigma$, inclusive, account for at least $1 - 1/k^2$ of the total probability of 1. In other words, the probability that **x** assumes a value within 2 standard deviations of the mean is at least $\frac{3}{4}$, the probability that it assumes a value within 3 standard deviations of the mean is at least $\frac{8}{9}$, the probability that it assumes a value within 4 standard deviations of the mean is at least $\frac{15}{16}$, and so forth. It is in this sense that σ controls the spread or dispersion of the distribution of **x**.

EXERCISES

1. Using the probabilities given on page 64, find the mean and the variance of the distribution of the number of heads obtained in three flips of a coin.

2. Given a random variable whose range is the set $\{-1, 1\}$ and whose probability distribution is $f(-1) = \frac{1}{2}$ and $f(1) = \frac{1}{2}$. Find the mean and the variance of this distribution.

3. Show that $E[(\mathbf{x} - c)^2]$ is a minimum when $c = \mu$.

4. Prove Theorem 4.5 for $r = 1$ and $r = 3$.

5. Show that $\text{var}(\mathbf{x} + c) = \text{var}(\mathbf{x})$.

6. Show that $\text{var}(a\mathbf{x} + b) = a^2 \text{var}(\mathbf{x})$.

7. Prove Theorem 4.5.

8. (*Symmetry and Skewness*) The symmetry or lack thereof (skewness) of a probability distribution is usually measured by means of the quantity

$$\alpha_3 = \frac{\mu_3}{\sigma^3}$$

Find α_3 for each of the following distributions, which have equal means and equal standard deviations:

(a) $f(1) = 0.05, f(2) = 0.15, f(3) = 0.30, f(4) = 0.30, f(5) = 0.15,$ $f(6) = 0.05$

(b) $f(1) = 0.05, f(2) = 0.20, f(3) = 0.15, f(4) = 0.45, f(5) = 0.10,$
$f(6) = 0.05.$

Also draw histograms of these two probability distribution and note that whereas the first is *symmetrical,* the second has a "tail" on the lefthand side and is said to be *negatively skewed.*

9. What is the least value of k in Chebyshev's Theorem for which the probability that $\mathbf{x}$ assumes a value greater than $\mu + k\sigma$ or less than $\mu - k\sigma$ is less than 0.05?

10. Letting $k\sigma = c$ in Chebyshev's Theorem, what does this theorem assert about the probability that $\mathbf{x}$ assumes a value greater than $\mu + c$ or less than $\mu - c$? What does it assert about the probability that $\mathbf{x}$ assumes a value greater than or equal to $\mu - c$ but less than or equal to $\mu + c$?

4.3 Moments of Special Probability Distributions

In this section we shall derive some of the lower moments, mainly μ and σ^2, of the *binomial, hypergeometric,* and *Poisson* distributions. Alternate and sometimes more elegant methods of obtaining these moments will be treated in Section 4.4. The means and variances of the *geometric, discrete uniform,* and *negative binomial* distributions are given in the exercises on pages 105 and 106 and also in the exercises following Section 4.4.

4.3.1 *Moments of the binomial distribution*

There are many ways in which one can derive the moments of the binomial distribution. The method which we shall use here has the advantage that it follows directly from the definition of moments. Alternate derivations based on moment generating functions and theory concerning the distribution of sums of random variables will be given in Sections 4.4.1 and 7.4.

THEOREM 4.7:
The mean and variance of the binomial distribution $b(x; n, \theta)$ are

$$\mu = n\theta \qquad \textit{and} \qquad \sigma^2 = n\theta(1 - \theta) \tag{4.3.1}$$

Substituting (3.2.1), the formula for $b(x; n, \theta)$, into (4.2.1) with

$r = 1$, let us derive the formula for μ by writing

$$\mu = \sum_{x=0}^{n} x \cdot \binom{n}{x} \theta^x (1 - \theta)^{n-x}$$

$$= \sum_{x=1}^{n} \frac{n!}{(x - 1)!(n - x)!} \theta^x (1 - \theta)^{n-x}$$

omitting the term where $x = 0$, which is 0, and cancelling the x against the first factor in $x!$. Then, factoring out the factor n in $n! = n(n - 1)!$ and one factor θ we get

$$\mu = n\theta \sum_{x=1}^{n} \binom{n - 1}{x - 1} \theta^{x-1} (1 - \theta)^{n-x}$$

and if we let $y = x - 1$ and $m = n - 1$, this becomes

$$\mu = n\theta \sum_{y=0}^{m} \binom{m}{y} \theta^y (1 - \theta)^{m-y}$$

Since the summation on the righthand side of this last equation is equal to

$$\sum_{y=0}^{m} b(y; m, \theta) = 1,$$

it follows that $\mu = n\theta$.

To derive the formula for σ^2, let us first determine $E[\mathbf{x}(\mathbf{x} - 1)]$ duplicating, for all practical purposes, the steps used above. We thus get

$$E[\mathbf{x}(\mathbf{x} - 1)] = \sum_{x=0}^{n} x(x - 1)\binom{n}{x} \theta^x (1 - \theta)^{n-x}$$

$$= \sum_{x=2}^{n} \frac{n!}{(x - 2)!(n - x)!} \theta^x (1 - \theta)^{n-x}$$

$$= n(n - 1)\theta^2 \sum_{x=2}^{n} \binom{n - 2}{x - 2} \theta^{x-2} (1 - \theta)^{n-x}$$

and letting $y = x - 2$ and $m = n - 2$

$$E[\mathbf{x}(\mathbf{x} - 1)] = n(n - 1)\theta^2 \sum_{y=0}^{m} \binom{m}{y} \theta^y (1 - \theta)^{m-y}$$

$$= n(n - 1)\theta^2$$

Since $E[\mathbf{x}(\mathbf{x} - 1)] = E(\mathbf{x}^2) - E(\mathbf{x})$ we get

$$\mu_2' = E(\mathbf{x}^2) = E[\mathbf{x}(\mathbf{x} - 1)] + E(\mathbf{x}) = n(n - 1)\theta^2 + n\theta$$

and using the formula $\sigma^2 = \mu_2' - \mu^2$ (see page 96), we finally obtain

$$\begin{aligned}\sigma^2 &= n(n - 1)\theta^2 + n\theta - n^2\theta^2 \\ &= n\theta(1 - \theta).\end{aligned}$$

The fact that the mean of a binomial distribution equals $n\theta$ should really have been expected. If a coin is flipped 400 times, we expect on the average $400(\frac{1}{2}) = 200$ heads; if a balanced die is rolled 120 times, we expect on the average $120(\frac{1}{6}) = 20$ sixes; and if the probability that any one person will answer a mail questionaire is 0.10, we expect on the average $1000(0.10) = 100$ responses to 1000 questionaires. The formula for the variance of a binomial distribution does not have any immediate (intuitive) significance, but, being a measure of variation or dispersion, it has many important applications. To illustrate one, let us consider the following modification: suppose we are not interested in the random variable $\mathbf{x}$ having the binomial distribution $b(x; n, \theta)$, but in the random variable $\mathbf{x}/n$, namely, *the proportion of successes in n trials.* Using the results just obtained together with Theorem 4.4 and Exercise 6 on page 98, we obtain

$$E\left(\frac{\mathbf{x}}{n}\right) = \theta \quad \text{and} \quad \text{var}\left(\frac{\mathbf{x}}{n}\right) = \frac{\theta(1 - \theta)}{n} \tag{4.3.2}$$

If we now apply Chebyshev's Theorem in the form in which it is given in Exercise 10 on page 99, we can assert that *for any positive constant c, the probability that* $\mathbf{x}/n$ *assumes a value greater than* $\theta + c$ *or less than* $\theta - c$ *is less than* $\frac{\theta(1 - \theta)}{nc^2}$. Hence, when $n \to \infty$, the probability that $\mathbf{x}/n$ assumes a value which differs from θ by more than any arbitrary constant c approaches 0. In other words, when $n \to \infty$, the probability that $\mathbf{x}/n$ assumes a value arbitrarily close to θ approaches 1. Using Chebyshev's Theorem, thus, in connection with the binomial distribution, it is often referred to as the *Law of Large Numbers*. Note that the Law of Large Numbers applies to the proportion of successes, not to their actual number. It is a fallacy to assume that when n is large the value of $\mathbf{x}$, the number of successes, must necessarily be close to $n\theta$.

4.3.2 *Moments of the hypergeometric distribution*

Using methods which are very similar to those employed in Section 4.3.1, let us now prove the following theorem concerning the mean and variance of the hypergeometric distribution:

THEOREM 4.8:
The mean and variance of the hypergeometric distribution $h(x; n, a, b)$ *are*

$$\mu = \frac{na}{a+b}$$

$$\sigma^2 = \frac{nab(a+b-n)}{(a+b)^2(a+b-1)} \qquad (4.3.3)$$

To derive the formula for μ, let us substitute (3.2.2), the formula for $h(x; n, a, b)$, into (4.2.1) with $r = 1$, getting

$$\mu = \sum_{x=0}^{n} x \cdot \frac{\binom{a}{x}\binom{b}{n-x}}{\binom{a+b}{n}}$$

$$= \sum_{x=1}^{n} \frac{a!}{(x-1)!(a-x)!} \cdot \frac{\binom{b}{n-x}}{\binom{a+b}{n}}$$

Then, factoring out $a/\binom{a+b}{n}$ we obtain

$$\mu = \frac{a}{\binom{a+b}{n}} \sum_{x=1}^{n} \binom{a-1}{x-1}\binom{b}{n-x}$$

and letting $y = x - 1$ and $m = n - 1$, this becomes

$$\mu = \frac{a}{\binom{a+b}{n}} \sum_{y=0}^{m} \binom{a-1}{y}\binom{b}{m-y}$$

Using Theorem 2.9 on page 27, we finally get

$$\mu = \frac{a}{\binom{a+b}{n}} \cdot \binom{a+b-1}{n-1} = \frac{na}{a+b}$$

To derive the formula for σ^2, we proceed as in the case of the binomial distribution, namely, by first finding $E[\mathbf{x}(\mathbf{x}-1)]$. Leaving it to the reader to show that

$$E[\mathbf{x}(\mathbf{x}-1)] = \frac{a(a-1)n(n-1)}{(a+b)(a+b-1)}$$

in Exercise 3 on page 104, we obtain the desired result by substituting this expression for $E[\mathbf{x}(\mathbf{x}-1)]$ into

$$\sigma^2 = E[\mathbf{x}(\mathbf{x}-1)] + \mu - \mu^2$$

where $\mu = na/(a+b)$.

4.3.3 *Moments of the Poisson distribution*

Having derived the Poisson distribution as a limiting case of the binomial distribution when $n \to \infty$, $\theta \to 0$, and $n\theta = \lambda$ is fixed, we can obtain the mean and the variance of the Poisson distribution by applying the same limiting process to the mean and the variance of the binomial distribution. We thus find that

THEOREM 4.9:
The mean and variance of the Poisson distribution $f(x; \lambda)$ are

$$\mu = \lambda \quad \text{and} \quad \sigma^2 = \lambda \tag{4.3.4}$$

These formulas can also be derived directly, that is, without reference to the corresponding moments of the binomial distribution. For instance, for the mean of the Poisson distribution we can write

$$\mu = \sum_{x=0}^{\infty} x \cdot \frac{\lambda^x e^{-\lambda}}{x!} = \lambda \sum_{x=1}^{\infty} \frac{\lambda^{x-1} e^{-\lambda}}{(x-1)!}$$

starting the summation with 1 since the term corresponding to $x = 0$ is 0, cancelling the x against the first factor in $x! = x(x-1)!$, and factoring out λ. Then, letting $y = x - 1$, we get

$$\mu = \lambda \sum_{y=0}^{\infty} \frac{\lambda^y e^{-\lambda}}{y!} = \lambda \sum_{y=0}^{\infty} f(y; \lambda) = \lambda$$

The formula for σ^2 may, similarly, be derived by first finding $E[\mathbf{x}(\mathbf{x} - 1)]$ as in the case of the binomial and hypergeometric distributions. A recursion formula which readily yields moments about the mean of the Poisson distribution is given in Exercise 6 below.

EXERCISES

1. A balanced coin is flipped 16 times. Using Chebyshev's Theorem, what can we assert about the probability of getting more than 14 or fewer than 2 heads? Use Table I on page 355 to find the *exact* probability of getting more than 14 or fewer than 2 heads in 16 flips of a balanced coin.

2. A balanced coin is flipped 100 times. Using Chebyshev's Theorem, what can we assert about the probability of getting more than 62 or fewer than 38 heads? Note how much Chebyshev's Inequality "gives away" by comparing your result with the actual probability of getting more than 62 or fewer than 38 heads in 100 flips of a balanced coin, namely, 0.012.

3. Show that for a random variable having the hypergeometric distribution $h(x; n, a, b)$ the expected value of $\mathbf{x}(\mathbf{x} - 1)$ is

$$\frac{a(a-1)n(n-1)}{(a+b)(a+b-1)}$$

4. Show that the mean of the hypergeometric distribution equals that of the binomial distribution with $\theta = a/(a + b)$, and when n is very small compared to $a + b$, the variance of the hypergeometric distribution approaches that of the binomial distribution with $\theta = a/(a + b)$. Also show that for $n > 1$ the variance of the hypergeometric distribution is always less than the variance of the binomial distribution with $\theta = a/(a + b)$.

5. Show that for the Poisson distribution $f(x; \lambda)$ the expected value of $\mathbf{x}(\mathbf{x} - 1)$ is λ^2.

6. Differentiating with respect to λ both sides of the equation

$$\mu_r = \sum_{x=0}^{\infty} (x - \lambda)^r \frac{\lambda^x e^{-\lambda}}{x!}$$

derive the following *recursion formula* for the moments about the mean of the Poisson distribution:

$$\mu_{r+1} = \lambda\left[r\mu_{r-1} + \frac{d\mu_r}{d\lambda}\right]$$

for $r = 1, 2, 3, \ldots$. Use this recursion formula together with the fact that $\mu_0 = 1$ and $\mu_1 = 0$ to find μ_2, μ_3, and μ_4.

7. (*Moments of the discrete uniform distribution*) Using the special sums given in the Appendix on page 352, find the mean and the variance of the discrete uniform distribution

$$f(x) = \frac{1}{n} \qquad \text{for } x = 1, 2, \ldots, n.$$

8. (*Moments of the geometric distribution*) Writing the mean of the geometric distribution as

$$\begin{aligned}\sum_{x=1}^{\infty} x\cdot\theta(1-\theta)^{x-1} = \theta + \theta(1-\theta) + \theta(1-\theta)^2 + \theta(1-\theta)^3 + \ldots \\ + \theta(1-\theta) + \theta(1-\theta)^2 + \theta(1-\theta)^3 + \ldots \\ + \theta(1-\theta)^2 + \theta(1-\theta)^3 + \ldots \\ + \theta(1-\theta)^3 + \ldots \\ \ldots\ldots\ldots\end{aligned}$$

use the formula for the sum of an infinite geometric progression first for each row and then for the row totals to show that $\mu = 1/\theta$.

9. (*Moments of the geometric distribution*) Differentiating with respect to θ both sides of the equation

$$\sum_{x=1}^{\infty} \theta(1-\theta)^{x-1} = 1$$

show that the mean of the geometric distribution is $\mu = 1/\theta$. Also, differentiating both sides twice with respect to θ, show that $\mu_2' = (2 - \theta)/\theta^2$ and, hence, that $\sigma^2 = (1 - \theta)/\theta^2$.

10. (*Moments of the negative binomial distribution*) Using steps similar to those employed in deriving the formula for the mean of the binomial distribution, show that the mean of the negative binomial distribution is $\mu = k/\theta$. Also show that the variance of the negative binomial distribution is

$$\sigma^2 = \frac{k}{\theta}\left(\frac{1}{\theta} - 1\right)$$

by first evaluating $E[\mathbf{x}(\mathbf{x} + 1)]$.

11. (*Factorial moments*) The moments of some probability distributions are most easily found by first evaluating quantities such as $E[\mathbf{x}(\mathbf{x} - 1)]$, $E[\mathbf{x}(\mathbf{x} - 1)(\mathbf{x} - 2)]$, ..., which are called *factorial moments* of $\mathbf{x}$. Writing the rth factorial moment of $\mathbf{x}$ as

$$\mu'_{(r)} = E[\mathbf{x}(\mathbf{x} - 1) \cdot \ldots \cdot (\mathbf{x} - r + 1)]$$

express μ'_2, μ'_3, and μ'_4 in terms of factorial moments.

4.4 Moment Generating Functions

It must have been apparent from the examples and the exercises of the preceding sections that the task of finding the moments of a probability distribution can be very tedious and sometimes very tricky. Fortunately, there exists a general method, based on so-called *moment generating functions*, which often provides considerable simplifications. *Given a random variable* $\mathbf{x}$, *the moment generating function of its probability distribution is given by the expected value of* $e^{t\mathbf{x}}$, *namely*

$$M_{\mathbf{x}}(t) = E(e^{t\mathbf{x}}) = \sum_i e^{tx_i} f(x_i) \tag{4.4.1}$$

with the summation extending over all x_i *within the range of* $\mathbf{x}$. (If the range of $\mathbf{x}$ is infinite, the infinite series in (4.4.1) may diverge for certain values of t; in that case the moment generating function does not exist for those values of t.)

Expanding e^{tx_i} as

$$1 + tx_i + \frac{t^2x_i^2}{2!} + \ldots + \frac{t^rx_i^r}{r!} + \ldots$$

we obtain

$$M_x(t) = \sum_i \left[1 + tx_i + \frac{t^2x_i^2}{2!} + \ldots + \frac{t^r x_i^r}{r!} + \ldots\right] f(x_i)$$

$$= \sum_i f(x_i) + t \cdot \sum_i x_i f(x_i) + \frac{t^2}{2!} \cdot \sum_i x_i^2 f(x_i)$$

$$+ \ldots + \frac{t^r}{r!} \cdot \sum_i x_i^r f(x_i) + \ldots$$

$$= 1 + \mu t + \mu_2' \cdot \frac{t^2}{2!} + \ldots + \mu_r' \cdot \frac{t^r}{r!} + \ldots \tag{4.4.2}$$

and this explains why $M_x(t)$ is called a moment generating function: *if we write $M_x(t)$ as a power series in t, the coefficient of $t^r/r!$ is the r'th moment about the origin.* Note that in $M_x(t)$ the independent variable is t; the subscript **x** is used to indicate that we are referring to the distribution of the random variable **x**.

The main difficulty in using the series expansion of a moment generating function for obtaining moments is usually *not* that of finding $M_x(t)$, but that of expanding $M_x(t)$ as a power series in t. If we are interested only in the first few moments of a distribution, their determination can usually be simplified by making use of the fact that the coefficient of $t^r/r!$ in the Maclaurin's series of $M_x(t)$ is the rth derivative of $M_x(t)$ with respect to t at $t = 0$. We thus have

THEOREM 4.10:

$$\left[\frac{d^r M_x(t)}{dt^r}\right]_{t=0} = \mu_r' = E(x^r)$$

As we have defined $M_x(t)$, it generates moments about the origin. A modification in its definition (see Exercise 6 on page 111) facilitates finding factorial moments and another modification, to be discussed in Chapter 6, yields a generating function which gives directly moments about the mean.

Moment generating functions have many interesting and important properties which we shall discuss later in Chapter 6. For the time being we shall study them only in connection with the problem of finding moments and in Section 4.4.3 in connection with a problem involving limiting distributions.

4.4.1 *The moment generating function of the binomial distribution*

Let us illustrate the process of finding moments by use of moment generating functions first with reference to the binomial distribution. Substituting the formula for $b(x; n, \theta)$ into (4.4.1), we get

$$M_X(t) = \sum_{x=0}^{n} e^{xt}\binom{n}{x}\theta^x(1-\theta)^{n-x}$$

$$= \sum_{x=0}^{n} \binom{n}{x}(\theta e^t)^x(1-\theta)^{n-x}$$

Recognizing this last summation as the binomial expansion of $[\theta e^t + (1-\theta)]^n$, we find that

THEOREM 4.11:

The moment generating function of the binomial distribution $b(x; n, \theta)$ *is given by*

$$M_X(t) = [1 + \theta(e^t - 1)]^n \qquad (4.4.3)$$

Differentiating this moment generating function twice with respect to t, we obtain

$$M_X'(t) = n\theta e^t[1 + \theta(e^t - 1)]^{n-1}$$

$$M_X''(t) = n\theta e^t[1 + \theta(e^t - 1)]^{n-1} + n(n-1)\theta^2 e^{2t}[1 + \theta(e^t - 1)]^{n-2}$$

$$= n\theta e^t(1 - \theta + n\theta e^t)[1 + \theta(e^t - 1)]^{n-2}$$

and substituting $t = 0$ we get $\mu_1' = n\theta$ and $\mu_2' = n\theta(1 - \theta + n\theta)$. We thus have

$$\mu = \mu_1' = n\theta \qquad \text{and} \qquad \sigma^2 = \mu_2' - \mu^2 = n\theta(1-\theta)$$

which agrees with the results obtained earlier on page 99. For the binomial distribution it is somewhat easier to find moments with the moment generating function than to evaluate them directly. It is easier yet with the so-called *factorial moment generating function* explained in Exercise 6 on page 111.

4.4.2 *The moment generating function of the Poisson distribution*

Omitting the hypergeometric distribution, for which the method of this section is difficult to apply, let us now find the moment generating function and subsequently the mean and the variance of the Poisson distribution. Substituting (3.2.3) into (4.4.1), we get

$$M_x(t) = \sum_{x=0}^{\infty} e^{xt} \cdot \frac{\lambda^x e^{-\lambda}}{x!}$$

$$= e^{-\lambda} \sum_{x=0}^{\infty} \frac{(\lambda e^t)^x}{x!}$$

and recognizing the last summation as the Maclaurin series of e^y with $y = \lambda e^t$, we find that

THEOREM 4.12:
The moment generating function of the Poisson distribution $f(x; \lambda)$ is given by

$$M_x(t) = e^{\lambda(e^t - 1)} \tag{4.4.4}$$

Differentiating this moment generating function twice with respect to t, we obtain

$$M_x'(t) = \lambda e^t e^{\lambda(e^t-1)}$$

$$M_x''(t) = \lambda\, e^t e^{\lambda(e^t-1)} + \lambda^2 e^{2t} e^{\lambda(e^t-1)}$$

and substituting $t = 0$ we get $\mu_1' = \lambda$ and $\mu_2' = \lambda + \lambda^2$. We thus have

$$\mu = \mu_1' = \lambda \qquad \text{and} \qquad \sigma^2 = \mu_2' - \mu^2 = \lambda$$

which agrees with the results obtained earlier on page 103.

The moment generating functions of some of the other distributions we have discussed are given among the exercises which follow. In some instances it is easier to find moments directly, and in some instances the moment generating function technique provides considerable simplifications. The first is true, for example, for the hypergeometric distribution and the latter is true, for example, for the geometric distribution.

4.4.3 *Moment generating functions and limiting distributions*

In Chapter 3 we showed that when $n \to \infty$, $\theta \to 0$, and $n\theta = \lambda$ remains fixed, the binomial distribution approaches the Poisson distribution. In this section we shall show that under the same limiting conditions the moment generating function of the binomial distribution approaches that of the Poisson distribution.

Taking logarithms of both sides of (4.4.3), the moment generating function of the binomial distribution, we get

$$\ln M_x(t) = n \cdot \ln [1 + \theta(e^t - 1)]$$

and using the infinite series

$$\ln (1 + y) = y - \frac{y^2}{2} + \frac{y^3}{3} - \ldots + (-1)^{r-1}\frac{y^r}{r} + \ldots$$

for $-1 < y < 1$ to expand $\ln [1 + \theta(e^t - 1)]$, we obtain

$$\begin{aligned}\ln M_x(t) &= n\left[\theta(e^t - 1) - \frac{\theta^2(e^t - 1)^2}{2} + \ldots + (-1)^{r-1}\frac{\theta^r(e^t - 1)^r}{r} + \ldots\right] \\ &= \lambda\,(e^t - 1) - \lambda\,\theta\,\frac{(e^t - 1)^2}{2} + \ldots \\ &\qquad + (-1)^{r-1}\,\lambda\,\theta^{r-1}\,\frac{(e^t - 1)^r}{r} + \ldots\end{aligned}$$

for $-1 < \theta(e^t - 1) < 1$. If we now let $n \to \infty$, $\theta \to 0$, while $n\theta = \lambda$ remains fixed, we find that all terms on the righthand side except the first approach 0 and that $\ln M_x(t) \to \lambda(e^t - 1)$. Hence

$$M_x(t) \to e^{\lambda(e^t - 1)}$$

and it can be seen that the moment generating function of the binomial distribution approaches an expression which is readily identified as the moment generating function of the Poisson distribution.

The fact that the moment generating function of the binomial distribution approaches that of the Poisson distribution when $n \to \infty$, $\theta \to 0$, while $n\theta = \lambda$ remains fixed, does not by itself constitute proof that the binomial distribution approaches the Poisson distribution under these limiting conditions. After all, it is conceivable that two *different* distributions might have the identical moment generating function

$$M_x(t) = e^{\lambda(e^t - 1)}$$

However, there is a theorem to the effect that the correspondence between probability distributions and moment generating functions is one-to-one whenever the latter exist. In conjunction with this theorem we have, thus, shown in this section that the binomial distribution approaches the Poisson distribution under the given limiting conditions.

EXERCISES

1. Using the method of Section 4.4.1 find μ_3', μ_3, and $\alpha_3 = \mu_3/\sigma^3$ for the binomial distribution $b(x; n, \theta)$. Using the fact that $\alpha_3 = 0$ for symmetrical distributions, what can one say about the symmetry of the binomial distribution (a) when $\theta = \frac{1}{2}$, and (b) when n is large?

2. Using the method of Section 4.4.2, find μ_3', μ_3, and $\alpha_3 = \mu_3/\sigma^3$ for the Poisson distribution $f(x; \lambda)$. What can one say about the symmetry of the Poisson distribution when λ is large?

3. Can $M_{\mathbf{x}}(t) = t/(1 - t)$ be the moment generating function of the distribution of some random variable $\mathbf{x}$? Explain.

4. (*Moment generating function of the discrete uniform distribution*) Given the discrete uniform distribution

$$f(x) = \frac{1}{n} \quad \text{for} \quad x = 1, 2, 3, \ldots, n$$

show that its moment generating function is

$$M_{\mathbf{x}}(t) = \frac{e^t(1 - e^{nt})}{n(1 - e^t)}$$

Also find the mean of this distribution by evaluating lim $M_{\mathbf{x}}'(t)$ as $t \to 0$.

5. (*Moment generating function of the geometric distribution*) Show that the moment generating function of the geometric distribution (see Exercise 14 on page 77) is

$$M_{\mathbf{x}}(t) = \frac{\theta e^t}{1 - e^t(1 - \theta)}$$

Also use this moment generating function to find the mean and the variance of the geometric distribution and compare your results with those of Exercise 9 on page 105.

6. (*Factorial moment generating functions*) Given a random variable $\mathbf{x}$, the factorial moment generating function of its probability distribution is

the expected value of $t^{\mathbf{x}}$, namely,

$$F_{\mathbf{x}}(t) = E(t^{\mathbf{x}}) = \sum_i t^{x_i} f(x_i)$$

with the summation extending over all x_i within the range of **x**.

(a) Show that the rth derivative of $F_{\mathbf{x}}(t)$ with respect to t at $t = 1$ is $\mu'_{(r)}$, the rth factorial moment which we defined in Exercise 11 on page 106.

(b) Find the factorial moment generating function of the binomial distribution and use it to determine μ and σ^2.

(c) Find the factorial moment generating function of the Poisson distribution and use it to determine μ and σ^2.

4.5 Product Moments

Given a pair of random variables **x** and **y**, the *r'th and s'th product moment (about the origin) of their joint distribution* is

$$E(\mathbf{x}^r\mathbf{y}^s) = \sum_i \sum_j x_i^r y_j^s f(x_i, y_j) \tag{4.5.1}$$

with the summation extending over all pairs (x_i, y_j) for which $f(x_i, y_j)$ is defined. (More general product moments can, similarly, be defined for problems involving more than two random variables.) Analogous to (4.2.2) we also define the *r'th and s'th product moment about the respective means* as

$$E[(\mathbf{x} - \mu_{\mathbf{x}})^r(\mathbf{y} - \mu_{\mathbf{y}})^s] = \sum_i \sum_j (x_i - \mu_{\mathbf{x}})^r(y_j - \mu_{\mathbf{y}})^s f(x_i, y_j) \tag{4.5.2}$$

where $\mu_{\mathbf{x}}$ and $\mu_{\mathbf{y}}$ are, respectively, the means of the marginal distributions of **x** and **y**.

In statistics, the case where $r = 1$ and $s = 1$ is of special interest; $E[(\mathbf{x} - \mu_{\mathbf{x}})(\mathbf{y} - \mu_{\mathbf{y}})]$ is called the *covariance* of the joint distribution of **x** and **y**, and it is written symbolically as $\sigma_{\mathbf{xy}}$, cov(**x**, **y**), or C(**x**, **y**). In a sense, the covariance measures a relationship between the values that are assumed by **x** and **y**. If there is a high probability that large values of **x** go with large values of **y** and small values of **x** go with small values of **y**, the covariance is *positive*; if there is a high probability that large values of **x** go with small values of **y** and vice versa, the covariance is *negative*. Furthermore, as the reader will be asked to show in Exercise 3 below, *if* **x** *and* **y** *are independent, their covariance is* 0. (The fact that the converse of this is *not* true will be illustrated later in Chapter 13.)

As in the case of ordinary moments, product moments about the respective means are usually obtained by expressing them in terms of product moments about the origin. For the covariance we, thus, have

$$\sigma_{\mathbf{xy}} = E(\mathbf{xy}) - \mu_{\mathbf{x}}\mu_{\mathbf{y}} \tag{4.5.3}$$

which the reader will be asked to prove in Exercise 2 below.

To give an illustration, let us find the covariance for the bivariate distribution on page 82. Having shown on page 93 that $E(\mathbf{xy}) = \frac{1}{18}$, we have only to find $\mu_{\mathbf{x}}$ and $\mu_{\mathbf{y}}$ and substitute into (4.5.3). Since the expected number of threes and the expected number of fives for one roll of a pair of balanced dice both equal $2(\frac{1}{6}) = \frac{1}{3}$, we find that

$$\sigma_{\mathbf{xy}} = \frac{1}{18} - \left(\frac{1}{3}\right)^2 = -\frac{1}{18}.$$

The negative value of $\sigma_{\mathbf{xy}}$ implies the obvious fact that if there are many threes there cannot be many fives and vice versa.

EXERCISES

1. Find the covariance of the bivariate distribution of Exercise 1 on page 88.

2. Prove that $\text{cov}(\mathbf{x}, \mathbf{y}) = E(\mathbf{xy}) - \mu_{\mathbf{x}}\mu_{\mathbf{y}}$.

3. Prove that if **x** and **y** are independent, the covariance of their joint distribution is 0.

4. (*Joint moment generating functions*) When dealing with k random variables $\mathbf{x}_1, \mathbf{x}_2, \ldots, \mathbf{x}_k$, we define the *joint moment generating function* of their joint distribution as

$$E(e^{t_1\mathbf{x}_1 + t_2\mathbf{x}_2 + \cdots + t_k\mathbf{x}_k})$$

(a) Show that the partial derivative of the joint moment generating function with respect to t_i at $t_1 = t_2 = \ldots = t_k = 0$ is $E(\mathbf{x}_i)$.

(b) Show that the second partial derivative of the joint moment generating function with respect to t_i and t_j at $t_1 = t_2 = \ldots = t_k = 0$ is $E(\mathbf{x}_i\mathbf{x}_j)$.

(c) Show that the joint moment generating function of the multinomial distribution (3.3.6) is

$$(\theta_1 e^{t_1} + \theta_2 e^{t_2} + \ldots + \theta_k e^{t_k})^n$$

and, hence, that for $i \neq j$

$$\text{cov}\,(\mathbf{x}_i, \mathbf{x}_j) = -n\theta_i\theta_j$$

4.6 Mathematical Expectation and Decision Making

It is not unreasonable to suggest that a person's behavior is *rational* if in situations involving uncertainties and risks he chooses the alternative which has the highest mathematical expectation. To illustrate, let us consider the following problem: someone who is in charge of a party (whose purpose is to raise funds for a worthy cause) has to decide whether to plan an outdoor picnic or a buffet supper to be held indoors. He has the information that *if it does not rain* the picnic will yield a profit of \$500 while the buffet supper will yield a profit of \$170; *if it rains* the picnic will yield a profit of \$80 while the buffet supper will yield a profit of \$440. Also, he is told by the weatherman that the probability that it will rain on the day for which the affair is planned is $\frac{1}{3}$. Using this information, he might reason as follows: if the dinner is held outdoors the *expected profit* is

$$500(\tfrac{2}{3}) + 80(\tfrac{1}{3}) = \$360$$

if it is held indoors the *expected profit* is

$$170(\tfrac{2}{3}) + 440(\tfrac{1}{3}) = \$260$$

and, basing his decision on the idea of *maximizing expected profits,* he plans to hold the affair outdoors.

To consider a more complicated example in which a decision is based on this same criterion, suppose that Mr. Jones rents out a piece of heavy roadbuilding equipment for periods of t hours. He is paid \$50 an hour, but his equipment tends to overheat and if it overheats x times during the t hours for which it is rented out, it costs x^2 dollars to repair the damage. Suppose, furthermore, that the number of times his equipment overheats in t hours is a random variable having a Poisson distribution with $\lambda = 2t$. What Mr. Jones would like to know is for how many hours at a time he should rent out his equipment so as to maximize his expected profit. If $\mathbf{x}$ is the number of times his equipment overheats in t hours, his profit is $P(\mathbf{x}) = 50t - \mathbf{x}^2$ and his expected profit is thus

$$E[P(\mathbf{x})] = 50t - E(\mathbf{x}^2)$$

Having shown in Section 4.4.2 that $E(\mathbf{x}^2) = \lambda^2 + \lambda$, we obtain

$$E[P(\mathbf{x})] = 50t - [(2t)^2 + 2t] = 48t - 4t^2$$

and, differentiating with respect to t, we find that the expected profit is maximized when $48 - 8t = 0$, that is, when $t = 6$. We have, thus, shown that Mr. Jones can expect his business to be most profitable if he rents his equipment out for 6 hours at a time.

The main difficulty in applying the method of decision making which we have illustrated is that, in actual practice, we seldom know the exact "cash values" for all the risks that are involved; also, we seldom have adequate information about all relevant probabilities. Some further examples in which decisions are based on the idea of maximizing expected profits are given at the end of Chapter 6.

EXERCISES

1. A company operating a chain of drugstores plans to open a new store in one of two locations. The management of the company figures that in the first location the store will show an annual profit of \$20,000 if it is successful and an annual loss of \$2000 if it is not. So far as the second location is concerned, the store will show an annual profit of \$25,000 if it is successful and an annual loss of \$5000 if it is not. If the probability of success is $\frac{1}{2}$ for each location, where should the company open the new store so as to maximize its expected profit?

2. How would the management's decision have been affected in Exercise 1 if the probability of success had been $\frac{1}{4}$ instead of $\frac{1}{2}$ for each store? What if the probability of success had been $\frac{3}{8}$ for each store?

3. Where would the company referred to in Exercise 1 build the new store if there were no information about the probability of success and its management consisted of *confirmed pessimists*? What if its management consisted of *confirmed optimists*?

4. Suppose that in the first example in the text the decision is to be based on the outcome of a chance experiment (some gambling device) which will lead to a picnic with the probability θ and an indoor buffet supper with the probability $1 - \theta$. For what value of θ is the expected profit the same regardless of whether it rains?

5. A manufacturer makes a certain piece of machinery for the government. He is paid \$1000 if it is shipped in perfect condition and \$750 if it is not shipped in perfect condition. To test a piece of this machinery before it is shipped costs \$10 and if it is found to be defective it costs another \$50 to correct for the imperfection. Is it more profitable for the manufacturer to ship each piece of machinery with inspection or without inspection, if he knows that 2 per cent of these pieces of machinery are defective when they come off his assembly line? What if he knows that 6 per cent of these pieces of machinery are defective?

6. In the beginning of each week a department store stocks a number of "Bon Voyage" baskets and the number it could sell during the week is a random variable having the uniform distribution $f(x) = \frac{1}{10}$ for $x = 1, 2, \ldots,$ and 10. If there is a profit of \$6 for each basket sold and a loss (due to spoilage) of \$2 for each basket not sold during the week, show that if the store stocks n baskets at the beginning of the week the expected profit is $\frac{1}{10}(64n - 4n^2)$. How many of these baskets should the store stock at the beginning of the week so as to maximize expected profits?

Chapter 5

Probability Densities

5.1 Introduction

When dealing with sample spaces containing more than a countable infinity of elements, that is, in the *continuous case*, it will be necessary to express probability measures in terms of integrals. This has the consequence that we will not be able to assign a probability to each subset of the sample space, as was specified in the postulates of probability in Section 2.3.1. For instance, if a dart is thrown at a target, whose center serves as the origin of a rectangular system of coordinates, we cannot ask for the probability of hitting a point whose coordinates are both rational numbers. This particular problem could be handled if we used Lebesgue integrals instead of the Riemann integrals to which one is introduced in the usual introductory course in calculus, but then there would be other sets to which no probabilities can be assigned. Fortunately, the subsets of continuous sample spaces to which we will be unable to assign probabilities are very abstruse and of no practical significance so far as the work of this book is concerned.

5.2 Probability Densities and Distribution Functions

In Section 3.1 we introduced the concept of a *distribution function*, defining its values $F(x)$ as the probabilities that a random variable $\mathbf{x}$ assumes a value less than or equal to x, for $-\infty \leq x \leq \infty$. At the time we restricted ourselves to discrete random variables and the graphs of their distribution functions looked like that of Figure 5.1. In the discrete case, the values of the distribution function increase in "jumps," presenting thus the picture of a step-function like that of Figures 3.1 and 5.1.

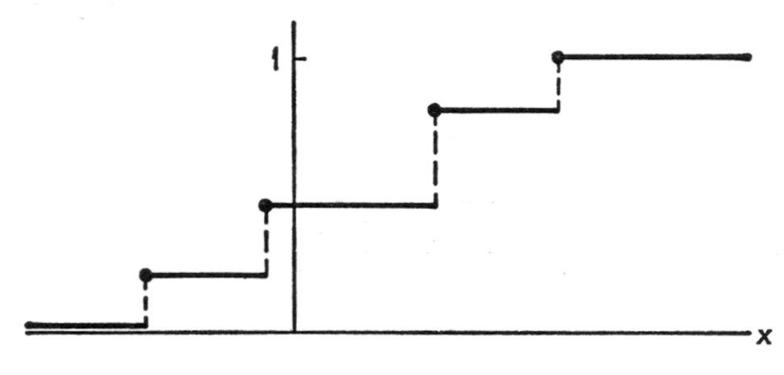

Figure 5.1

Now let us consider the case where the range of **x** consists of the set of all real numbers and the graph of the distribution function is a continuous curve somewhat like that of Figure 5.2. Although there

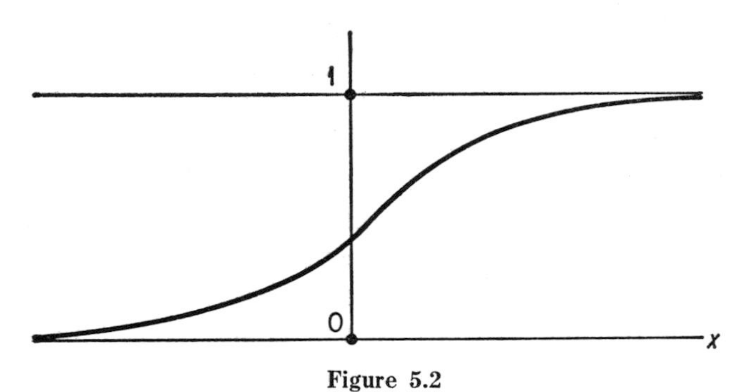

Figure 5.2

are other possibilities, *we shall limit ourselves to the case where the distribution function is continuous and* $F'(x) = f(x)$, *its derivative at* x, *exists for all but a finite set of values of* x.

Since the properties of distribution functions referred to in Exercise 5 on page 66 hold also in the continuous case, that is, $F(-\infty) = 0$, $F(\infty) = 1$, and $F(a) \leq F(b)$ if $a < b$, we can use the fundamental theorem of integral calculus and write

$$\int_{-\infty}^{x} f(t)\, dt = F(x) - F(-\infty) = F(x) \qquad (5.2.1)$$

Hence, the probability that a random variable **x** assumes a value less than or equal to x is

$$\int_{-\infty}^{x} f(t)\, dt$$

where $f(t)$ is the derivative of the distribution function of **x** at t.

An immediate consequence of (5.2.1) is that *for any two constants a and b, with a < b, the probability that* **x** *assumes a value greater than a but less than or equal to b is*

$$\begin{aligned} F(b) - F(a) &= \int_{-\infty}^{b} f(x)\, dx - \int_{-\infty}^{a} f(x)\, dx \\ &= \int_{a}^{b} f(x)\, dx \end{aligned}$$

In view of the assumption that the distribution function is continuous, the probability that **x** assumes a value *less than* any real number x equals the probability that it will assume a value *less than or equal* to x. Hence, *in the continuous case the probability that* **x** *assumes any given value within its range is equal to zero and the probability that it assumes a value on the interval from a to b, including or excluding either endpoint, is equal to*

$$\int_{a}^{b} f(x)\, dx$$

Referring to Figure 5.3 we find that the probability that the random variable **x** assumes a value on the interval from a to b is given by the shaded area, namely, the area under the curve from a to b.

Let us point out again that a probability of 0 does not mean that the corresponding event cannot happen. As a matter of fact,

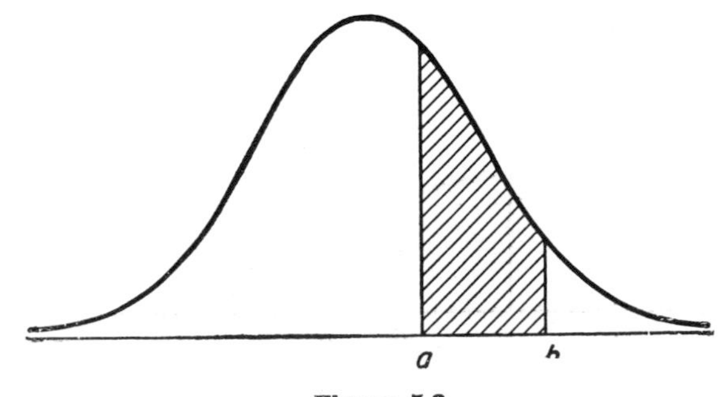

Figure 5.3

in the continuous case **x** has to assume some value x even though the probability that it will assume this value is 0.

Borrowing again from the language of physics, we refer to $f(x)$ as the *probability density* or as the value of the *probability density function* at x. To illustrate this analogy, let us consider first Figures 5.4 and 5.5, and then Figures 5.6 and 5.7. In Figure 5.4 there are

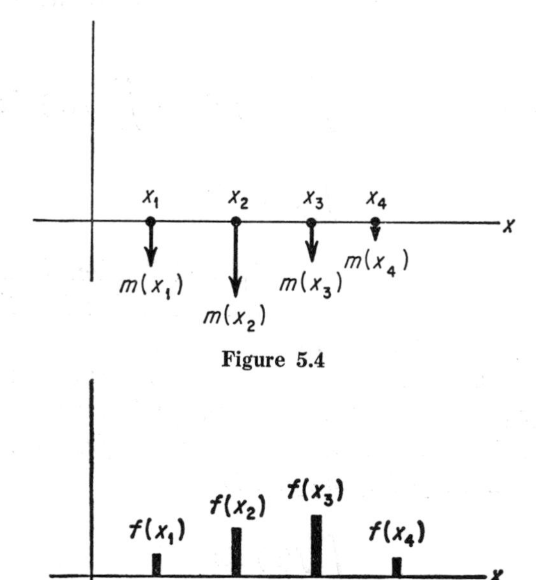

Figure 5.4

Figure 5.5

several *point masses* $m(x_i)$ resting on the x-axis at the points x_i; in Figure 5.5, illustrating a probability distribution in the discrete case, there are *probabilities* $f(x_i)$ associated with the points x_i. In Figure 5.6 there is a bar with a variable cross-section resting on

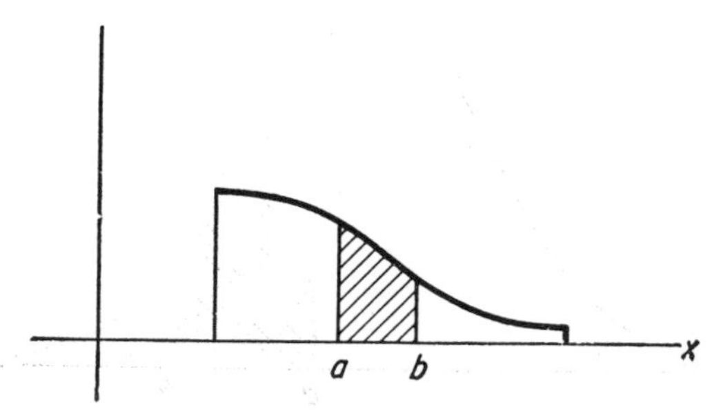

Figure 5.6

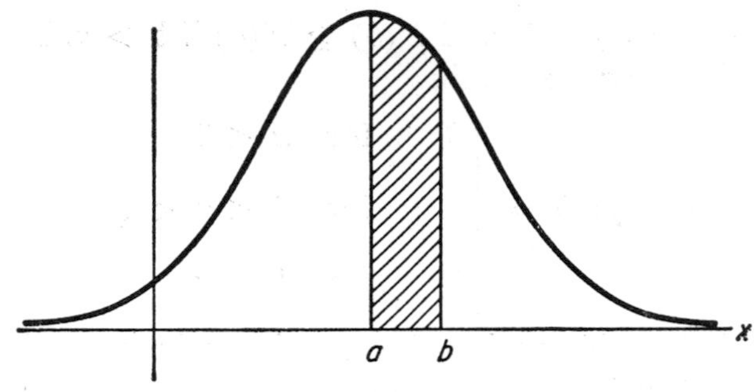

Figure 5.7

the x-axis and for any given value of x we can only speak of its *density* $\rho(x)$, that is, its mass per unit cross section. Integrating the density $\rho(x)$ from a to b, we obtain the mass of that section of the bar which lies between a and b. Similarly, in Figure 5.7, illustrating a probability density in the continuous case, we can only speak of the *probability density* $f(x)$ for any given value of x. To obtain the probability that **x** assumes a value between a and b, we must integrate the probability density $f(x)$ from a to b, just as we obtained the mass of the bar by integrating the density $\rho(x)$ from a to b.

To illustrate the concepts of distribution function and probability density in the continuous case, let us consider first the distribution function whose graph is shown in Figure 5.8; it is given by

$$F(x) = \begin{cases} 0 & \text{for} \quad x \leq 0 \\ x & \text{for} \quad 0 < x < 1 \\ 1 & \text{for} \quad 1 \leq x \end{cases}$$

Note that this function can serve as a distribution function because

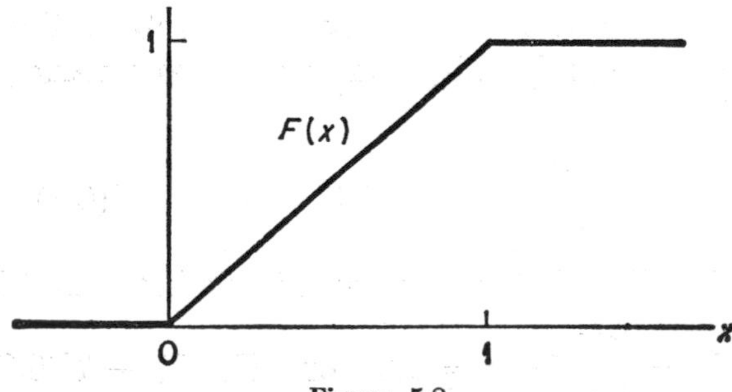

Figure 5.8

$F(-\infty) = 0$, $F(\infty) = 1$, and $F(b) \geq F(a)$ if $b > a$. Differentiating with respect to x, we obtain

$$f(x) = \begin{cases} 0 & \text{for } x < 0 \\ 1 & \text{for } 0 < x < 1 \\ 0 & \text{for } 1 < x \end{cases}$$

and we find that this probability density, whose graph is shown in Figure 5.9, is defined for all values of x except 0 and 1. So far as

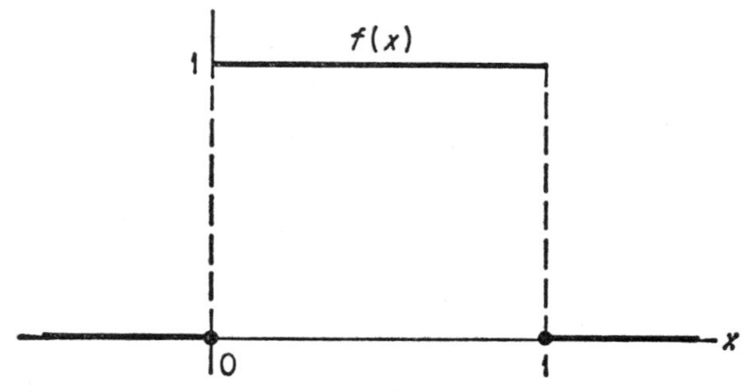

Figure 5.9

questions of probability are concerned, it does not matter how $f(x)$ is defined at these two points. We shall put $f(0)$ and $f(1)$ both equal to 0, and we can thus say that the random variable **x**, with which we are concerned in this example, has the probability density

$$f(x) = \begin{cases} 1 & \text{for } 0 < x < 1 \\ 0 & \text{elsewhere} \end{cases}$$

where "elsewhere" means all other real values of x.

Using either the probability density or the distribution function with which we began, we can now evaluate probabilities concerning **x**. For instance, the probability that **x** assumes a value less than or equal to 0.3 is

$$\int_0^{0.3} f(x)\, dx = \int_0^{0.3} 1 \cdot dx = 0.3 \qquad \text{or} \qquad F(0.3) = 0.3$$

Also, the probability that **x** assumes a value between 0.2 and 0.8 is

$$\int_{0.2}^{0.8} f(x)\, dx = \int_{0.2}^{0.8} 1 \cdot dx = 0.6 \quad \text{or} \quad F(0.8) - F(0.2) = 0.6$$

In the preceding example we gave the distribution function, derived the probability density, and then calculated some probabilities. Now let us consider an example where we are given a probability density, namely,

$$f(x) = \begin{cases} 2e^{-2x} & \text{for } x > 0 \\ 0 & \text{for } x \leq 0 \end{cases}$$

To verify whether this actually defines a probability density, we have to check whether (1) $f(x) \geq 0$ *for each value of* x, *and* (2)

$$\int_{-\infty}^{\infty} f(x)\, dx = 1$$

The first of these conditions is to assure that the probability which we assign to any given interval is non-negative; the second condition is necessary to assure that the probability for the entire sample space is equal to 1. As it can easily be verified that these conditions are satisfied, let us integrate on x, getting

$$F(x) = \begin{cases} 1 - e^{-2x} & \text{for } x > 0 \\ 0 & \text{for } x \leq 0 \end{cases}$$

The graph of this distribution function is shown in Figure 5.11; that of the corresponding probability density is shown in Figure 5.10.

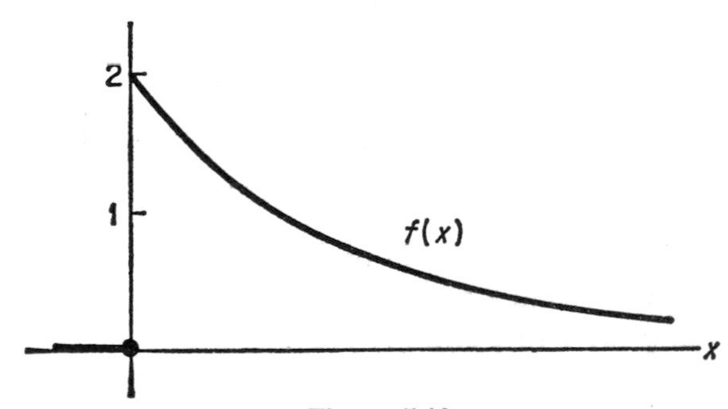

Figure 5.10

To determine probabilities about the random variable considered in this second example, we can again use either $f(x)$ or $F(x)$. (Of course, in actual practice we would use one or the other, but not both.) For instance, the probability that the random variable

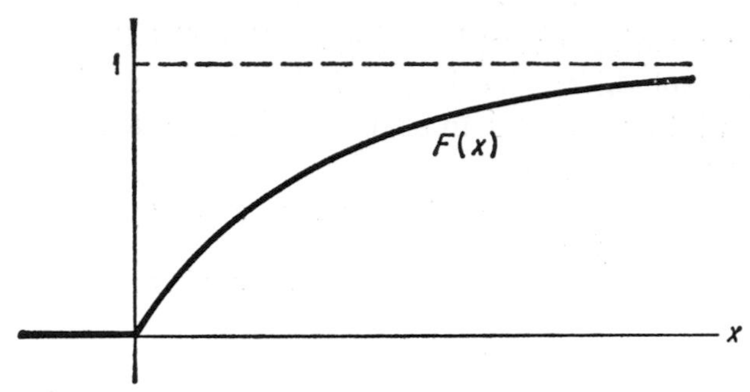

Figure 5.11

assumes a value on the interval from 2 to 4, we get

$$\int_2^4 2e^{-2x}\,dx = e^{-4} - e^{-8}$$

or

$$F(4) - F(2) = (1 - e^{-8}) - (1 - e^{4}) = e^{-4} - e^{-8}$$

which equals approximately 0.018.

EXERCISES

1. The distribution function of a random variable is given by

$$F(x) = \begin{cases} 1 - \dfrac{1}{x} & \text{for } x \geq 1 \\ 0 & \text{for } x < 1 \end{cases}$$

Find the corresponding probability density and sketch the graphs of both $F(x)$ and $f(x)$. At what point or points is $f(x)$ undefined?

2. Referring to the random variable of Exercise 1, find the probabilities that its value is less than 2 and that its value lies on the interval from 5 to 10 by using (a) $F(x)$, and (b) $f(x)$.

3. Given the probability density

$$f(x) = \begin{cases} kx(1 - x) & \text{for } 0 < x < 1 \\ 0 & \text{elsewhere} \end{cases}$$

find k and then calculate the probability that a random variable having this probability density assumes a value greater than or equal to 0.2.

4. Find the distribution function which corresponds to the probability density of Exercise 3. Also use the distribution function to check the value obtained for the probability asked for in Exercise 3.

5. Given the probability density

$$f(x) = \begin{cases} x & \text{for } 0 < x \leq 1 \\ 2 - x & \text{for } 1 \leq x < 2 \\ 0 & \text{elsewhere} \end{cases}$$

find the corresponding distribution function and sketch the graphs of $f(x)$ and $F(x)$.

6. If a random variable has the probability density of Exercise 5, find

(a) the probability that it assumes a value less than 0.5

(b) the probability that it assumes a value greater than 1.3

(c) the probability that it assumes a value on the interval from 0.2 to 1.2.

7. The distribution function of a random variable is given by

$$F(x) = \begin{cases} 1 - (1 + x)e^{-x} & \text{for } x \geq 0 \\ 0 & \text{for } x < 0 \end{cases}$$

Find the corresponding probability density. Are there any points at which $f(x)$ is not defined?

8. If a random variable has the distribution function of Exercise 7, find the probability that it assumes a value less than or equal to 1.

5.3 Special Probability Densities

In this section we shall present several important probability densities, the *uniform distribution*, the *exponential distribution*, the *gamma distribution*, and the *normal distribution*.* The *beta distribution* will be introduced in Exercise 6 on page 130 and the *Cauchy distribution* in Section 5.4. Three very important densities, the *t-distribution*, the *F-distribution*, and the *Chi-square distribution*

* It would be more appropriate to refer to these probability densities as the *uniform density*, the *exponential density*, and so forth, but the practice of referring to them as distributions is deeply entrenched in the language of statistics.

will be presented later in Chapter 8. Some applications of the probability densities introduced in this section are given in the set of exercises beginning on page 131.

5.3.1 *The uniform distribution*

The probability density which we used as an illustration on page 122 is a special case of the *uniform distribution*

$$f(x) = \begin{cases} \dfrac{1}{\beta - \alpha} & \text{for} \quad \alpha < x < \beta \\ 0 & \text{elsewhere} \end{cases} \tag{5.3.1}$$

where α and β are real constants with $\alpha < \beta$. Although the uniform density has some direct applications, its main value lies in the fact that due to its simplicity it readily lends itself to the task of illustrating various aspects of statistical theory.

5.3.2 *The exponential distribution*

The second illustration in Section 5.2 was a special case of the *exponential distribution*

$$f(x) = \begin{cases} \dfrac{1}{\theta} e^{-(x/\theta)} & \text{for} \quad x > 0 \\ 0 & \text{elsewhere} \end{cases} \tag{5.3.2}$$

with $\theta > 0$. As can easily be verified, the integral of this probability density, from $-\infty$ to ∞, is equal to 1.

To illustrate how an exponential distribution might arise in actual practice, let us first calculate the probability that a random variable having the exponential distribution (5.3.2) does *not* assume a value less than or equal to x, namely,

$$1 - F(x) = \int_x^\infty f(x)\, dx = \int_x^\infty \frac{1}{\theta} e^{-(x/\theta)}\, dx = e^{-(x/\theta)}$$

What we would like to show is that $e^{-(x/\theta)}$ is also the probability that a piece of electronic equipment will *not* fail prior to time x if the probability of failure during any small time interval Δx is $1/\theta\ \Delta x$, independent of x (see also Exercise 12 on page 76). Dividing the interval from 0 to x into n equal parts $\Delta x = x/n$, the probability that the piece of equipment will not fail during one of these intervals is $1 - 1/\theta\, \Delta x$, provided that Δx is very small. For large n, the probability that the piece of equipment will not fail during the time interval from 0 to x is, thus, $(1 - 1/\theta\, \Delta x)^n$, which can be written

$$\left(1 - \frac{1}{\theta}\,\Delta x\right)^{(x/\Delta x)} = \left[\left(1 - \frac{\Delta x}{\theta}\right)^{-(\theta/\Delta x)}\right]^{-(x/\theta)}$$

If we now let Δx approach 0, the expression inside the brackets approaches e, and the probability that the piece of equipment does not fail prior to time x approaches $e^{-(x/\theta)}$. The exponential distribution, thus, provides the appropriate *model* for calculating probabilities concerning the "lifetime" of the given piece of equipment. Of course, this result does not necessarily apply to other kinds of equipment.

5.3.3 *The gamma distribution*

Another probability density which plays an important role in statistics is the *gamma distribution*

$$f(x) = \begin{cases} kx^{\alpha-1}e^{-(x/\beta)} & \text{for } x > 0 \\ 0 & \text{for } x \leq 0 \end{cases} \tag{5.3.3}$$

where $\alpha > 0$, $\beta > 0$, and k must be such that the integral of $f(x)$ from $-\infty$ to ∞ is equal to 1. To evaluate k let us make the substitution $y = x/\beta$ and we get

$$k \int_0^\infty x^{\alpha-1}e^{-(x/\beta)}\, dx = k\beta^\alpha \int_0^\infty y^{\alpha-1}e^{-y}\, dy = 1$$

This last integral, which depends on α alone, is the well-known *gamma function*

$$\Gamma(\alpha) = \int_0^\infty y^{\alpha-1}e^{-y}\, dy \qquad \text{for } \alpha > 0 \tag{5.3.4}$$

studied ordinarily in elementary or advanced calculus. Integrating by parts, it can be shown that the gamma function satisfies the recursion formula

$$\Gamma(\alpha) = (\alpha - 1)\Gamma(\alpha - 1) \tag{5.3.5}$$

see Exercise 2 on page 130. In particular, when $\alpha = n$, where n is a positive integer, $\Gamma(n) = (n-1)!$

Returning now to the problem of evaluating the constant k in (5.3.3), we obtain $k\beta^\alpha\Gamma(\alpha) = 1$ and, hence

$$k = \frac{1}{\beta^\alpha \Gamma(\alpha)}$$

If α is a positive integer, $\Gamma(\alpha) = (\alpha - 1)!$ and k can, thus, readily be found; otherwise $\Gamma(\alpha)$ must be obtained from a table of values of the gamma function. The graphs of several gamma distributions are shown in Figure 5.12.

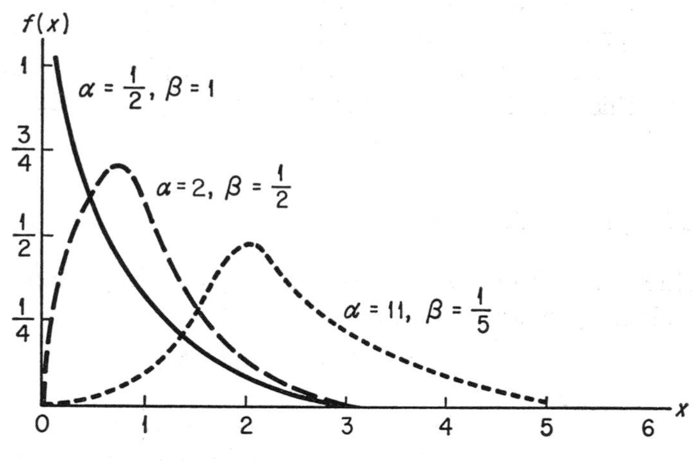

Figure 5.12

Special cases of the gamma distribution play an important role in the theory of statistics. For $\alpha = 1$ we obtain the exponential distribution of Section (5.3.2), and for $\alpha = n/2$ and $\beta = 2$ we obtain the *Chi-square distribution* which we shall study later in Chapter 8. In addition to the applications given in the exercises on page 132, an application of the gamma distribution to a problem of theoretical physics is given in Exercise 4 on page 136.

5.3.4 *The normal distribution*

The *normal distribution* is in many respects the cornerstone of modern statistical theory. It was studied first in the eighteenth century when scientists observed an astonishing degree of regularity in errors of measurement. They found that the patterns (distributions) which they observed were closely approximated by a continuous curve which they referred to as the "normal curve of errors" and attributed to the laws of chance. The mathematical properties of this continuous distribution and its theoretical basis were first investigated by Pierre Laplace (1749–1827), Abraham de Moivre (1667–1745), and Carl Gauss (1777–1855). In honor of the last, normal distributions are sometimes referred to also as *Gaussian*

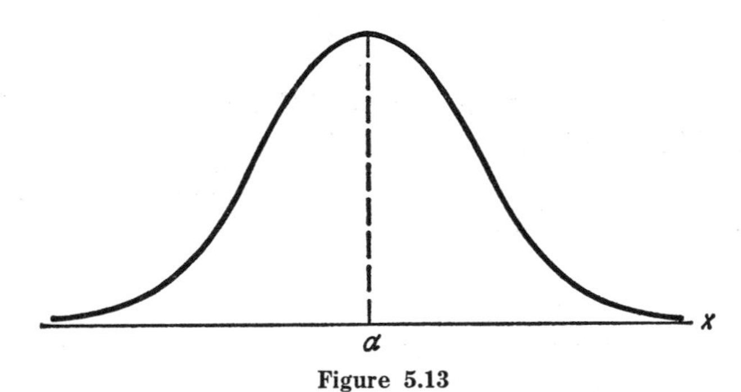

Figure 5.13

distributions. The equation of the *normal distribution*, whose graph is shown in Figure 5.13, is

$$f(x) = k \cdot e^{-\frac{1}{2}\left(\frac{x-\alpha}{\beta}\right)^2} \quad \text{for} \quad -\infty < x < \infty \tag{5.3.6}$$

where α and β are real constants, $\beta > 0$, and k must be such that the integral of $f(x)$ from $-\infty$ to ∞ is equal to 1. The significance of the parameters α and β will be discussed in Section 6.3.3.

To evaluate k, let us make the change of variable $u = (x - \alpha)/\beta$ in the integral of $f(x)$ from $-\infty$ to ∞, getting

$$k\beta \int_{-\infty}^{\infty} e^{-(1/2)u^2}\, du = 1 \quad \text{or} \quad \int_{-\infty}^{\infty} e^{-(1/2)u^2}\, du = \frac{1}{k\beta}$$

Squaring both sides of the last equation, writing v in the second integral instead of u, we obtain

$$\int_{-\infty}^{\infty} e^{-(1/2)u^2}\, du \cdot \int_{-\infty}^{\infty} e^{-(1/2)v^2}\, dv = \frac{1}{k^2\beta^2}$$

or

$$\int_{-\infty}^{\infty}\int_{-\infty}^{\infty} e^{-(1/2)(u^2+v^2)}\, du\, dv = \frac{1}{k^2\beta^2}$$

Changing now to polar coordinates, that is, letting $u = r \cdot \cos \theta$ and $v = r \cdot \sin \theta$, we get

$$\int_0^{2\pi} \int_0^{\infty} r \cdot e^{-(1/2)r^2} \, dr \, d\theta = \frac{1}{k^2\beta^2}$$

and straightforward methods of elementary calculus show that the lefthand member of this equation is equal to 2π. Thus, $2\pi = 1/k^2\beta^2$ and

$$k = \frac{1}{\beta\sqrt{2\pi}}$$

Further mathematical properties of the normal distribution will be discussed in Chapters 6 and 8. In fact, most of Chapter 8 will be devoted to the normal distribution and distributions closely related to the normal distribution.

EXERCISES

1. If the random variable **x** has the exponential density (5.3.2), find c such that the probability that **x** assumes a value greater than c is $\frac{1}{2}$.

2. Use integration by parts to show that $\Gamma(\alpha) = (\alpha - 1)\ \Gamma(\alpha - 1)$ for $\alpha > 1$.

3. Making the substitution $x = y^2/2$, show that the gamma function is also given by

$$\Gamma(\alpha) = 2^{1-\alpha} \int_0^{\infty} y^{2\alpha-1} e^{-(1/2)y^2} \, dy \qquad \text{for} \quad \alpha > 0$$

   Use this form of the gamma function to show that $\Gamma(\frac{1}{2}) = \sqrt{\pi}$.

4. Find the probability that the value of a random variable is greater than 2, if the random variable has a gamma distribution with

   (a) $\alpha = 2$ and $\beta = 1$

   (b) $\alpha = 3$ and $\beta = 2$

5. Show that the maximum of the normal distribution is at $x = \alpha$ and that its two inflection points are at $x = \alpha + \beta$ and $x = \alpha - \beta$.

6. (*Beta distribution*) A random variable is said to have the *beta distribution* if its probability density is

$$f(x) = \begin{cases} k \cdot x^{\alpha-1}(1 - x)^{\beta-1} & \text{for} \quad 0 < x < 1 \\ 0 & \text{elsewhere} \end{cases} \qquad (5.3.7)$$

where $\alpha > 0$, $\beta > 0$, and k is such that the integral of $f(x)$ from 0 to 1 is equal to 1. Find k for the special case where $\alpha = 4$ and $\beta = 2$, and verify that this agrees with the general result according to which

$$k = \frac{\Gamma(\alpha + \beta)}{\Gamma(\alpha)\Gamma(\beta)}$$

Also find the distribution function of a random variable having the beta distribution with $\alpha = 3$ and $\beta = 3$.

7. (*Pearson curves*) It was shown by Karl Pearson, one of the founders of modern statistics, that the differential equation

$$\frac{1}{f(x)} \cdot \frac{d[f(x)]}{dx} = \frac{d - x}{a + bx + cx^2}$$

yields most of the distributions that are important in statistics if appropriate values are chosen for the constants a, b, c, and d. Verify that this differential equation gives

(a) the normal distribution if $b = c = 0$ and $a > 0$

(b) the exponential distribution if $a = c = d = 0$ and $b > 0$

(c) the gamma distribution if $a = c = 0$, $b > 0$, and $d > -b$

(d) the beta distribution if $a = 0$, $b = -c$, and $d > 1 - b$.

5.3.5 *Some applications*

The following set of exercises deals with applications of the uniform, exponential, gamma, and beta distributions. Applications of the normal distribution, based on a special table, are given in some of the exercises following Section 6.3.3 and in later parts of this book.

EXERCISES

1. Given a line AB, whose midpoint is C and whose length is a. A point X is chosen at random on this line, that is, **x**, its distance from A, has the uniform density $f(x) = 1/a$ for $0 < x < a$. What is the probability that AX, BX, and AC can form a triangle?

2. Suppose that it is reasonable to treat the length of telephone calls made by the executives of a certain company as a random variable having an exponential distribution with $\theta = 4$; time is measured in minutes. What is the probability that a telephone call made by one of these executives will last at least 2 minutes? What is the probability that one of these calls which has already lasted 2 minutes will last at least another 2 minutes?

3. If families are selected at random in a certain densely populated area, their annual income in excess of \$4000 can be treated as a random variable having an exponential distribution with $\theta = 2000$. What is the probability that 3 out of 4 families selected in this area (at random and independently) have incomes in excess of \$5000?

4. In a large department store, the December sales volume of nylon stockings (in ten thousands of pairs) can be treated as a random variable whose distribution is closely approximated by a gamma distribution with $\alpha = 3$ and $\beta = 1$. What is the probability that during the month of December this store will sell at least 40,000 pairs of nylon stockings?

5. In a certain city, the daily consumption of electric power (in millions of kilowatt-hours) can be treated as a random variable having a gamma distribution with $\alpha = 2$ and $\beta = 3$. If the power plant of this city has a daily capacity of 10 million kilowatt-hours, what is the probability that this power supply is inadequate on any given day?

6. The daily proportion of perfect tiles fired in a certain kiln can be treated as a random variable having a beta distribution with $\alpha = 18$ and $\beta = 2$. What is the probability that on a given day less than 90 per cent of the tiles fired in this kiln are perfect?

5.4 Change of Variable

Let us now study the problem of obtaining the probability density of a random variable **y**, given the probability density of a random variable **x** and a relationship of the form $y = h(x)$ between values of **x** and values of **y**. In what follows we shall assume that the function given by $y = h(x)$ is differentiable and either increasing or decreasing for all values within the range of **x**. Note that under these conditions the inverse function, given by $x = H(y)$, exists and that it is differentiable except where $h'(x) = 0$.

THEOREM 5.1:

If the probability density of **x** *is given by* $f(x)$ *and the function given by* $y = h(x)$ *is differentiable and either increasing or de-*

creasing for all values within the range of **x**, *the probability density of* **y** *is given by*

$$g(y) = f(x) \cdot \left| \frac{dx}{dy} \right| \qquad \frac{dy}{dx} \neq 0 \tag{5.4.1}$$

This theorem will have to be proved in two parts, depending on whether the function given by $y = h(x)$ is increasing or decreasing. The second part, where the function is assumed to be decreasing, will be left to the reader (see Exercise 1 on page 136).

Writing $F_{\mathbf{x}}(a)$ for the value of the distribution function of **x** at a, the probability that **x** assumes a value less than or equal to a is

$$F_{\mathbf{x}}(a) = \int_{-\infty}^{a} f(x)\, dx$$

Under the assumption that the function given by $y = h(x)$ is *increasing*, $F_{\mathbf{x}}(a)$ also equals the probability that **y** assumes a value less than or equal to $h(a)$, namely,

$$F_{\mathbf{y}}[h(a)] = \int_{-\infty}^{a} f(x)\, dx \tag{5.4.2}$$

If we now perform the change of variable $y = h(x)$ and $x = H(y)$ in the integral on the righthand side of (5.4.2), we get

$$F_{\mathbf{y}}[(h(a)] = \int_{-\infty}^{h(a)} f[H(y)]H'(y)\, dy \tag{5.4.3}$$

for any real number $h(a)$ within the range of **y**. Hence, the integrand in (5.4.3) gives the probability density of **y**, provided that $H'(y)$ exists, and

$$g(y) = f[H(y)]H'(y) \qquad \frac{1}{H'(y)} \neq 0$$

This can also be written

$$g(y) = f(x) \cdot \frac{dx}{dy} = f(x) \cdot \left| \frac{dx}{dy} \right| \qquad \frac{dy}{dx} \neq 0$$

since $H(y) = x$ and $H'(y) = dx/dy$ was assumed to be non-negative.

To illustrate the use of Theorem 5.1, let us consider the situation described in Figure 5.14. Assuming that the double arrow is spun so that θ has a uniform density from $-(\pi/2)$ to $\pi/2$, suppose we want to find the probability density of **x**, the coordinate of the point

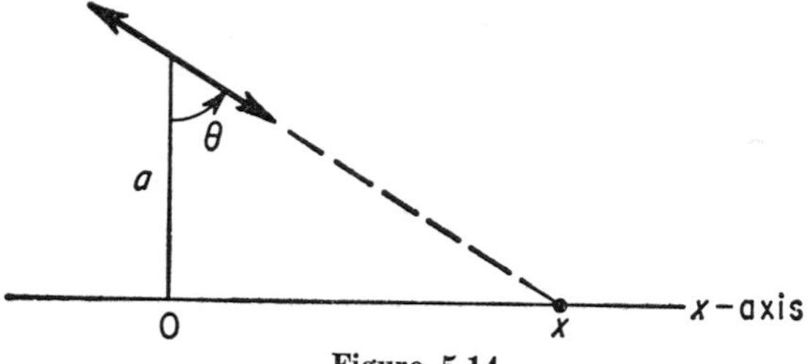

Figure 5.14

to which the arrow points in Figure 5.14. In other words, we are given

$$f(\theta) = \begin{cases} \dfrac{1}{\pi} & \text{for } -\dfrac{\pi}{2} < \theta < \dfrac{\pi}{2} \\ 0 & \text{elsewhere} \end{cases}$$

and, as is apparent from Figure 5.14, the relationship between x and θ is given by $x = a \cdot \tan \theta$, where $a > 0$. Hence

$$\frac{d\theta}{dx} = \frac{a}{a^2 + x^2}$$

and according to Theorem 5.1

$$g(x) = \frac{1}{\pi} \cdot \frac{a}{a^2 + x^2} \qquad \text{for} \quad -\infty < x < \infty \tag{5.4.4}$$

where $a > 0$.

The probability density given by (5.4.4) is called the *Cauchy distribution* and its graph is shown in Figure 5.15. It plays an important role in illustrating various aspects of statistical theory; as we shall see in Chapter 6, *its moments do not exist.*

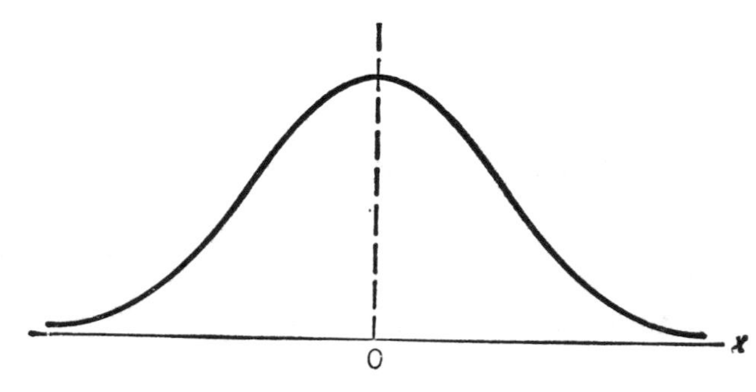

Figure 5.15

The following is another interesting result obtained with Theorem 5.1. Let us consider a random variable **x** having a continuous probability density $f(x)$, and let us suppose that we want to find the probability density of the random variable **y**, which assumes the value

$$y = \int_{-\infty}^{x} f(x)\,dx = F(x) \tag{5.4.5}$$

when **x** assumes the value x. As can be seen from Figure 5.16, for any given x, y is the area under the graph of $f(x)$ to the left of x.

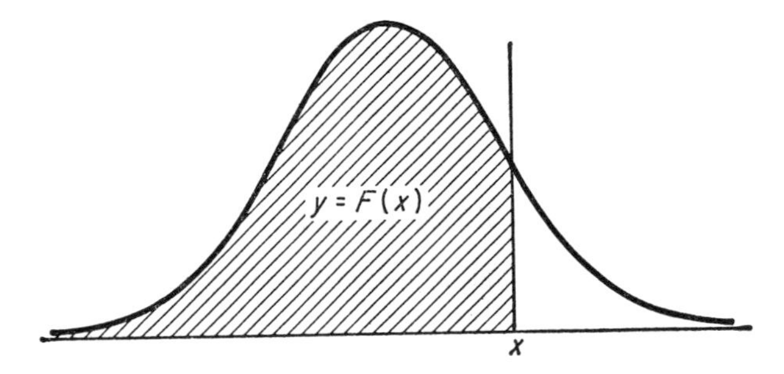

Figure 5.16

Differentiating $y = F(x)$ with respect to x, we get

$$\frac{dy}{dx} = F'(x) = f(x)$$

and according to Theorem 5.1 we have

$$g(y) = f(x)\cdot\frac{1}{f(x)} = 1 \qquad \text{for} \quad 0 < y < 1 \tag{5.4.6}$$

The probability density of y is, thus, the uniform density on the interval from 0 to 1. The change of variable which we have performed here is often referred to as the *probability integral transformation.*

In both of the preceding examples the conditions of Theorem 5.1 were met inasmuch as the functions relating the two variables were increasing. Now let us consider a random variable **x** having a normal distribution with $\alpha = 0$ and $\beta = 1$, namely,

$$f(x) = \frac{1}{\sqrt{2\pi}}\,e^{-(1/2)x^2} \qquad \text{for} \quad -\infty < x < \infty$$

and let us find the probability density of **y**, where $y = x^2$. Since this function is decreasing for negative values of x and increasing for positive values of x, the conditions of Theorem 5.1 are not met. However, in view of the symmetry of this normal distribution, $f(-x) = f(x)$, and the fact that $-x$ and x yield the same value of y, we can treat the probability density of **x** *for the moment* as if it were

$$f^*(x) = \frac{2}{\sqrt{2\pi}} e^{-(1/2)x^2} \qquad \text{for} \quad x > 0$$

and 0 elsewhere. Now Theorem 5.1 leads to

$$g(y) = \frac{2}{\sqrt{2\pi}} e^{-(1/2)y} \frac{1}{2\sqrt{y}} = \frac{1}{\sqrt{2\pi}} y^{-(1/2)} e^{-(1/2)y} \qquad \text{for} \quad y > 0$$

and this is readily identified as a gamma distribution with $\alpha = \frac{1}{2}$ and $\beta = 2$.

EXERCISES

1. Prove Theorem 5.1 when the function given by $y = h(x)$ is *decreasing.*

2. Given the random variable **x** with the probability density

$$f(x) = \begin{cases} \dfrac{x^2}{9} & \text{for} \quad 0 < x < 3 \\ 0 & \text{elsewhere} \end{cases}$$

find the probability density of **y**, where $y = x^3$.

3. Given a random variable **x** with the probability density

$$f(x) = \begin{cases} \dfrac{kx^3}{(1 + 2x)^6} & \text{for} \quad x > 0 \\ 0 & \text{elsewhere} \end{cases}$$

where k is an appropriate constant, show that the random variable **y**, where $y = 2x/(1 + 2x)$, has a beta distribution.

4. According to the Maxwell-Boltzmann law, the probability density of **v**, the velocity of a gas molecule is

$$f(v) = \begin{cases} kv^2 e^{-\beta v^2} & \text{for} \quad v > 0 \\ 0 & \text{elsewhere} \end{cases}$$

where β depends on its mass and the absolute temperature and k is an appropriate constant. Show that the probability density of the kinetic energy $\mathbf{E}$, where $E = \frac{1}{2}mv^2$, is a gamma distribution.

5.5 Multivariate Probability Densities

Let us now generalize the work of Section 5.2 by considering n random variables $\mathbf{x}_1, \mathbf{x}_2, \ldots, \mathbf{x}_n$. If the probability that $\mathbf{x}_1$ assumes a value less than or equal to a_1, $\mathbf{x}_2$ assumes a value less than or equal to $a_2, \ldots,$ and $\mathbf{x}_n$ assumes a value less than or equal to a_n, is given by

$$F(a_1, a_2, \ldots, a_n) = \int_{-\infty}^{a_1}\int_{-\infty}^{a_2}\cdots\int_{-\infty}^{a_n} f(x_1, x_2, \ldots, x_n)\, dx_1\, dx_2 \ldots dx_n \tag{5.5.1}$$

for all real constants $a_1, a_2, \ldots,$ and a_n, then $f(x_1, x_2, \ldots, x_n)$ is referred to as a value of the *joint probability density* of the n random variables and $F(x_1, x_2, \ldots, x_n)$ as a value of their *joint distribution function.*

To give an example of a joint probability density, let us consider the one whose graph is shown partially in Figure 5.17, namely,

$$f(x_1, x_2) = \begin{cases} e^{-(x_1+x_2)} & \text{for} \quad x_1 > 0 \text{ and } x_2 > 0 \\ 0 & \text{elsewhere} \end{cases}$$

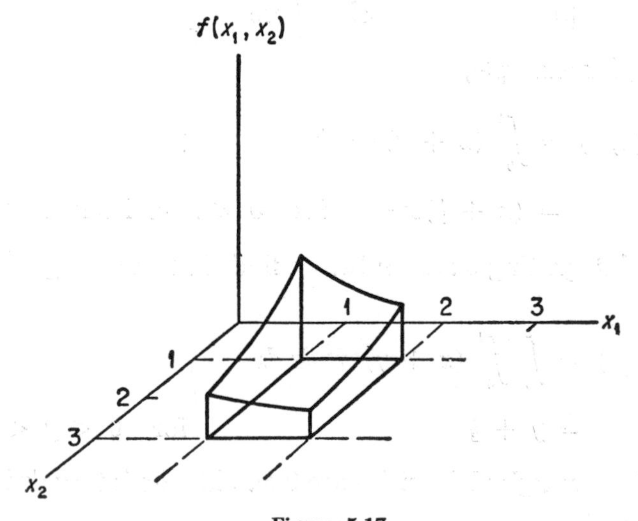

Figure 5.17

In this *bivariate* example, probabilities are given by volumes under the surface; for instance, the probability that $\mathbf{x}_1$ assumes a value between 1 and 2 and $\mathbf{x}_2$ assumes a value between 1 and 3 is given by the volume of the solid indicated in Figure 5.17. It equals

$$\int_1^2 \int_1^3 e^{-(x_1+x_2)}\, dx_1\, dx_2 = e^{-2} - e^{-3} - e^{-4} + e^{-5} = 0.074$$

It will be left to the reader to show that for this example the joint distribution function is given by

$$F(x_1, x_2) = \begin{cases} (1 - e^{-x_1})(1 - e^{-x_2}) & \text{for } x_1 > 0 \text{ and } x_2 > 0 \\ 0 & \text{elsewhere} \end{cases}$$

Given the joint probability density of n random variables, the *joint marginal density* of any k of these random variables is obtained by integrating out, from $-\infty$ to ∞, the other $n - k$ variables. Another way of putting this is that the *joint marginal distribution function* of any k of these random variables is given by (5.5.1) with ∞ substituted for the a's corresponding to the other $n - k$ random variables.

Thus, if the joint probability density of three random variable $\mathbf{x}$, $\mathbf{y}$, and $\mathbf{z}$ is given by

$$f(x, y, z) = \begin{cases} (x + y)e^{-z} & \text{for } 0 < x < 1, 0 < y < 1, 0 < z \\ 0 & \text{elsewhere} \end{cases}$$

we obtain, for example,

$$\begin{aligned} f(x, z) &= \int_0^1 (x + y)e^{-z}\, dy \\ &= (x + \tfrac{1}{2})e^{-z} \qquad \text{for } 0 < x < 1 \text{ and } 0 < z \end{aligned}$$

Similarly, integrating out x and z, we find that the marginal density of $\mathbf{y}$ is

$$\begin{aligned} \phi(y) &= \int_0^\infty \int_0^1 (x + y)e^{-z}\, dz\, dx \\ &= y + \tfrac{1}{2} \qquad \text{for } 0 < y < 1 \end{aligned}$$

Both of these marginal densities are 0 outside the intervals indicated for x, y, and z.

Analogous to (3.3.3), we shall define the *conditional probability density* of $\mathbf{x}_1$ given that $\mathbf{x}_2$ assumes the value x_2 as

$$f_1(x_1 \mid x_2) = \frac{f(x_1, x_2)}{g(x_2)} \qquad g(x_2) \neq 0 \tag{5.5.2}$$

where $f(x_1, x_2)$ and $g(x_2)$ are, respectively, values of the joint probability density of $\mathbf{x}_1$ and $\mathbf{x}_2$ and the marginal density of $\mathbf{x}_2$.

For instance, if two random variables $\mathbf{x}_1$ and $\mathbf{x}_2$ have the joint probability density

$$f(x_1, x_2) = \begin{cases} \frac{2}{3}(x_1 + 2x_2) & \text{for } 0 < x_1 < 1 \text{ and } 0 < x_2 < 1 \\ 0 & \text{elsewhere} \end{cases}$$

the marginal density of $\mathbf{x}_2$ is

$$g(x_2) = \int_0^1 \tfrac{2}{3}(x_1 + 2x_2)\, dx_1 = \tfrac{1}{3}(1 + 4x_2) \qquad \text{for } 0 < x_2 < 1$$

and $g(x_2) = 0$ elsewhere. Hence, the conditional probability density of $\mathbf{x}_1$ given that $\mathbf{x}_2$ assumes the value x_2 is

$$f_1(x_1 \mid x_2) = \frac{\frac{2}{3}(x_1 + 2x_2)}{\frac{1}{3}(1 + 4x_2)} = \frac{2x_1 + 4x_2}{1 + 4x_2} \qquad \text{for } 0 < x_1 < 1$$

and $f_1(x_1 \mid x_2) = 0$ elsewhere. Using this conditional probability density we can now find, for example, the probability that $\mathbf{x}_1$ will assume a value on the interval from 0 to $\frac{1}{2}$, given that the value of $\mathbf{x}_2$ is 1/2; it is

$$\int_0^{1/2} \frac{2x_1 + 4(1/2)}{1 + 4(1/2)}\, dx_1 = \frac{5}{12}$$

In Figure 5.18 this probability is the ratio of the area of trapezoid *ABCD* to the area of trapezoid *ABEF*.

The concept of a conditional probability density can easily be extended to apply to problems involving more than two random variables. For instance,

$$\frac{f(x_1, x_2, x_3)}{g(x_1, x_2)} \qquad g(x_1, x_2) \neq 0$$

gives the conditional probability density of $\mathbf{x}_3$ given that $\mathbf{x}_1$ and $\mathbf{x}_2$ assume the values x_1 and x_2, and

$$\frac{f(x_1, x_2, x_3, x_4)}{g(x_4)} \qquad g(x_4) \neq 0$$

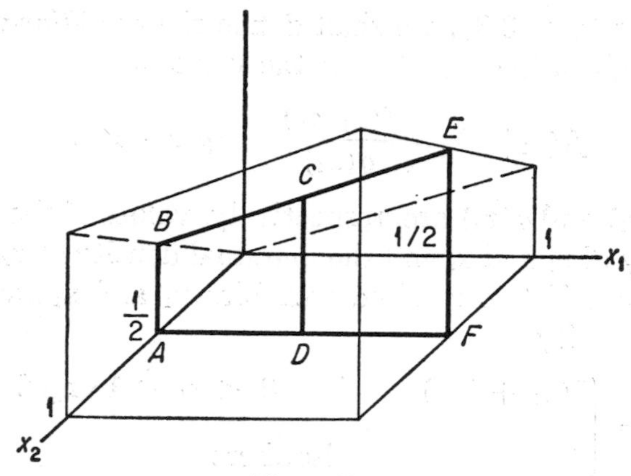

Figure 5.18

gives the joint conditional density of $\mathbf{x}_1$, $\mathbf{x}_2$, and $\mathbf{x}_3$, given that the value of $\mathbf{x}_4$ is x_4.

As in the discrete case, questions of *independence* are of special importance in connection with the joint distribution of continuous random variables. Analogous to (3.3.5) let us say, by definition, that *the random variables* $\mathbf{x}_1$, $\mathbf{x}_2$, ..., *and* $\mathbf{x}_n$ *are independent if and only if*

$$f(x_1, x_2, \ldots, x_n) = \prod_{i=1}^{n} f_i(x_i) \tag{5.5.3}$$

for all values within the ranges of these random variables for which $f(x_1, x_2, \ldots, x_n)$ *is defined.* As before, $f(x_1, x_2, \ldots, x_n)$ and $f_i(x_i)$ are, respectively, values of the joint probability density of the n random variables and the marginal density of $\mathbf{x}_i$.

Using this definition of independence, it can easily be verified that in the example on page 138, where $f(x, y, z) = (x + y)e^{-z}$, the three random variables are *not independent.* On the other hand, $\mathbf{x}$ and $\mathbf{z}$ are *pairwise independent* and so are the random variables $\mathbf{y}$ and $\mathbf{z}$. Also, in the example on page 137, where $f(x_1, x_2) = e^{-(x_1+x_2)}$, the two random variables are *independent,* since

$$f(x_1) = e^{-x_1} \quad \text{for} \quad x_1 > 0$$

$$g(x_2) = e^{-x_2} \quad \text{for} \quad x_2 > 0$$

and $f(x_1, x_2) = f(x_1)g(x_2)$ for all positive values of $\mathbf{x}_1$ and $\mathbf{x}_2$. [For negative or zero values of $\mathbf{x}_1$ and $\mathbf{x}_2$ the joint density as well as the marginal densities are identically zero; hence $f(x_1, x_2) = f(x_1)g(x_2)$ also in that case.]

EXERCISES

1. Find k if the joint probability density of $\mathbf{x}_1$ and $\mathbf{x}_2$ is given by

$$f(x_1, x_2) = \begin{cases} ke^{-3x_1-4x_2} & \text{for} \quad x_1 > 0 \text{ and } x_2 > 0 \\ 0 & \text{elsewhere} \end{cases}$$

Also find the probability that the value of $\mathbf{x}_1$ falls between 0 and 1 while that of $\mathbf{x}_2$ falls between 0 and 2.

2. Find the equation of the joint distribution function of the two random variables of Exercise 1 and use it to verify the probability asked for in that exercise.

3. Given the joint density

$$f(x_1, x_2) = \begin{cases} \dfrac{k}{(1 + x_1 + x_2)^3} & \text{for} \quad x_1 > 0 \text{ and } x_2 > 0 \\ 0 & \text{elsewhere} \end{cases}$$

find k and the marginal densities of $\mathbf{x}_1$ and $\mathbf{x}_2$. Also find the conditional density of $\mathbf{x}_1$ given that $\mathbf{x}_2$ assumes the value x_2.

4. Given the joint probability density

$$f(x, y, z) = \begin{cases} \frac{4}{9}\, xyz^2 & \text{for} \quad 0 < x < 1, 0 < y < 1, 0 < z < 3 \\ 0 & \text{elsewhere} \end{cases}$$

find (a) the joint marginal density of $\mathbf{x}$ and $\mathbf{z}$, and (b) the marginal density of $\mathbf{x}$. Also evaluate the probability that $\mathbf{x}$ assumes a value on the interval from 0 to $\frac{1}{2}$, $\mathbf{y}$ assumes a value on the interval from $\frac{1}{3}$ to $\frac{2}{3}$, and $\mathbf{z}$ assumes a value on the interval from 1 to 2.

5. Given the joint probability density

$$f(x_1, x_2) = \begin{cases} 2 & \text{for} \quad 0 < x_1 < 1 \text{ and } 0 < x_1 < x_2 < 1 \\ 0 & \text{elsewhere} \end{cases}$$

find the marginal densities of $\mathbf{x}_1$ and $\mathbf{x}_2$ and check whether the two random variables are independent. Also find the conditional probability that $\mathbf{x}_1$ will assume a value on the interval from $\frac{1}{4}$ to $\frac{1}{2}$, given that $\mathbf{x}_2$ assumes the value $\frac{1}{2}$.

6. Referring to the illustration in the text on page 138, show that **x** and **z** are independent, but that **x**, **y**, and **z** are not independent.

7. Check whether the two random variables of Exercise 3 are independent.

8. (a) Given $f(x, y) = \frac{1}{81}x^2y^2$ for $0 < x < 3$ and $0 < y < 3$, and $f(x, y) = 0$ elsewhere, check whether **x** and **y** are independent.

   (b) Given $f(x, y) = \frac{2}{81}x^2y^2$ for $0 < x < y$ and $0 < y < 3$, and $f(x, y) = 0$ elsewhere, check whether **x** and **y** are independent.

9. Suppose that the price of a certain item (in dollars), which depends on the cost of production and prices of raw materials, may be looked upon as a random variable having the uniform density

$$f(p) = \begin{cases} 5 & \text{for } 0.20 < p < 0.40 \\ 0 & \text{elsewhere} \end{cases}$$

For a fixed price p, total sales (in 10,000 units) may be looked upon as a random variable having the conditional exponential distribution

$$f(s \mid p) = \begin{cases} p \cdot e^{-ps} & \text{for } s > 0 \\ 0 & \text{elsewhere} \end{cases}$$

What is the probability that sales of this item will exceed 25,000 units?

Chapter 6

Mathematical Expectation: Continuous Random Variables

6.1 Mathematical Expectation

Analogous to (4.1.1) we shall define the mathematical expectation of $\mathbf{x}$, a random variable whose probability density is given by $f(x)$, as

$$E(\mathbf{x}) = \int_{-\infty}^{\infty} x \cdot f(x)\, dx \tag{6.1.1}$$

This differs from (4.1.1) only inasmuch as integration has taken the place of summation. Similarly, we shall make the more general definition that the mathematical expectation of $g(\mathbf{x})$, the random variable whose value is $g(x)$ when the value of $\mathbf{x}$ is x, is

$$E[g(\mathbf{x})] = \int_{-\infty}^{\infty} g(x) f(x)\, dx \tag{6.1.2}$$

analogous to (4.1.2). If the integrals given by (6.1.1) or (6.1.2) do not converge, the corresponding mathematical expectations do not exist. See, for example, Exercise 6 on page 151.

Most of the discussion of Sections 4.1 and 4.2 applies also to the continuous case. Leaving it to the reader to verify that Theorems 4.1, 4.2, and 4.3 hold also when $\mathbf{x}$ is a continuous random variable, let us prove the following theorem, whose first part is equivalent to Theorem 4.4:

THEOREM 6.1:

(1) $E(a\mathbf{x} + b) = aE(\mathbf{x}) + b$

(2) $E[(a\mathbf{x} + b)^2] = a^2E(\mathbf{x}^2) + 2abE(\mathbf{x}) + b^2$

To prove the first part of this theorem we have only to write

$$\begin{aligned} E(a\mathbf{x} + b) &= \int_{-\infty}^{\infty} (ax + b)f(x)\,dx \\ &= a\int_{-\infty}^{\infty} xf(x)\,dx + b\int_{-\infty}^{\infty} f(x)\,dx \\ &= aE(\mathbf{x}) + b \end{aligned}$$

and to prove the second part

$$\begin{aligned} E[(a\mathbf{x} + b)^2] &= \int_{-\infty}^{\infty} (ax + b)^2 f(x)\,dx \\ &= a^2\int_{-\infty}^{\infty} x^2 f(x)\,dx + 2ab\int_{-\infty}^{\infty} xf(x)\,dx + b^2\int_{-\infty}^{\infty} f(x)\,dx \\ &= a^2E(\mathbf{x}^2) + 2abE(\mathbf{x}) + b^2 \end{aligned}$$

As in Section 4.1, we extend the concept of mathematical expectation to functions of several random variables by means of the following definition:

$$E[g(\mathbf{x}_1, \mathbf{x}_2, \ldots, \mathbf{x}_n)] = \int_{-\infty}^{\infty} \cdots \int_{-\infty}^{\infty} g(x_1, x_2, \ldots, x_n) f(x_1, x_2, \ldots, x_n)\,dx_1 \ldots dx_n \qquad (6.1.3)$$

where $f(x_1, x_2, \ldots, x_n)$ gives the joint probability density of the random variables $\mathbf{x}_1, \mathbf{x}_2, \ldots, \mathbf{x}_n$. To define a random variable, the function given by $g(x_1, x_2, \ldots, x_n)$ will, as before, have to be single-valued.

6.2 Moments

As in Section 4.2, if $g(\mathbf{x}) = \mathbf{x}^r$, formula (6.1.2) yields the *r'th moment about the origin* of the distribution of $\mathbf{x}$. Using the same symbolism as in the discrete case, we shall write

$$\mu_r' = E(\mathbf{x}^r) = \int_{-\infty}^{\infty} x^r f(x)\, dx \tag{6.2.1}$$

Similarly, the *r'th moment about the mean* is given by

$$\mu_r = E[(\mathbf{x} - \mu)^r] = \int_{-\infty}^{\infty} (x - \mu)^r f(x)\, dx \tag{6.2.2}$$

where, as before, $\mu_1' = \mu$ is called the *mean* of the distribution of $\mathbf{x}$. Also, we shall again refer to μ_2 as the *variance* of the distribution of $\mathbf{x}$ and write it as σ^2, $V(\mathbf{x})$, or $\text{var}(\mathbf{x})$. Note that Theorem 4.5, and hence, the various relationships among moments about the origin and moments about the mean hold also in the continuous case. Thus, in particular, we again have $\sigma^2 = \mu_2' - \mu^2$.

When tabulating values of probability densities, probability distributions, or distribution functions, it is sometimes desirable (or even necessary) to consider them in their *standard form.* Generally speaking, *the distribution of a random variable is said to be in its standard form if* $\mu = 0$ *and* $\sigma = 1$. If the probability density or the probability distribution of a random variable $\mathbf{x}$ has the mean μ and the variance σ^2, we refer to the random variable $\mathbf{y} = (\mathbf{x} - \mu)/\sigma$ as the *standardized random variable corresponding to* $\mathbf{x}$. Using Theorem 6.1 with $a = 1/\sigma$ and $b = -(\mu/\sigma)$ it can easily be verified that, indeed,

$$E(\mathbf{y}) = E\left(\frac{\mathbf{x} - \mu}{\sigma}\right) = 0$$

and

$$\text{var}(\mathbf{y}) = E\left[\left(\frac{\mathbf{x} - \mu}{\sigma}\right)^2\right] - E\left(\frac{\mathbf{x} - \mu}{\sigma}\right)^2 = 1$$

The distribution of $\mathbf{y}$ is, thus, the distribution of $\mathbf{x}$ *transformed into its standard form.* The need for considering standardized random variables and standardized distributions will be illustrated in Sections 6.3.3 and 6.4.3 and in later parts of the book.

6.3 Moments of Special Probability Densities

As in the discrete case, we can find the moments of probability densities by deriving them directly with (6.2.1) and (6.2.2) or by using moment generating functions, to be defined for the continuous case in Section 6.4. Only experience can tell whether one method is more suitable than the other for any given distribution.

6.3.1 *Moments of the uniform distribution*

Substituting the formula for the uniform distribution on the interval from α to β into (6.2.1), we find that the rth moment about the origin is

$$\mu_r' = \int_\alpha^\beta \frac{1}{\beta - \alpha} x^r \, dx = \frac{\beta^{r+1} - \alpha^{r+1}}{(\beta - \alpha)(r + 1)} \tag{6.3.1}$$

This gives, in particular

$$\mu_1' = \frac{\alpha + \beta}{2} \quad \text{and} \quad \mu_2' = \frac{\beta^2 + \alpha\beta + \alpha^2}{3}$$

and, hence,

THEOREM 6.2:

The mean and variance of the uniform distribution on the interval from α to β are

$$\mu = \frac{\alpha + \beta}{2} \quad \textit{and} \quad \sigma^2 = \frac{(\beta - \alpha)^2}{12} \tag{6.3.2}$$

6.3.2 *Moments of the gamma distribution*

Substituting (5.3.3) into (6.2.1), we find that for the gamma distribution the rth moment about the origin is

$$\mu_r' = \frac{1}{\beta^\alpha \Gamma(\alpha)} \int_0^\infty x^{r+\alpha-1} e^{-(x/\beta)} \, dx$$

Setting $y = x/\beta$ and recognizing the resulting integral as $\Gamma(r + \alpha)$, we obtain

$$\mu_r' = \frac{\beta^r \Gamma(\alpha + r)}{\Gamma(\alpha)} \tag{6.3.3}$$

In particular

$$\mu_1' = \frac{\beta\Gamma(\alpha + 1)}{\Gamma(\alpha)} = \beta\alpha \quad \text{and} \quad \mu_2' = \frac{\beta^2\Gamma(\alpha + 2)}{\Gamma(\alpha)} = \beta^2(\alpha + 1)\alpha$$

and, hence,

THEOREM 6.3:

The mean and variance of the gamma distribution are

$$\mu = \beta\alpha \quad \textit{and} \quad \sigma^2 = \beta^2\alpha \tag{6.3.4}$$

Considering the exponential distribution of Section 5.3.2 as a special gamma distribution with $\alpha = 1$ and $\beta = \theta$, (6.3.3) becomes

$$\mu_r' = \frac{\theta^r \Gamma(1 + r)}{\Gamma(1)} = r!\theta^r \tag{6.3.5}$$

and, in particular,

THEOREM 6.4:

The mean and variance of the exponential distribution are

$$\mu = \theta \quad \textit{and} \quad \sigma^2 = \theta^2 \tag{6.3.6}$$

6.3.3 *Moments of the normal distribution*

Let us now show that the parameters α and β of the normal distribution as defined by (5.3.6) on page 129, are, in fact, its mean and its standard deviation. Since

$$\mu = \int_{-\infty}^{\infty} x \cdot \frac{1}{\beta\sqrt{2\pi}} e^{-\frac{1}{2}\left(\frac{x-\alpha}{\beta}\right)^2} dx$$

setting $y = \dfrac{x - \alpha}{\beta}$ yields

$$\mu = \frac{1}{\sqrt{2\pi}} \int_{-\infty}^{\infty} (\beta y + \alpha) e^{-(1/2)y^2}\, dy$$

$$= \frac{\beta}{\sqrt{2\pi}} \int_{-\infty}^{\infty} y \cdot e^{-(1/2)y^2}\, dy + \alpha \left[\frac{1}{\sqrt{2\pi}} \int_{-\infty}^{\infty} e^{-(1/2)y^2}\, dy\right]$$

The first of these two integrals is equal to 0 since the integrand $\phi(y)$ is such that $\phi(-y) = -\phi(y)$. Furthermore, the quantity in brackets equals 1, it is the integral from $-\infty$ to ∞ of a normal density with $\alpha = 0$ and $\beta = 1$, and we thus get

$$\mu = \alpha$$

Using this result we can now write the variance of a normal density with the parameters $\alpha = \mu$ and β as

$$\sigma^2 = \frac{1}{\beta\sqrt{2\pi}} \int_{-\infty}^{\infty} (x - \mu)^2 e^{-\frac{1}{2}\left(\frac{x-\mu}{\beta}\right)^2} dx$$

Setting $y = \dfrac{x - \mu}{\beta}$, this becomes

$$\sigma^2 = \frac{\beta^2}{\sqrt{2\pi}} \int_{-\infty}^{\infty} y^2 e^{-(1/2)y^2} dy = \frac{2\beta^2}{\sqrt{2\pi}} \int_0^{\infty} y^2 e^{-(1/2)y^2} dy$$

since the integrand $\theta(y)$ is such that $\theta(-y) = \theta(y)$. If we then set $z = \frac{1}{2}y^2$, we get

$$\sigma^2 = \frac{2\beta^2}{\sqrt{\pi}} \int_0^{\infty} z^{1/2} e^{-z} dz$$

and this last integral can readily be identified as $\Gamma(\frac{3}{2})$. Having shown in Exercise 3 on page 130 that $\Gamma(\frac{1}{2}) = \sqrt{\pi}$, we can now use the recursion formula $\Gamma(\alpha) = (\alpha - 1)\Gamma(\alpha - 1)$ and write $\Gamma(\frac{3}{2}) = \frac{1}{2}\Gamma(\frac{1}{2}) = \frac{1}{2}\sqrt{\pi}$. We thus get

$$\sigma^2 = \frac{2\beta^2}{\sqrt{\pi}} \cdot \Gamma\left(\frac{3}{2}\right) = \frac{2\beta^2}{\sqrt{\pi}} \frac{\sqrt{\pi}}{2} = \beta^2$$

and this completes the proof that β^2 is the *variance* of the normal distribution. *The normal distribution with the mean* μ *and the variance* σ^2 *is thus given by*

$$N(x; \mu, \sigma^2) = \frac{1}{\sigma\sqrt{2\pi}} e^{-\frac{1}{2}\left(\frac{x-\mu}{\sigma}\right)^2} \quad \text{for} \quad -\infty < x < \infty \qquad (6.3.7)$$

and we often refer to it symbolically simply as $N(\mu, \sigma^2)$.

Since the normal distribution plays a central role in statistical theory as well as in applications, areas under the *standard normal distribution* $N(x; 0, 1)$ are given in Table III. More specifically, Table III contains the values of

$$\int_0^z N(x; 0, 1)\, dx = \int_0^z \frac{1}{\sqrt{2\pi}} e^{-(1/2)x^2} dx$$

for $z = 0.00, 0.01, 0.02, \ldots, 3.08$, and 3.09 (see Figure 6.1). In view of the symmetry of the normal distribution about its mean, $N(x - \mu; \mu, \sigma^2) = N(\mu - x; \mu, \sigma^2)$, it is unnecessary to extend Table III to negative values of z.

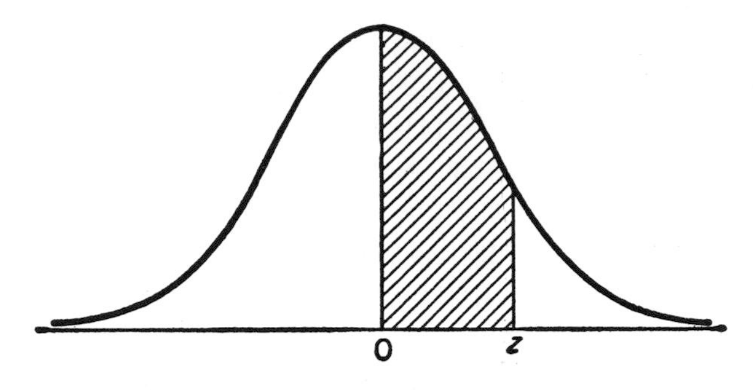

Figure 6.1

To illustrate the use of Table III, suppose that the random variable **z** has the standard normal distribution. We thus find that the probability that **z** assumes a value less than or equal to 1.53 is $0.5000 + 0.4370 = 0.9370$, the probability that it assumes a value greater than -0.62 is $0.5000 + 0.2324 = 0.7324$, the probability that it assumes a value greater than 0.89 is $0.5000 - 0.3133 = 0.1867$, the probability that it assumes a value less than -1.55 is $0.5000 - 0.4394 = 0.0606$, the probability that it assumes a value between 1.25 and 1.45 is $0.4265 - 0.3944 = 0.0321$, and the proba-

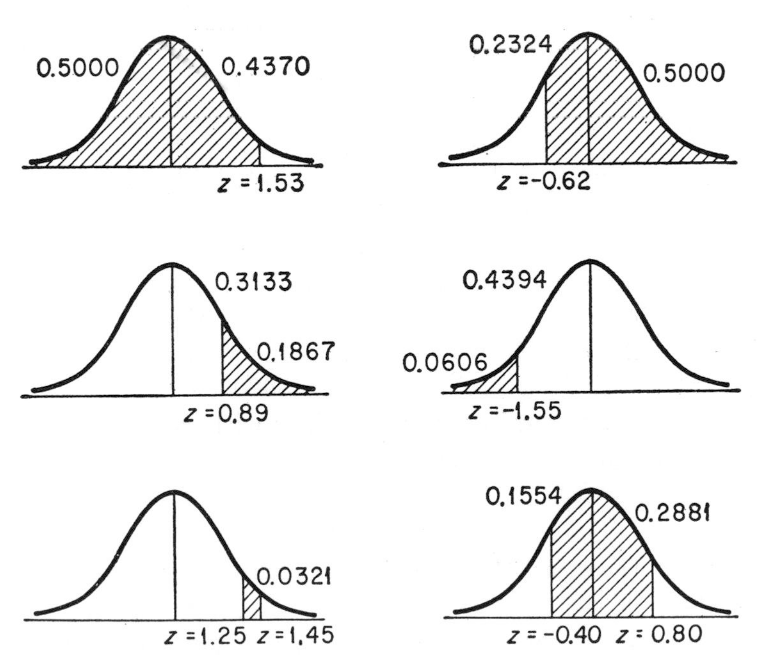

Figure 6.2

bility that it assumes a value between -0.40 and 0.80 is $0.1554 + 0.2881 = 0.4435$ (see Figure 6.2).

If we want to use Table III to find probabilities concerning a random variable **x** having the normal distribution $N(x;\ \mu,\ \sigma^2)$, we have only to make use of the fact that $\mathbf{z} = (\mathbf{x} - \mu)/\sigma$ is a random variable having the standard normal distribution $N(z;\ 0,\ 1)$. In other words, when **x** assumes the value x, the corresponding standardized random variable **z** (see page 145) assumes the value $(x - \mu)/\sigma$. Thus, to find the probability that **x** assumes a value between x_1 and x_2, we have only to look up the probability that a random variable having the standard normal distribution assumes a value between $(x_1 - \mu)/\sigma$ and $(x_2 - \mu)/\sigma$.

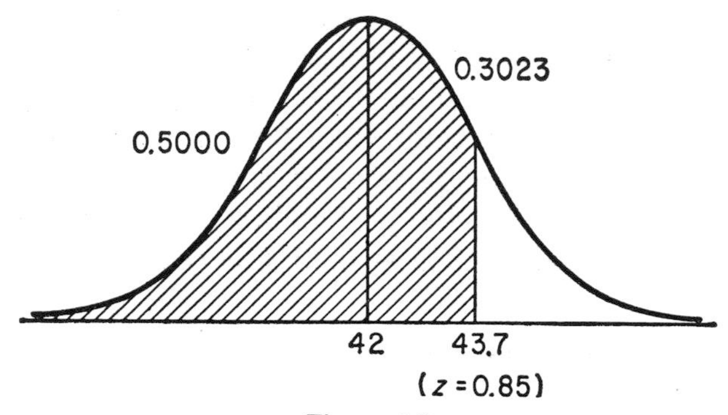

Figure 6.3

To give an example, let us find the probability that a random variable having the normal distribution $N(x; 42, 4)$ assumes a value less than or equal to 43.7. Since $\mu = 42$ and $\sigma = 2$, we shall have to look up the probability that a random variable having the standard normal distribution assumes a value less than or equal to $(43.7 - 42)/2 = 0.85$. The corresponding entry in Table III is 0.3023 and the desired probability is $0.5000 + 0.3023 = 0.8023$ (see Figure 6.3). Several exercises dealing with applications of the normal distribution are given below.

EXERCISES

1. Show that Theorems 4.1, 4.2, and 4.3 hold also when **x** is a continuous random variable.

2. Prove Chebyshev's Theorem for continuous random variables, duplicating the steps used in Section 4.2.1.

3. If the random variable **x** has the exponential distribution (5.3.2), show that the corresponding standardized random variable has the probability density

$$f(y) = \begin{cases} e^{-y-1} & \text{for } y > -1 \\ 0 & \text{elsewhere} \end{cases}$$

4. Find the mean and the variance of the probability density of Exercise 5 on page 125.

5. Check whether the mean and the variance of the following distribution exist:

$$f(x) = \begin{cases} \dfrac{2}{x^3} & \text{for } x > 1 \\ 0 & \text{elsewhere} \end{cases}$$

6. Show that the moments of the Cauchy distribution (see page 134) do not exist.

7. (*Moments of the beta distribution*) Find an expression for μ_r' of the beta distribution (see Exercise 6 on page 130) and then find its mean and variance. *Hint*: make use of the fact that

$$\int_0^1 x^{\alpha-1}(1 - x)^{\beta-1}\,dx = \frac{\Gamma(\alpha)\Gamma(\beta)}{\Gamma(\alpha + \beta)}$$

8. Referring to Exercise 5 on page 132, what is the mean daily consumption of electric power in the given city? Using Chebyshev's theorem, what can we say about the probability that on a certain day the consumption of electric power in this city will be greater than 15 million kilowatt-hours?

9. If **z** is a random variable having the standard normal distribution, use Table III to find

(a) the probability that **z** assumes a value greater than 2.68

(b) the probability that **z** assumes a value less than 1.73

(c) the probability that **z** assumes a value greater than -0.66

(d) the probability that **z** assumes a value less than -1.88

(e) the probability that **z** assumes a value between -1.05 and -1.65

(f) the probability that **z** assumes a value between -0.05 and 1.05

10. If $\mathbf{z}$ is a random variable having the standard normal distribution, use Table III to find z so that

(a) the probability that $\mathbf{z}$ assumes a value between 0 and z is 0.4515

(b) the probability that $\mathbf{z}$ assumes a value greater than z is 0.3121

(c) the probability that $\mathbf{z}$ assumes a value less than z is 0.4562

(d) the probability that $\mathbf{z}$ assumes a value between $-z$ and z is 0.7416

11. According to Chebyshev's Theorem, the probability that a random variable assumes a value within 2 standard deviations of the mean is at least $\frac{3}{4}$ and the probability that it assumes a value within 3 standard deviations of the mean is at least $\frac{8}{9}$. What are the corresponding probabilities for a random variable having a normal distribution?

12. Suppose that the number of telephone calls made daily in a certain community is a random variable whose distribution can be closely approximated by a normal distribution with $\mu = 352$ and $\sigma = 31$. What is the probability that on any given day the number of telephone calls made in this community will exceed 400? (*Hint*: since the number of telephone calls made is a *discrete* random variable, find the probability that a random variable having the given normal distribution assumes a value greater than 400.5.)

13. The density of certain glass bricks is a random variable having a normal distribution with $\mu = 2.480$ and $\sigma = 0.03$. Below what density can we expect to find the lightest 20 per cent of these bricks?

14. If one ball bearing is selected at random from a very large shipment, its diameter is a random variable whose distribution is normal with $\mu = 0.397$ in. and $\sigma = 0.005$ in. What is the probability that the diameter of a ball bearing thus selected will exceed 0.400 in.?

15. The lifetime of a certain kind of battery is a random variable having a normal distribution with $\mu = 300$ hours and $\sigma = 35$ hours. Find the probability that one of these batteries will have a lifetime of more than 320 hours. Also find the value above which we can expect to find the best 25 per cent of these batteries.

6.4 Moment Generating Functions

As in the discrete case, the *moment generating function* of the distribution of $\mathbf{x}$ is given by $M_{\mathbf{x}}(t) = E(e^{t\mathbf{x}})$, although now we have

$$M_{\mathbf{x}}(t) = E(e^{t\mathbf{x}}) = \int_{-\infty}^{\infty} e^{tx} f(x)\, dx \qquad (6.4.1)$$

Using this definition, it can easily be shown that, as before, when $M_{\mathbf{x}}(t)$ is expanded as a power series in t; the coefficient of $t^r/r!$ is μ_r'; also the rth derivative of $M_{\mathbf{x}}(t)$ with respect to t at $t = 0$ is again equal to μ_r', provided of course that this moment exists. [To avoid questions concerning the existence of $M_{\mathbf{x}}(t)$, it is preferable in some respects to use characteristic functions instead of moment generating functions, the characteristic function of the distribution of $\mathbf{x}$ being given by $E(e^{it\mathbf{x}})$, where t is real and $i^2 = -1$.]

6.4.1 *Some properties of moment generating functions*

When using moment generating functions to find moments of distributions or in proofs of statistical theory, it is helpful to refer to some of their special properties. Although we shall prove the theorems which follow with reference to probability densities, they apply also in the discrete case.

THEOREM 6.5:

$$M_{\mathbf{x}+a}(t) = e^{at}M_{\mathbf{x}}(t) \tag{6.4.2}$$

To prove this theorem we have only to write

$$\begin{aligned} M_{\mathbf{x}+a}(t) = E[e^{(\mathbf{x}+a)t}] &= \int_{-\infty}^{\infty} e^{(x+a)t}f(x)\,dx \\ &= e^{at}\int_{-\infty}^{\infty} e^{xt}f(x)\,dx \\ &= e^{at}M_{\mathbf{x}}(t) \end{aligned}$$

Theorem 6.5 is of special importance when $a = -\mu$. Differentiating r times with respect to t gives

$$\frac{d^rM_{\mathbf{x}-\mu}(t)}{dt^r} = \int_{-\infty}^{\infty} (x - \mu)^r e^{(x-\mu)t}f(x)\,dx$$

and at $t = 0$ this yields

$$\int_{-\infty}^{\infty} (x - \mu)^r f(x)\,dx = \mu_r$$

$M_{\mathbf{x}-\mu}(t)$ thus generates moments about the mean.

To give an example of such a generating function for moments about the mean, let us refer to the Poisson distribution, whose moment generating function is given by

$$M_{\mathbf{x}}(t) = e^{\lambda(e^t-1)}$$

according to (4.4.4). Since $\mu = \lambda$ in this case, Theorem 6.5 yields

$$M_{\mathbf{x}-\mu}(t) = e^{-\lambda t}e^{\lambda(e^t-1)} = e^{\lambda(e^t-t-1)}$$

and it will be left to the reader to verify that $M''_{\mathbf{x}-\mu}(0) = \sigma^2 = \lambda$.

Another important property of moment generating functions is expressed by the following theorem:

THEOREM 6.6:

$$M_{b\mathbf{x}}(t) = M_{\mathbf{x}}(bt) \tag{6.4.3}$$

To prove this theorem we have only to write

$$M_{b\mathbf{x}}(t) = E(e^{b\mathbf{x}t}) = \int_{-\infty}^{\infty} e^{bxt}f(x)\,dx$$

$$= \int_{-\infty}^{\infty} e^{x(bt)}f(x)\,dx$$

$$= M_{\mathbf{x}}(bt)$$

Combining Theorems 6.5 and 6.6 we get

$$M_{b(\mathbf{x}+a)}(t) = e^{abt}M_{\mathbf{x}}(bt) \tag{6.4.4}$$

and in the special case where $a = -\mu$ and $b = 1/\sigma$, this becomes

THEOREM 6.7:

$$M_{(\mathbf{x}-\mu)/\sigma}(t) = e^{-(\mu t/\sigma)}M_{\mathbf{x}}(t/\sigma) \tag{6.4.5}$$

which is of particular importance when dealing with *standardized* random variables.

6.4.2 *Moment generating functions of special distributions*

In this section we shall derive the moment generating functions of the gamma distribution and the normal distribution. Others will be obtained in the exercises which follow and in later chapters.

THEOREM 6.8:

The moment generating function of the gamma distribution is given by

$$M_x(t) = (1 - \beta t)^{-\alpha} \tag{6.4.6}$$

Substituting (5.3.3) for the probability density in (6.4.1), we obtain

$$\begin{aligned} M_x(t) &= \int_0^\infty e^{xt} \frac{1}{\beta^\alpha \Gamma(\alpha)} x^{\alpha-1} e^{-x/\beta}\, dx \\ &= \frac{1}{\beta^\alpha \Gamma(\alpha)} \int_0^\infty x^{\alpha-1} e^{-x\left(\frac{1}{\beta}-t\right)}\, dx \end{aligned}$$

and setting $y = x\left(\frac{1}{\beta} - t\right)$, we get

$$\begin{aligned} M_x(t) &= \frac{1}{\beta^\alpha \Gamma(\alpha)\left(\frac{1}{\beta} - t\right)^\alpha} \int_0^\infty y^{\alpha-1} e^{-y}\, dy \\ &= \frac{1}{\Gamma(\alpha)(1 - \beta t)^\alpha} \int_0^\infty y^{\alpha-1} e^{-y}\, dy \end{aligned}$$

Identifying this last integral as $\Gamma(\alpha)$, completes the proof of Theorem 6.8.

Using the binomial theorem to expand (6.4.6) as a power series in t, we obtain

$$\begin{aligned} M_x(t) = 1 &+ \alpha\beta t + \alpha(\alpha + 1)\beta^2 \cdot \frac{t^2}{2!} \\ &+ \alpha(\alpha + 1)(\alpha + 2)\beta^3 \cdot \frac{t^3}{3!} + \cdots \end{aligned} \tag{6.4.7}$$

and it follows that

$$\mu_1' = \alpha\beta, \quad \mu_2' = \alpha(\alpha + 1)\beta^2, \quad \text{and} \quad \mu_3' = \alpha(\alpha + 1)(\alpha + 2)\beta^3.$$

This verifies the result obtained in Section 6.3.2, namely, that the mean of the gamma distribution is $\mu = \alpha\beta$ and that the variance of the gamma distribution is $\sigma^2 = \alpha\beta^2$.

THEOREM 6.9:

The moment generating function of the normal distribution $N(x; \mu, \sigma^2)$ *is given by*

$$M_x(t) = e^{\mu t + (1/2) t^2 \sigma^2} \tag{6.4.8}$$

Substituting (6.3.7) for the probability density in (6.4.1), we obtain

$$M_x(t) = \int_{-\infty}^{\infty} e^{xt} \frac{1}{\sigma\sqrt{2\pi}} e^{-\frac{1}{2}\left(\frac{x-\mu}{\sigma}\right)^2} dx$$

$$= \frac{1}{\sigma\sqrt{2\pi}} \int_{-\infty}^{\infty} e^{-\left(\frac{1}{2\sigma^2}\right)[-2xt\sigma^2 + (x-\mu)^2]} dx$$

Completing the square in the exponent, we have

$$-2xt\sigma^2 + (x - \mu)^2 = [x - (\mu + t\sigma^2)]^2 - 2\mu t\sigma^2 - t^2\sigma^4$$

and we can thus write

$$M_x(t) = e^{\mu t + (1/2) t^2\sigma^2} \left[\frac{1}{\sigma\sqrt{2\pi}} \int_{-\infty}^{\infty} e^{-\frac{1}{2}\left[\frac{x-(\mu+t\sigma^2)}{\sigma}\right]^2} dx \right]$$

Identifying the quantity inside the brackets as the integral from $-\infty$ to ∞ of a normal density with the mean $\mu + t\sigma^2$ and the standard deviation σ, *and hence equalling* 1, we finally get

$$M_x(t) = e^{\mu t + (1/2) t^2\sigma^2}$$

and this completes the proof of Theorem 6.9.

Applying Theorems 6.5 and 6.7, we find that the corresponding *generating function for moments about the mean* is given by

$$M_{x-\mu}(t) = e^{(1/2) t^2\sigma^2} \tag{6.4.9}$$

and that the *moment generating function of the standard normal distribution* is given by

$$M_{(x-\mu)/\sigma}(t) = e^{(1/2) t^2} \tag{6.4.10}$$

Finding the third and fourth derivatives of this function at $t = 0$, the reader will be asked to show in Exercise 5 below that for any normal distribution $\alpha_3 = \mu_3/\sigma^3 = 0$ and that $\alpha_4 = \mu_4/\sigma^4 = 3$.

EXERCISES

1. Using the generating function for moments about the mean of the Poisson distribution as given on page 154, verify that the second derivative at $t = 0$ is equal to λ.

2. Given $f(x) = \frac{1}{2}e^{-|x|}$ for $-\infty < x < \infty$, show that the moment generating function of this distribution is

$$M_x(t) = \frac{1}{1 - t^2}$$

Also find the variance of this distribution (a) by expanding $M_x(t)$ as an infinite series and (b) by finding its first and second derivatives at $t = 0$.

3. Given that for a certain distribution $\mu'_r = r!$, find an expression for the corresponding moment generating function and identify the distribution.

4. Finding the first and second derivatives of the moment generating function of the gamma distribution, verify that the mean of the gamma distribution is $\mu = \alpha\beta$ and that its variance is $\sigma^2 = \alpha\beta^2$.

5. Using (6.4.10) show that for the standard normal distribution $\alpha_3 = \mu_3/\sigma^3 = 0$ and $\alpha_4 = \mu_4/\sigma^4 = 3$ by evaluating the third and fourth derivatives of its moment generating function. Explain why this result holds for *any* normal distribution.

6. Using (4.4.3) find $M_{x-\mu}(t)$ for the binomial distribution and, differentiating twice with respect to t, verify the formula for σ^2.

7. (*Cumulants*) If we let $K_x(t) = \ln M_{x-\mu}(t)$, the coefficient of $t^r/r!$ in the Maclaurin's series of $K_x(t)$ is called the *r'th cumulant* and it is written κ_r. Equating coefficients of like powers, show that

   (a) $\kappa_2 = \mu_2$ (c) $\kappa_4 = \mu_4 - 3\mu_2^2$

   (b) $\kappa_3 = \mu_3$ (d) $\kappa_5 = \mu_5 - 10\mu_3\mu_2$

   Using (6.4.9) also show that for a normal distribution $\kappa_2 = \sigma^2$ while all other cumulants are equal to 0.

6.4.3 *Moment generating functions and limiting distributions*

In Section 4.4.3 we showed that under certain limiting conditions the moment generating function of the binomial distribution approaches that of the Poisson distribution. *In this section we shall show that under different limiting conditions, when $n \to \infty$ while θ remains fixed, the moment generating function of the standardized binomial distribution approaches that of the standard normal distribution.*

Having shown in Section 4.4.1 that the moment generating function of the binomial distribution is given by

$$M_x(t) = [1 + \theta(e^t - 1)]^n$$

Theorem 6.7 on page 154 yields

$$M_{(x-\mu)/\sigma}(t) = e^{-(\mu t/\sigma)}[1 + \theta(e^{t/\sigma} - 1)]^n$$

where $\mu = n\theta$ and $\sigma = \sqrt{n\theta(1-\theta)}$. Taking logarithms on both sides, we then get

$$\ln M_{(x-\mu)/\sigma}(t) = -\frac{\mu t}{\sigma} + n \cdot \ln [1 + \theta(e^{t/\sigma} - 1)]$$

and making use of the Maclaurin series for $e^{t/\sigma}$, namely,

$$e^{t/\sigma} = 1 + (t/\sigma) + \tfrac{1}{2}(t/\sigma)^2 + \tfrac{1}{6}(t/\sigma)^3 + \dots$$

we obtain

$$\ln M_{(x-\mu)/\sigma}(t)$$

$$= -\frac{\mu t}{\sigma} + n \cdot \ln [1 + \theta\{(t/\sigma) + \tfrac{1}{2}(t/\sigma)^2 + \tfrac{1}{6}(t/\sigma)^3 + \dots\}]$$

To expand the logarithm in this last expression by means of the series

$$\ln (1 + x) = x - \tfrac{1}{2}x^2 + \tfrac{1}{3}x^3 - \dots \qquad |x| < 1$$

it is necessary that the quantity in braces is sufficiently small. Since we shall be interested in the limit when $n \to \infty$ and, hence, $\sigma = \sqrt{n\theta(1-\theta)} \to \infty$, this condition will be satisfied and we can write (for n sufficiently large)

$$\begin{aligned}\ln M_{(x-\mu)/\sigma}(t) = &-\frac{\mu t}{\sigma} + n\theta[(t/\sigma) + \tfrac{1}{2}(t/\sigma)^2 + \tfrac{1}{6}(t/\sigma)^3 + \dots] \\ &- \frac{n\theta^2}{2}[(t/\sigma) + \tfrac{1}{2}(t/\sigma)^2 + \tfrac{1}{6}(t/\sigma)^3 + \dots]^2 \\ &+ \frac{n\theta^3}{3}[(t/\sigma) + \tfrac{1}{2}(t/\sigma)^2 + \tfrac{1}{6}(t/\sigma)^3 + \dots]^3 \\ &- \dots\dots\dots\end{aligned}$$

If we now collect powers of t, we get

$$\begin{aligned}\ln M_{(x-\mu)/\sigma}(t) &= \left(-\frac{\mu}{\sigma} + \frac{n\theta}{\sigma}\right)t + \left(\frac{n\theta}{2\sigma^2} - \frac{n\theta^2}{2\sigma^2}\right)t^2 \\ &\quad + \left(\frac{n\theta}{6\sigma^3} - \frac{n\theta^2}{2\sigma^3} + \frac{n\theta^3}{3\sigma^3}\right)t^3 + \dots \\ &= \frac{1}{\sigma}(-\mu + n\theta) + \frac{1}{\sigma^2}\left(\frac{n\theta - n\theta^2}{2}\right)t^2 \\ &\quad + \frac{n}{\sigma^3}\left(\frac{\theta - 3\theta^2 + 2\theta^3}{6}\right)t^3 + \dots\end{aligned}$$

and, substituting $\mu = n\theta$ and $\sigma = \sqrt{n\theta(1 - \theta)}$, it can be seen that the coefficient of t is 0, the coefficient of t^2 is $\frac{1}{2}$, and

$$\ln M_{(x-\mu)/\sigma}(t) = \tfrac{1}{2}t^2 + \frac{n}{\sigma^3}\left(\frac{\theta - 3\theta^2 + 2\theta^3}{6}\right)t^3 + \ldots$$

In general, for $r > 2$ the coefficient of t^r is a constant times n/σ^r and it approaches 0 when $n \to \infty$. We thus obtain

$$\lim_{n\to\infty} \ln M_{(x-\mu)/\sigma}(t) = \tfrac{1}{2}t^2$$

and, using the fact that the limit of a logarithm equals the logarithm of the limit (provided that these limits exist),

$$\lim_{n\to\infty} M_{(x-\mu)/\sigma}(t) = e^{(1/2)t^2} \tag{6.5.11}$$

which is the moment generating function of the standard normal distribution.

Referring again to the uniqueness theorem according to which a moment generating function, when it exists, determines a unique probability density or distribution, we can now say that *when $n \to \infty$ the standardized binomial distribution approaches the standard normal distribution*. This result can also be obtained directly, without the use of moment generating functions, and a reference to such a proof is given in the Bibliography on page 163. A third proof, based on the *Central Limit Theorem*, will be touched upon in Chapter 7.

Although, strictly speaking, the result which we have obtained applies when $n \to \infty$, normal distributions are often used to *approximate* binomial distributions even when n is relatively small. When using normal distributions to approximate binomial distributions we must account for the fact that we are approximating a *discrete* probability distribution with a *continuous* probability density; we do this by representing 0 by the interval from $-\frac{1}{2}$ to $\frac{1}{2}$, 1 by the interval from $\frac{1}{2}$ to $1\frac{1}{2}$, 2 by the interval from $1\frac{1}{2}$ to $2\frac{1}{2}$, ..., and, in general, the integer r by the interval from $r - \frac{1}{2}$ to $r + \frac{1}{2}$.

Thus, if we want to approximate the binomial probability of getting 5 successes in 12 trials with $\theta = \frac{1}{2}$, we must find the probability that a random variable having a normal distribution with $\mu = 12(\frac{1}{2}) = 6$ and $\sigma = \sqrt{12(\frac{1}{2})(\frac{1}{2})} = 1.73$ assumes a value between $4\frac{1}{2}$ and $5\frac{1}{2}$ (see Exercise 3 below). Similarly, to approximate the probability of getting 35 or more sixes in 180 rolls of a balanced die, we must find the probability that a random variable having a normal distribution with $\mu = 180(\frac{1}{6}) = 30$ and

$$\sigma = \sqrt{180(\tfrac{1}{6})(\tfrac{5}{6})} = 5$$

assumes a value greater than 34.5 (see Exercise 4 below).

EXERCISES

1. Using (4.4.4) and Theorem 6.7 find the moment generating function of the standardized Poisson distribution. Then show that when $\lambda \to \infty$ the moment generating function of the standardized Poisson distribution approaches that of the standard normal distribution.

2. Using (6.4.6) and Theorem 6.7, find the moment generating function of the standardized gamma distribution. Then show that when $\alpha \to \infty$ the moment generating function of the standardized gamma distribution approaches that of the standard normal distribution.

3. Use the normal distribution to approximate $b(5; 12, \frac{1}{2})$, that is, the binomial probability of getting 5 successes in 12 trials when $\theta = \frac{1}{2}$.

4. Use the normal distribution to approximate the probability of getting 35 or more sixes in 180 rolls of a balanced die.

5. If 60 per cent of all visitors to a certain historical site come from the East, what is the probability that among 100 visitors to this site at least 70 come from the East?

6. A true-false test contains 200 questions. What is the probability that a student who answers each question by flipping a coin (heads is "true" and tails is "false") will get fewer than 90 correct answers?

7. It is known that on the average 1 per cent of certain fuzes delivered to an arsenal are duds. What is the probability that in a sample of 400 there are 5 or more duds?

8. A manufacturer knows that on the average 2 per cent of his product is defective. What is the probability that in a lot of 100 there will be 3 defectives?

6.5 Product Moments

As in the discrete case, the *r'th and s'th product moment (about the origin) of the joint density of two random variables* is $E(\mathbf{x}^r\mathbf{y}^s)$ and the corresponding *product moment about the respective means* is $E[(\mathbf{x} - \mu_\mathbf{x})^r(\mathbf{y} - \mu_\mathbf{y})^s]$. In particular, the *covariance* is again defined as $E[(\mathbf{x} - \mu_\mathbf{x})(\mathbf{y} - \mu_\mathbf{y})]$, although we now have

$$\operatorname{cov}(\mathbf{x}, \mathbf{y}) = \int_{-\infty}^{\infty}\int_{-\infty}^{\infty} (x - \mu_\mathbf{x})(y - \mu_\mathbf{y})f(x, y)\, dx\, dy \qquad (6.5.1)$$

Expanding the integrand in (6.5.1), it can again be shown that

$$\operatorname{cov}(\mathbf{x}, \mathbf{y}) = E(\mathbf{xy}) - \mu_\mathbf{x}\mu_\mathbf{y} \qquad (6.5.2)$$

Applications of the covariance to problems of regression and correlation will be treated in Chapter 13.

EXERCISES

1. Find the covariance for the joint density of Exercise 1 on page 141.

2. Find the covariance for the joint density of Exercise 5 on page 141.

3. Show that if two continuous random variables are independent, the covariance of their joint distribution is equal to 0.

6.6 Mathematical Expectation and Decision Making

To give a further illustration of how the idea of maximizing expected profits is used in making rational decisions, let us consider the following example which is similar to Exercise 6 on page 116. In the beginning of each month a department store stocks x units of a certain item; there is a profit of a dollars for each unit sold and a loss of b dollars for each unit not sold during the month. If sales volume is a random variable whose distribution can be approximated by the uniform density

$$f(v) = \frac{1}{v_2 - v_1} \qquad \text{for} \quad v_1 < v < v_2$$

how many units of the given item should the department store stock at the beginning of each month so as to maximize expected profits?

If the store stocks x units, there is a demand for v, and $v \geq x$, the department store's profit is $P(x) = ax$; if $v < x$, its profit is $P(x) =$

$av - b(x - v)$. Hence, the expected profit is

$$\frac{1}{v_2 - v_1}\int_x^{v_2} ax\,dv + \frac{1}{v_2 - v_1}\int_{v_1}^{x} [av - b(x - v)]\,dv$$

$$= \frac{1}{v_2 - v_1}\left[x(av_2 + bv_1) - \tfrac{1}{2}(a + b)(x^2 - v_1^2)\right]$$

and, differentiating with respect to x, we find that its maximum is attained at

$$x = \frac{a(v_2 - v_1)}{a + b} + v_1$$

If this is not at integer, the correct result is given by one of the two integers between which x is contained. For instance, for $a = 8$, $b = 1$, $v_1 = 20$, and $v_2 = 40$, we get $x = 37\frac{7}{9}$; substituting $x = 37$ and $x = 38$ into the expression for the expected profit, we find that the maximum is attained at $x = 38$.

EXERCISES

1. Suppose that the example in the text is modified to the extent that there is a loss of c dollars in goodwill for the loss of each sale due to lack of the item. Find an expression for the number of units the department store should stock so as to maximize expected profits. How many units should the department store stock for $a = 10$, $b = 4$, $c = 1$, $v_1 = 10$, and $v_2 = 40$?

2. Mr. Miller is a contractor who bids on road construction jobs. He has found from experience that if his cost estimate of a job is C dollars, the lowest opposing bid may be looked upon as a random variable having the uniform density

$$f(x) = \begin{cases} \dfrac{1}{C} & \text{for } \dfrac{C}{2} < x < \dfrac{3C}{2} \\ 0 & \text{elsewhere} \end{cases}$$

Show that in order to maximize his expected profit, Mr. Miller should always add 25 per cent to his cost estimate when submitting his bids.

BIBLIOGRAPHY

A direct proof that the standardized binomial distribution approaches the standard normal distribution when $n \rightarrow \infty$ may be found in

Kenney, J. F., and E. S., Keeping, *Mathematics of Statistics, Part II*, 2nd ed., New York: D. Van Nostrand & Company, Inc., 1951, p. 33.

Further examples in which decisions are based on the criterion of maximizing expected profits may be found in texts on *Operations Research* and, for example, in

Wadsworth, G. P., and J. G. Bryan, *Introduction to Probability and Random Variables*, New York: McGraw-Hill Book Co., Inc., 1960, p. 192.

Chapter 7

Sums of Random Variables

7.1 Introduction

Given a sample space over which we define the random variables $\mathbf{x}_1, \mathbf{x}_2, \ldots,$ and $\mathbf{x}_n$, their *sum* is the random variable $\mathbf{y}$, whose value is equal to $x_1 + x_2 + \ldots + x_n$ when $\mathbf{x}_1$ assumes the value x_1, $\mathbf{x}_2$ assumes the value $x_2, \ldots,$ and $\mathbf{x}_n$ assumes the value x_n. We thus write $\mathbf{y} = \mathbf{x}_1 + \mathbf{x}_2 + \ldots + \mathbf{x}_n$.

Sums of random variables play an important role in the development of statistical theory; in fact, distribution theory connected with the random variables $\mathbf{x}_1 + \mathbf{x}_2 + \ldots + \mathbf{x}_n$ and

$$\frac{\mathbf{x}_1 + \mathbf{x}_2 + \ldots + \mathbf{x}_n}{n}$$

is basic to many of the procedures which we shall study in the remainder of this book. Leaving applications to later chapters, we shall concern ourselves here with the problem of finding the distributions of sums of random variables given the joint distributions of the $\mathbf{x}_i$, and the problem of expressing the moments of distributions of random variables of the form $a_1\mathbf{x}_1 + a_2\mathbf{x}_2 + \ldots + a_n\mathbf{x}_n$ in terms of the moments and product moments of the joint distributions of the $\mathbf{x}_i$.

To illustrate a straightforward method of obtaining the probability density (or distribution) of the sum of two or more random variables, we have only to refer to Figures 7.1 and 7.2. In the case of *two* random variables, the probability that $\mathbf{y} = \mathbf{x}_1 + \mathbf{x}_2$ assumes a

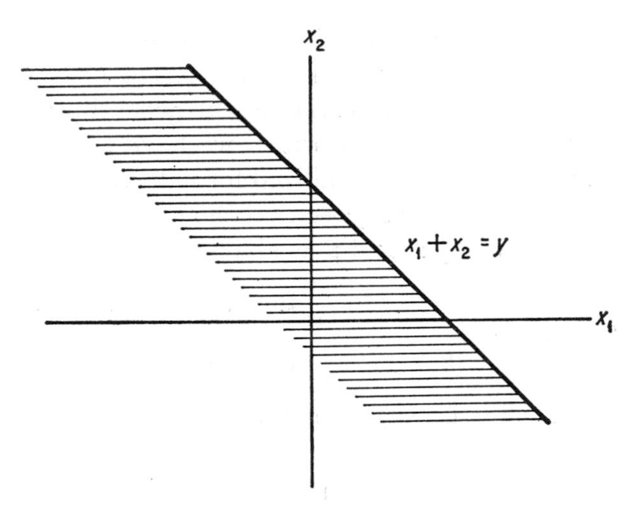

Figure 7.1

value less than or equal to y, namely, $F(y)$, is obtained by integrating the joint probability density of $\mathbf{x}_1$ and $\mathbf{x}_2$ over the shaded region of Figure 7.1. (In the discrete case, the integral is replaced by a sum.) The probability density of $\mathbf{y} = \mathbf{x}_1 + \mathbf{x}_2$ can then be obtained by making use of the fact that $f(y) = d[F(y)]/dy$. In the case of *three* random variable, $F(y)$ is obtained by integrating the joint density of $\mathbf{x}_1$, $\mathbf{x}_2$, and $\mathbf{x}_3$ over the volume which lies below

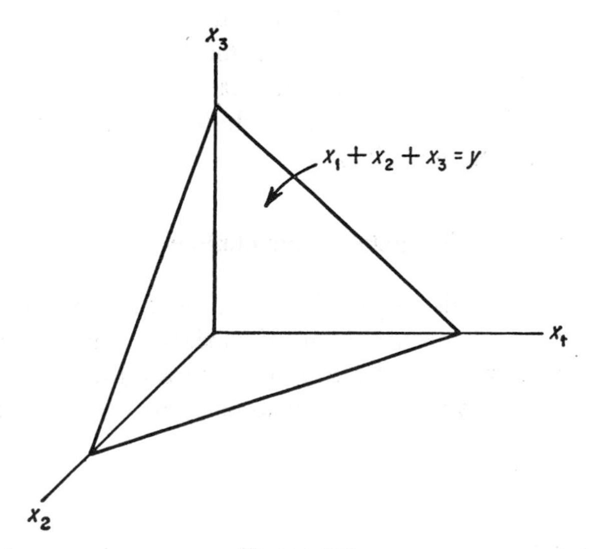

Figure 7.2

the plane indicated in Figure 7.2; the probability density of $\mathbf{y} = \mathbf{x}_1 + \mathbf{x}_2 + \mathbf{x}_3$ is then given by the derivative of $F(y)$ with respect to y. In the case of n random variables the general procedure is the same, although the region over which we have to integrate has n dimensions and it cannot be visualized for $n > 3$.

To give an illustration, suppose that the joint probability density of two random variables $\mathbf{x}_1$ and $\mathbf{x}_2$ is given by

$$f(x_1, x_2) = \begin{cases} 2e^{-x_1-2x_2} & \text{for} \quad x_1 > 0 \quad \text{and} \quad x_2 > 0 \\ 0 & \text{elsewhere} \end{cases}$$

Integrating this joint density over the shaded region of Figure 7.1, we get

$$F(y) = \int_0^y \left[\int_0^{y-x_2} f(x_1, x_2)\, dx_1 \right] dx_2 = \int_0^y \left[\int_0^{y-x_2} 2e^{-x_1-2x_2}\, dx_1 \right] dx_2$$

$$= 1 - 2e^{-y} + e^{-2y}$$

and, differentiating with respect to y, this gives

$$f(y) = 2(e^{-y} - e^{-2y}) \qquad \text{for} \quad y > 0$$

and $f(y) = 0$ for $y \leq 0$.

In the next two sections we shall introduce two other general techniques for finding the distributions of sums of random variables. As will be explained on page 170, the method of Section 7.2 has the same theoretical foundation as the method outlined above. The method of Section 7.3 has many interesting and important applications, but it is limited to the case where the random variables $\mathbf{x}_1$, $\mathbf{x}_2$, . . ., and $\mathbf{x}_n$ are independent.

7.2 Sums of Random Variables—Convolutions

The method of this section is based, essentially, on the work of Section 5.4, namely, on a change of variable. Considering first the case of two random variables $\mathbf{x}_1$ and $\mathbf{x}_2$ whose joint density is given by $f(x_1, x_2)$, we can write the joint density of $\mathbf{y} = \mathbf{x}_1 + \mathbf{x}_2$ and $\mathbf{x}_2$ as

$$g(y, x_2) = f(x_1, x_2) \left| \frac{dx_1}{dy} \right| \tag{7.2.1}$$

in accordance with (5.4.1). We are, in fact, changing variable from

$\mathbf{x}_1$ to $\mathbf{y}$ treating x_2 as a constant in $y = x_1 + x_2$. Hence,

$$\left| \frac{dx_1}{dy} \right| = 1$$

and (7.2.1) becomes

$$g(y, x_2) = f(y - x_2, x_2)$$

Finally, integrating out x_2 from $-\infty$ to ∞, we find that the (marginal) density of $\mathbf{y} = \mathbf{x}_1 + \mathbf{x}_2$ is given by

$$f(y) = \int_{-\infty}^{\infty} f(y - x_2, x_2)\, dx_2 \tag{7.2.2}$$

In particular, when $\mathbf{x}_1$ and $\mathbf{x}_2$ are independent and $f(x_1, x_2) = f_1(x_1)f_2(x_2)$, (7.2.2) becomes

$$f(y) = \int_{-\infty}^{\infty} f_1(y - x_2)f_2(x_2)\, dx_2 \tag{7.2.3}$$

The integrals in (7.2.2) and (7.2.3) are called *convolution integrals*, or simply *convolutions*. Note that if we reverse the roles played by $\mathbf{x}_1$ and $\mathbf{x}_2$, we also have

$$f(y) = \int_{-\infty}^{\infty} f(x_1, y - x_1)\, dx_1 \tag{7.2.4}$$

analogous to (7.2.2) and

$$f(y) = \int_{-\infty}^{\infty} f_1(x_1)f_2(y - x_1)\, dx_1 \tag{7.2.5}$$

analogous to (7.2.3) when $\mathbf{x}_1$ and $\mathbf{x}_2$ are independent.

To illustrate the use of a convolution integral in determining the probability density of the sum of two random variables, suppose that

$$f(x_1, x_2) = \frac{1}{\pi^2} \cdot \frac{1}{1 + x_1^2} \cdot \frac{1}{1 + x_2^2} \qquad \text{for} \qquad \begin{array}{c} -\infty < x_1 < \infty \\ -\infty < x_2 < \infty \end{array}$$

namely, that $\mathbf{x}_1$ and $\mathbf{x}_2$ are independent random variables having the same *Cauchy distribution* (see page 134). Substitution into (7.2.2) yields

$$f(y) = \frac{1}{\pi^2} \int_{-\infty}^{\infty} \frac{1}{1 + (y - x_2)^2} \cdot \frac{1}{1 + x_2^2}\, dx_2$$

and integrating, by the method of partial fractions, this becomes

$$f(y) = \frac{1}{\pi} \frac{1/2}{(1/2)^2 + y^2} \qquad \text{for} \quad -\infty < y < \infty$$

This result is interesting inasmuch as it shows that the distribution of the sum of two independent random variables having the same Cauchy distribution is *also* a Cauchy distribution.

To consider another example, suppose that $\mathbf{x}_1$ and $\mathbf{x}_2$ are independent random variables having uniform distributions on the interval from 0 to 1, namely, that

$$f(x_1, x_2) = \begin{cases} 1 & \text{for} \quad 0 < x_1 < 1 \quad \text{and} \quad 0 < x_2 < 1 \\ 0 & \text{elsewhere} \end{cases}$$

Substituting into (7.2.2) or (7.2.3) in this example, we shall have to be careful to account for the fact that *neither x_1 nor x_2 can exceed y, their sum, or be less than $y - 1$.* Hence, when $0 < y < 1$, (7.2.2) gives

$$f(y) = \int_0^y 1 \cdot dx_2 = y$$

and when $1 < y < 2$, it gives

$$f(y) = \int_{y-1}^1 1 \cdot dx_2 = 2 - y$$

We have thus shown that the sum of two independent random variables with uniform densities on the interval from 0 to 1 has the *triangular density* of Figure 7.3.

Although we presented (and illustrated) convolutions with reference to the continuous case, the general method applies also to find the probability distribution of the sum of two *discrete* random

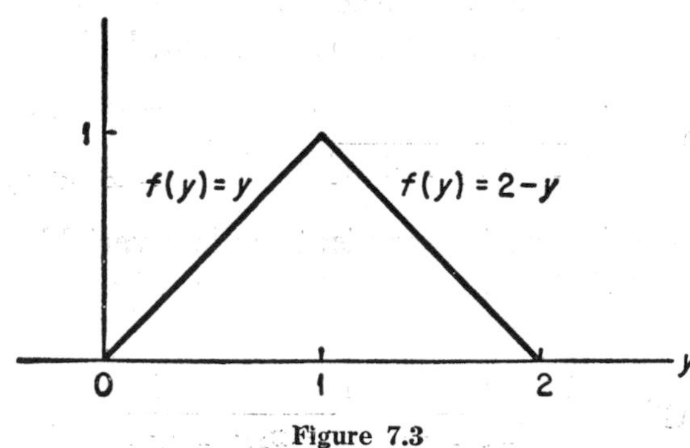

Figure 7.3

variables. Replacing integration with summation, (7.2.2) becomes

$$f(y) = \sum_{x_2} f(y - x_2, x_2) \tag{7.2.6}$$

and similar sums can be defined analogous to (7.2.3), (7.2.4), and (7.2.5).

To illustrate the use of (7.2.6), suppose that $\mathbf{x}_1$ and $\mathbf{x}_2$ are independent random variables having Poisson distributions with the parameters λ_1 and λ_2, namely,

$$f(x_1, x_2) = \frac{e^{-\lambda_1}\lambda_1^{x_1}}{x_1!}\frac{e^{-\lambda_2}\lambda_2^{x_2}}{x_2!} \qquad \text{for} \quad \begin{array}{l} x_1 = 0, 1, 2, \ldots \\ x_2 = 0, 1, 2, \ldots \end{array}$$

Substituting into (7.2.6) gives

$$f(y) = \sum_{x_2=0}^{y} \frac{e^{-(\lambda_1+\lambda_2)}\lambda_2^{x_2}\lambda_1^{y-x_2}}{x_2!(y - x_2)!}$$

where the summation goes from $x_2 = 0$ to $x_2 = y$, since x_2 cannot exceed $y = x_1 + x_2$. Factoring out $e^{-(\lambda_1+\lambda_2)}$ and multiplying and dividing by $y!$, we obtain

$$f(y) = \frac{e^{-(\lambda_1+\lambda_2)}}{y!} \sum_{x_2=0}^{y} \frac{y!}{x_2!(y - x_2)!}\lambda_2^{x_2}\lambda_1^{y-x_2}$$

and, identifying this sum as the binomial expansion of $(\lambda_1 + \lambda_2)^y$, we finally get

$$f(y) = \frac{e^{-(\lambda_1+\lambda_2)}(\lambda_1 + \lambda_2)^y}{y!} \qquad \text{for} \quad y = 0, 1, 2, \ldots$$

We have thus shown that *the sum of two independent random variables having Poisson distributions with the parameters λ_1 and λ_2 has a Poisson distribution with the parameter $\lambda_1 + \lambda_2$.*

So far we have considered only sums of two random variables; to find the distribution of sums of three or more, we could generalize (7.2.2) writing, for example,

$$f(y) = \int_{-\infty}^{\infty}\int_{-\infty}^{\infty} f(y - x_2 - x_3, x_2, x_3)\, dx_2\, dx_3 \tag{7.2.7}$$

for the probability density of $\mathbf{y} = \mathbf{x}_1 + \mathbf{x}_2 + \mathbf{x}_3$ and

$$f(y) = \int_{-\infty}^{\infty}\int_{-\infty}^{\infty}\int_{-\infty}^{\infty} f(y - x_2 - x_3 - x_4, x_2, x_3, x_4)\, dx_2\, dx_3\, dx_4 \tag{7.2.8}$$

for the probability density of $\mathbf{y} = \mathbf{x}_1 + \mathbf{x}_2 + \mathbf{x}_3 + \mathbf{x}_4$.

An alternate approach of finding the distribution of the sum of more than two random variables is to begin by finding the distribution of $\mathbf{y} = \mathbf{x}_1 + \mathbf{x}_2$, and then using the same method again to find the distribution of $\mathbf{u} = \mathbf{y} + \mathbf{x}_3$, $\mathbf{v} = \mathbf{u} + \mathbf{x}_4$, and so forth. This method is illustrated in Exercise 6 below.

Although the method of this section may seem different from that of Section 7.1, their theoretical foundation is the same. In the case of two random variables the method of Section 7.1 yields

$$F(y) = \int_{-\infty}^{\infty} \left[\int_{-\infty}^{y-x_2} f(x_1, x_2)\, dx_1 \right] dx_2$$

and, assuming that we can differentiate under the integral sign, we get

$$f(y) = \int_{-\infty}^{\infty} f(y - x_2, x_2)\, dx_2$$

namely, the convolution integral (7.2.2).

EXERCISES

1. Given that $\mathbf{x}_1$ and $\mathbf{x}_2$ have independent exponential densities with *unequal* parameters θ_1 and θ_2, see page 126, use the method indicated in Section 7.1 to find the probability density of $\mathbf{y} = \mathbf{x}_1 + \mathbf{x}_2$.

2. Find the probability density asked for in Exercise 1 when $\theta_1 = \theta_2$.

3. Repeat Exercise 1 using the method of Section 7.2.

4. Given that $\mathbf{x}_1$ and $\mathbf{x}_2$ are independent random variables having the same binomial distribution with the parameters n and θ, use the method of Section 7.2 to show that $\mathbf{y} = \mathbf{x}_1 + \mathbf{x}_2$ has the binomial distribution with the parameters $2n$ and θ.

5. Use the method of Section 7.1 to find the probability density of $\mathbf{y} = \mathbf{x}_1 + \mathbf{x}_2$, where $\mathbf{x}_1$ and $\mathbf{x}_2$ are independent random variables having uniform densities on the interval from 0 to 1.

6. Proceeding from the result on page 168, find the probability density of $\mathbf{u} = \mathbf{x}_1 + \mathbf{x}_2 + \mathbf{x}_3 = \mathbf{y} + \mathbf{x}_3$, where $\mathbf{x}_1$, $\mathbf{x}_2$, and $\mathbf{x}_3$ are independent random variables having uniform densities on the interval from 0 to 1. [*Hint*: note that $y \leq u \leq y + 1$ and that $f(u)$ will have to be found separately for $0 < u \leq 1$, $1 < u \leq 2$, and $2 < u < 3$.]

7.3 Sums of Independent Random Variables—Moment Generating Functions

The method of this section is based on the theorem that the moment generating function of the sum of n independent random variables equals the product of their moment generating functions, namely,

THEOREM 7.1:
If $\mathbf{x}_1, \mathbf{x}_2, \ldots,$ *and* $\mathbf{x}_n$ *are independent random variables with the moment generating functions* $M_{\mathbf{x}_1}(t), M_{\mathbf{x}_2}(t), \ldots, M_{\mathbf{x}_n}(t)$, *and* $\mathbf{y} = \mathbf{x}_1 + \mathbf{x}_2 + \ldots + \mathbf{x}_n$, *then*

$$M_{\mathbf{y}}(t) = \prod_{i=1}^{n} M_{\mathbf{x}_i}(t) \tag{7.3.1}$$

Making use of the fact that the random variables are independent and, hence, that $f(x_1, x_2, \ldots, x_n) = f_1(x_1)f_2(x_2) \cdot \ldots \cdot f_n(x_n)$, we have

$$\begin{aligned} M_{\mathbf{y}}(t) &= E(e^{\mathbf{y}t}) = E[e^{(\mathbf{x}_1+\mathbf{x}_2+\cdots+\mathbf{x}_n)t}] \\ &= \int_{-\infty}^{\infty} \cdots \int_{-\infty}^{\infty} e^{(x_1+x_2+\cdots+x_n)t} f(x_1, x_2, \ldots, x_n)\, dx_1\, dx_2 \ldots dx_n \\ &= \int_{-\infty}^{\infty} e^{x_1t} f_1(x_1)\, dx_1 \cdot \int_{-\infty}^{\infty} e^{x_2t} f_2(x_2)\, dx_2 \cdot \ldots \cdot \int_{-\infty}^{\infty} e^{x_nt} f_n(x_n)\, dx_n \\ &= \prod_{i=1}^{n} M_{\mathbf{x}_i}(t) \end{aligned}$$

and this completes the proof of Theorem 7.1 for the continuous case. (To prove it for discrete random variables we have only to replace the above integrals by sums.) Note that in order to find $f(y)$, the probability density or distribution of $\mathbf{y}$, we must be able to identify whatever density or distribution corresponds to $M_{\mathbf{y}}(t)$.

To illustrate the use of Theorem 7.1, suppose that $\mathbf{x}_1, \mathbf{x}_2, \ldots,$ and $\mathbf{x}_n$ are independent random variables having *exponential distributions* with the parameter θ. Since the exponential distribution is a gamma distribution with $\alpha = 1$ and $\beta = \theta$, we have $M_{\mathbf{x}_i}(t) = (1 - \theta t)^{-1}$ according to (6.4.6). Hence

$$M_{\mathbf{y}}(t) = \prod_{i=1}^{n} (1 - \theta t)^{-1} = (1 - \theta t)^{-n}$$

(see Appendix on page 352) and this moment generating function can readily be identified as that of a gamma distribution with $\alpha = n$ and $\beta = \theta$. Making use of the uniqueness theorem referred to on page 159, we have thus shown that the distribution of the sum of n independent random variables having exponential distributions with the same parameter θ is a gamma distribution with the parameters $\alpha = n$ and $\beta = \theta$.

To illustrate the use of Theorem 7.1 for discrete random variables, suppose that $\mathbf{x}_1, \mathbf{x}_2, \ldots,$ and $\mathbf{x}_n$ have independent *Poisson distributions* with parameters $\lambda_1, \lambda_2, \ldots, \lambda_n$. Making use of (4.4.4) we have

$$M_{\mathbf{x}_i}(t) = e^{\lambda_i(e^t-1)}$$

and, hence,

$$M_{\mathbf{y}}(t) = \prod_{i=1}^{n} e^{\lambda_i(e^t-1)} = e^{(\lambda_1+\lambda_2+\ldots+\lambda_n)(e^t-1)}$$

which can readily be identified as the moment generating function of a random variable having a Poisson distribution with the parameter $\lambda_1 + \lambda_2 + \ldots + \lambda_n$. Referring to the same uniqueness theorem as above, we have thus shown that the sum of n independent random variables having Poisson distributions with the parameters λ_i has a Poisson distribution with the parameter $\lambda_1 + \lambda_2 + \ldots + \lambda_n$. Note that for $n = 2$ we already proved this in Section 7.2.

Theorem 7.1 also provides an easy and elegant way of deriving the moment generating function of the binomial distribution. Suppose that $\mathbf{x}_1, \mathbf{x}_2, \ldots,$ and $\mathbf{x}_n$ are independent random variables having the same binomial distribution $b(x_i; 1, \theta)$, namely,

$$b(x_i; 1, \theta) = \begin{cases} 1 - \theta & \text{for } x_i = 0 \\ \theta & \text{for } x_i = 1 \end{cases}$$

The moment generating function of each of the $\mathbf{x}_i$ is

$$M_{\mathbf{x}_i}(t) = e^{0t}(1 - \theta) + e^{1\cdot t}\cdot\theta = 1 + \theta(e^t - 1)$$

and according to Theorem 7.1

$$M_{\mathbf{y}}(t) = \prod_{i=1}^{n} [1 + \theta(e^t - 1)] = [1 + \theta(e^t - 1)]^n$$

which is readily identified as the moment generating function of the binomial distribution with the parameters n and θ. Indeed, $\mathbf{y} = \mathbf{x}_1 + \mathbf{x}_2 + \ldots + \mathbf{x}_n$ *is* the number of successes in n trials, since $\mathbf{x}_1$ is the number of successes on the first trial, $\mathbf{x}_2$ is the number of successes on the second trial, and so forth.

EXERCISES

1. Repeat Exercise 4 on page 170 using the method of Section 7.3.

2. If n independent random variables have the normal distributions $N(x_i;\ \mu_i,\ \sigma_i^2)$ for $i = 1, 2, \ldots,$ and n, find the moment generating function of the distribution of their sum and identify the corresponding distribution.

3. If n independent random variables have the same geometric distribution (see Exercise 14 on page 77) find the moment generating function of the distribution of their sum and, if possible, identify the distribution.

4. If n independent random variables have gamma distributions with the same parameters α and β, find the moment generating function of their sum and, if possible, identify the distribution.

5. Prove the following theorem, which is a generalization of Theorem 7.1: if $\mathbf{x}_1, \mathbf{x}_2, \ldots, \mathbf{x}_n$ are independent random variables with the moment generating functions $M_{\mathbf{x}_i}(t)$ and

$$\mathbf{y} = \sum_{i=1}^{n} a_i\mathbf{x}_i,$$

where the a_i are constants, then

$$M_{\mathbf{y}}(t) = \prod_{i=1}^{n} M_{\mathbf{x}_i}(a_it)$$

6. Use the result obtained in Exercise 5 to show that if $\mathbf{x}_1, \mathbf{x}_2, \ldots,$ and $\mathbf{x}_n$ are independent random variables having normal distributions, then

$$\mathbf{y} = \sum_{i=1}^{n} a_i\mathbf{x}_i$$

has a normal distribution.

7.4 Moments of Linear Combinations of Random Variables

Given a set of random variables $\mathbf{x}_1, \mathbf{x}_2, \ldots,$ and $\mathbf{x}_n$, we shall call $\mathbf{y} = a_1\mathbf{x}_1 + a_2\mathbf{x}_2 + \ldots + a_n\mathbf{x}_n$ a *linear combination* of the $\mathbf{x}_i$. In particular, if $a_i = 1$ for all i, $\mathbf{y}$ is the sum of the random variables $\mathbf{x}_i$. In this section we shall derive expressions for the mean and the variance of a linear combination of n random variables and the covariance of two linear combinations of n random variables. Several applications of these results will be treated in Sections 7.4.1 through 7.4.4.

THEOREM 7.2:

If $\mathbf{x}_1, \mathbf{x}_2, \ldots, \mathbf{x}_n$ *are random variables,* $a_1, a_2, \ldots, a_n$ *are constants, and*

$$\mathbf{y} = \sum_{i=1}^{n} a_i \mathbf{x}_i,$$

then

$$E(\mathbf{y}) = \sum_{i=1}^{n} a_i E(\mathbf{x}_i) \tag{7.4.1}$$

and

$$\text{var}(\mathbf{y}) = \sum_{i=1}^{n} a_i^2 \text{ var}(\mathbf{x}_i) + 2 \sum_{i<j}\sum a_i a_j \text{ cov}(\mathbf{x}_i, \mathbf{x}_j) \tag{7.4.2}$$

where $\sum_{i<j}\sum$ *means that the summation extends over all values of* i *and* j*, from* 1 *to* n*, for which* $i < j$.

Using Theorems 4.2 and 4.3, or equivalent theorems for the continuous case, we have

$$E(a_1\mathbf{x}_1 + a_2\mathbf{x}_2 + \ldots + a_n\mathbf{x}_n)$$
$$= a_1E(\mathbf{x}_1) + a_2E(\mathbf{x}_2) + \ldots + a_nE(\mathbf{x}_n)$$

and this proves the first part of Theorem 7.2. To derive the expression for the variance of $\mathbf{y}$, let us write μ_i for $E(\mathbf{x}_i)$, getting thus

$$\text{var}(\mathbf{y}) = E([\mathbf{y} - E(\mathbf{y})]^2) = E\left(\left[\sum_{i=1}^{n} a_i\mathbf{x}_i - \sum_{i=1}^{n} a_iE(\mathbf{x}_i)\right]^2\right)$$

$$= E\left(\left[\sum_{i=1}^{n} a_i(\mathbf{x}_i - \mu_i)\right]^2\right)$$

Expanding this last expression, we obtain

$$\text{var}(\mathbf{y}) = \sum_{i=1}^{n} a_i^2 E[(\mathbf{x}_i - \mu_i)^2] + 2\sum_{i<j}\sum a_i a_j E[(\mathbf{x}_i - \mu_i)(\mathbf{x}_j - \mu_j)]$$

$$= \sum_{i=1}^{n} a_i^2 \text{ var}(\mathbf{x}_i) + 2\sum_{i<j}\sum a_i a_j \text{ cov}(\mathbf{x}_i, \mathbf{x}_j)$$

and this completes the proof of the second part of Theorem 7.2. Note that we made use of the fact that $\text{cov}(\mathbf{x}_i, \mathbf{x}_j) = \text{cov}(\mathbf{x}_j, \mathbf{x}_i)$.

An immediate corollary of this theorem is that if the random variables $\mathbf{x}_1, \mathbf{x}_2, \ldots,$ and $\mathbf{x}_n$ are *independent*, $\text{cov}(\mathbf{x}_i, \mathbf{x}_j) = 0$ for all $i \neq j$ and (7.4.2) becomes

$$\mathrm{var}(\mathbf{y}) = \sum_{i=1}^{n} a_i^2 \,\mathrm{var}(\mathbf{x}_i) \tag{7.4.3}$$

Several applications of this special formula are given in Sections 7.4.1 and 7.4.2; two applications of the more general formula, where the random variables $\mathbf{x}_i$ are not assumed to be independent, are given in Sections 7.4.3 and 7.4.4.

Another important theorem about linear combinations of random variables is the following, which concerns the covariance of two linear combinations of random variables:

THEOREM 7.3:

If $\mathbf{x}_1, \mathbf{x}_2, \ldots, \mathbf{x}_n$ *are random variables,* $a_1, a_2, \ldots, a_n$ *and* $b_1, b_2, \ldots, b_n$ *are constants,*

$$\mathbf{y}_1 = \sum_{i=1}^{n} a_i \mathbf{x}_i, \qquad \textit{and} \qquad \mathbf{y}_2 = \sum_{i=1}^{n} b_i \mathbf{x}_i,$$

then

$$\mathrm{cov}(\mathbf{y}_1, \mathbf{y}_2) = \sum_{i=1}^{n} a_i b_i \,\mathrm{var}(\mathbf{x}_i) + \sum\sum_{i<j} (a_i b_j + a_j b_i)\,\mathrm{cov}(\mathbf{x}_i, \mathbf{x}_j) \tag{7.4.4}$$

The proof of this theorem, which is very similar to that of Theorem 7.2, will be left to the reader. Analogous to (7.4.3), we have the corollary that if the random variables $\mathbf{x}_i$ are *independent,* (7.4.4) becomes

$$\mathrm{cov}(\mathbf{y}_1, \mathbf{y}_2) = \sum_{i=1}^{n} a_i b_i \,\mathrm{var}(\mathbf{x}_i) \tag{7.4.5}$$

A very important application of (7.4.5) will be given in Section 7.4.1.

7.4.1 *The distribution of the mean*

Given a set of measurements $x_1, x_2, \ldots,$ and x_n, their *average,* in colloquial language, is $(x_1 + x_2 + \ldots + x_n)/n$; in statistics we refer to it as the *mean* and denote it with the symbol $\bar{x}$ (x-bar). Means of observed data play an important role in applied statistics.

For instance, we may use the mean of the lifetimes of 12 batteries to *estimate* the "true average lifetime" of this kind of battery, we may use the mean income of 50 families in a certain area to *decide* whether family income in this area is below the national average, or we may use the means of the I.Q.'s of 20 students selected from each of two schools to *test the hypothesis* that the actual average I.Q. of students in one school is higher than that of the other.

If $x_1, x_2, \ldots,$ *and* x_n *are values assumed by a corresponding set of random variables* $\mathbf{x}_1, \mathbf{x}_2, \ldots,$ *and* $\mathbf{x}_n$*, which are independent and which have the same distribution, we refer to the* x*'s as a random sample.** Thus, if the lifetimes of the 12 batteries referred to in the preceding paragraph are values assumed by independent random variables having the exponential distribution

$$f(x) = \frac{1}{400} e^{-(x/400)} \qquad \text{for} \quad x > 0,$$

we refer to these measurements as a *random sample* from this "exponential population." Their mean, $\bar{x}$, is a value assumed by the random variable

$$\bar{\mathbf{x}} = \frac{\mathbf{x}_1 + \mathbf{x}_2 + \cdots + \mathbf{x}_n}{n}$$

In other words, the value of $\bar{\mathbf{x}}$ is equal to $\bar{x}$, when $\mathbf{x}_1$ assumes the value x_1, $\mathbf{x}_2$ assumes the value x_2, and so forth.

Since the distribution of $\bar{\mathbf{x}}$ plays an important role in the construction of statistical decision procedures, tests of hypotheses and methods of estimation or prediction, let us now prove the following theorem:

THEOREM 7.4:

If $\mathbf{x}_1, \mathbf{x}_2, \ldots,$ *and* $\mathbf{x}_n$ *are independent random variables having the same probability density or distribution with the mean* μ *and the variance* σ^2*, then*

$$E(\bar{\mathbf{x}}) = \mu \tag{7.4.6}$$

and

$$\operatorname{var}(\bar{\mathbf{x}}) = \sigma^2/n \tag{7.4.7}$$

It is customary to write $E(\bar{\mathbf{x}}) = \mu_{\bar{\mathbf{x}}}$ and $\operatorname{var}(\bar{\mathbf{x}}) = \sigma_{\bar{\mathbf{x}}}^2$, calling $\sigma_{\bar{\mathbf{x}}}$ the *standard error of the mean.*

* An alternate definition for the case where the random variables are not independent will be given in Section 7.4.3.

To prove Theorem 7.4 we have only to substitute $E(\mathbf{x}_i) = \mu$, $\text{var}(\mathbf{x}_i) = \sigma^2$, and $a_i = 1/n$ into (7.4.1) and (7.4.3). We thus get

$$E(\bar{\mathbf{x}}) = \sum_{i=1}^{n} \frac{1}{n} \cdot \mu = n \cdot \frac{1}{n} \cdot \mu = \mu$$

and

$$\text{var}(\bar{\mathbf{x}}) = \sum_{i=1}^{n} \frac{1}{n^2} \cdot \sigma^2 = n \cdot \frac{1}{n^2} \cdot \sigma^2 = \frac{\sigma^2}{n}$$

The formula $\sigma_{\bar{\mathbf{x}}} = \sigma/\sqrt{n}$ shows that the standard error of the mean decreases when n, the *sample size*, is increased. *This means that when n becomes larger and we actually have more information, sample means can be expected to be closer to μ, the quantity which $\bar{x}$ is usually supposed to estimate.* Referring to Chebyshev's Theorem as it is formulated in Exercise 10 on page 99, we can express this more precisely as follows:

For any positive constant c, the probability that $\bar{\mathbf{x}}$ assumes a value which differs from μ by more than c is less than σ^2/nc^2; when $n \to \infty$, this probability approaches 0.

Having defined $\bar{x}$ as a measure of the "center" of a set of data in the same sense in which μ defines the "center" of a distribution, we shall later, in Chapter 8, define a measure of the variability of a set of data, which, conceptually, is similar to σ^2. This measure of the variability of a set of data is based, essentially, on the deviations from the mean $x_1 - \bar{x}$, $x_2 - \bar{x}$, . . ., and $x_n - \bar{x}$. A very important property of these deviations from the mean is expressed by the following theorem, which we shall now prove for future reference:

THEOREM 7.5:

If $\mathbf{x}_1$, $\mathbf{x}_2$, . . ., and $\mathbf{x}_n$ are independent random variables having the same probability density or distribution with the variance σ^2, then

$$\text{cov}(\mathbf{x}_r - \bar{\mathbf{x}}, \bar{\mathbf{x}}) = 0 \qquad (7.4.8)$$

for $r = 1, 2, \ldots,$ *or* n.

To prove this theorem we have only to substitute appropriate values for the a's and b's of (7.4.5). Since

$$x_r - \bar{x} = \frac{n-1}{n} \cdot x_r - \frac{1}{n}\left[\left(\sum_{i=1}^{n} x_i\right) - x_r\right]$$

it follows that $a_r = (n-1)/n$ while all the other a's are equal to $-(1/n)$. Substituting these values together with $b_i = 1/n$ and

$\text{var}(\mathbf{x}_i) = \sigma^2$ into (7.4.5) we get

$$\begin{aligned}\text{cov}(\mathbf{x}_r - \bar{\mathbf{x}}, \bar{\mathbf{x}}) &= \sum_{i=1}^{n} a_i b_i \,\text{var}(\mathbf{x}_i) \\ &= \frac{1}{n}\cdot\sigma^2\left[\frac{n-1}{n} + \left(-\frac{1}{n}\right) + \left(-\frac{1}{n}\right) + \cdots + \left(-\frac{1}{n}\right)\right] \\ &= 0\end{aligned}$$

EXERCISES

1. Given the independent random variables $\mathbf{x}_1$, $\mathbf{x}_2$, and $\mathbf{x}_3$, whose means are 2, 1, and 4, and whose variances are 9, 20, and 12, find

(a) the mean and the variance of $2\mathbf{x}_1 + 3\mathbf{x}_2 + \mathbf{x}_3$

(b) the mean and the variance of $\mathbf{x}_1 - 2\mathbf{x}_2 + 5\mathbf{x}_3$

2. Repeat Exercise 1 if $\mathbf{x}_1$, $\mathbf{x}_2$, and $\mathbf{x}_3$ are not independent and $\text{cov}(\mathbf{x}_1, \mathbf{x}_2) = 1$, $\text{cov}(\mathbf{x}_1, \mathbf{x}_3) = -2$, and $\text{cov}(\mathbf{x}_2, \mathbf{x}_3) = 3$.

3. Prove Theorem 7.3 on page 175 and the corollary given by (7.4.5).

4. Given the random variables $\mathbf{x}$ and $\mathbf{y}$, find expressions for $\text{var}(\mathbf{x} + \mathbf{y})$, $\text{var}(\mathbf{x} - \mathbf{y})$, and $\text{cov}(\mathbf{x} + \mathbf{y}, \mathbf{x} - \mathbf{y})$ in terms of the variances and covariance of $\mathbf{x}$ and $\mathbf{y}$.

5. If $\mathbf{x}$ is the number of successes obtained in n independent trials and the probability of success in the ith trial is θ_i, show that

(a) $E(\mathbf{x}) = n\theta$, where $\theta = \sum_{i=1}^{n} \frac{\theta_i}{n}$

(b) $\text{var}(\mathbf{x}) = n\theta(1 - \theta) - \sum_{i=1}^{n} (\theta_i - \theta)^2$

(c) Use the results obtained in parts (a) and (b) to find the mean and the variance of the binomial distribution.

6. If $\mathbf{x}_1, \mathbf{x}_2, \ldots,$ and $\mathbf{x}_n$ have the multinomial distribution (3.3.6), find the mean and the variance of $\mathbf{x}_r + \mathbf{x}_s$, the sum of any two of these random variables. It is assumed that $n > 2$. [*Hint*: use the previously obtained results that $E(\mathbf{x}_i) = n\theta_i$, $\text{var}(\mathbf{x}_i) = n\theta_i(1 - \theta_i)$, and $\text{cov}(\mathbf{x}_i, \mathbf{x}_j) = -n\theta_i\theta_j$.]

7. A random sample of size 100 is taken from a population whose mean is 80 and whose variance is 400. Using Chebyshev's theorem, with what probability can we assert that the mean of the sample will not differ from $\mu = 80$ by more than 8? (The first sentence is meant to imply that the common distribution of the corresponding random variables has the mean $\mu = 80$ and the variance $\sigma^2 = 400$.)

8. A random sample of size 64 is taken from a population whose mean is 50 and whose variance is 256. Using Chebyshev's theorem, what can we assert with a probability of at least 0.99 about the possible difference between $\bar{x}$ and $\mu = 50$? (See comment to Exercise 7.)

7.4.2 *Differences between means and differences between proportions*

There are many problems of applied statistics in which we must decide whether differences between the means (or other descriptive measures) of two samples may be attributed to chance. For instance, if 50 men took on the average 4 minutes 24 seconds to perform a certain task while 50 women took on the average 4 minutes 31 seconds, we may want to decide whether there is actually a difference in the speed with which men and women (in general) can perform this task. Similarly, if one manufacturing process produced 15 defective pieces in a sample of size 400 while another produced 20 defective pieces in a sample of 350, it may be of interest to know whether this is really indicative of a difference in the merits of the two processes.

In order to develop theory which is pertinent to the analysis of problems of this kind, let us depart slightly from the notation of Section 7.4. Let us consider $n_1 + n_2$ random variables, writing the first n_1 as $\mathbf{x}_{11}, \mathbf{x}_{12}, \mathbf{x}_{13}, \ldots, \mathbf{x}_{1n_1}$, and the remaining n_2 as $\mathbf{x}_{21}, \mathbf{x}_{22}, \mathbf{x}_{23}, \ldots, \mathbf{x}_{2n_2}$. If these random variables are independent and if, furthermore, the first n_1 have identical distributions and so do the remaining n_2, then the values which they assume are referred to as *two independent random samples*. Using this notation, let us now prove the following theorem:

THEOREM 7.6:

If $\mathbf{x}_{11}, \mathbf{x}_{12}, \ldots, \mathbf{x}_{1n_1}, \mathbf{x}_{21}, \mathbf{x}_{22}, \ldots, \mathbf{x}_{2n_2}$ *are independent random variables, the first* n_1 *have identical distributions with the mean* μ_1 *and the variance* σ_1^2, *and the remaining* n_2 *have identical distribu-*

tions with the mean μ_2 and the variance σ_2^2, then

$$E(\bar{\mathbf{x}}_1 - \bar{\mathbf{x}}_2) = \mu_1 - \mu_2 \tag{7.4.9}$$

and

$$\text{var}(\bar{\mathbf{x}}_1 - \bar{\mathbf{x}}_2) = \frac{\sigma_1^2}{n_1} + \frac{\sigma_2^2}{n_2} \tag{7.4.10}$$

where

$$\bar{\mathbf{x}}_1 = \frac{1}{n_1}\sum_{i=1}^{n_1} \mathbf{x}_{1i} \qquad \textit{and} \qquad \bar{\mathbf{x}}_2 = \frac{1}{n_2}\sum_{i=1}^{n_2} \mathbf{x}_{2i}$$

It is customary to refer to the positive square root of $\text{var}(\bar{\mathbf{x}}_1 - \bar{\mathbf{x}}_2)$ as the *standard error of the difference between two means.*

To prove this theorem we have only to substitute $1/n_1$ for the first n_1 a's and $-(1/n_2)$ for the remaining n_2 a's in (7.4.1) and (7.4.3). We thus get

$$E(\bar{\mathbf{x}}_1 - \bar{\mathbf{x}}_2) = \sum_{i=1}^{n_1} \frac{1}{n_1}\mu_1 + \sum_{i=1}^{n_2}\left(-\frac{1}{n_2}\right)\mu_2$$

$$= \mu_1 - \mu_2$$

and

$$\text{var}(\bar{\mathbf{x}}_1 - \bar{\mathbf{x}}_2) = \sum_{i=1}^{n_1}\left(\frac{1}{n_1}\right)^2\sigma_1^2 + \sum_{i=1}^{n_2}\left(-\frac{1}{n_2}\right)^2\sigma_2^2$$

$$= \frac{\sigma_1^2}{n_1} + \frac{\sigma_2^2}{n_2}$$

and this completes the proof of the theorem.

An important special case arises when the first n_1 random variables have binomial distributions with $n = 1$ and $\theta = \theta_1$ while the other n_2 random variables have binomial distributions with $n = 1$ and $\theta = \theta_2$. In that case $\bar{\mathbf{x}}_1$ is the *proportion* of successes in the first n_1 trials, which we shall write as $\mathbf{f}_1$, and $\bar{\mathbf{x}}_2$ is the *proportion* of successes in the other n_2 trials, which we shall write as $\mathbf{f}_2$. Substituting $\mu_1 = \theta_1$, $\mu_2 = \theta_2$, $\sigma_1^2 = \theta_1(1 - \theta_1)$, and $\sigma_2^2 = \theta_2(1 - \theta_2)$ into (7.4.9) and (7.4.10), we thus get

$$E(\mathbf{f}_1 - \mathbf{f}_2) = \theta_1 - \theta_2 \tag{7.4.11}$$

and

$$\text{var}(\mathbf{f}_1 - \mathbf{f}_2) = \frac{\theta_1(1 - \theta_1)}{n_1} + \frac{\theta_2(1 - \theta_2)}{n_2} \tag{7.4.12}$$

It is customary to refer to the positive square root of $\text{var}(\mathbf{f}_1 - \mathbf{f}_2)$ as the *standard error of the difference between two proportions.*

We have taken up this theory at this time because it follows immediately from the work of Section 7.4. Various applications will be presented in Chapter 10 and 12.

EXERCISES

1. Samples of size 100 are taken from two populations having $\mu_1 = \mu_2$, $\sigma_1 = 30$, and $\sigma_2 = 40$. (This means that the distribution common to the first 100 random variables has $\sigma_1 = 30$, the distribution common to the other 100 random variables has $\sigma_2 = 40$, and the two distributions have equal means.) Using Chebyshev's theorem, what can we assert with a probability of at least 0.75 about the possible size of the difference between the sample means?

2. The actual proportion of men favoring a certain piece of legislation is 0.60 while that of women favoring this piece of legislation is 0.50. If 400 men and 400 women are interviewed about this piece of legislation, what can we assert with a probability of at least 0.99 about the possible size of the difference between the sample proportions of men and women who favor this piece of legislation? Use Chebyshev's theorem and assume that the conditions underlying the binomial distribution can (at least approximately) be met.

7.4.3 *Sampling from finite populations*

If an experiment consists of selecting one or more values from a finite set of numbers $\{c_1, c_2, \ldots, c_N\}$, this set is referred to as a *finite population* and the numbers selected are referred to as a *sample from a finite population.* (If two or more of the c's are equal, imagine that they are given subscripts as on page 21, so that we can nevertheless refer to them as a set.) Thus, the weights of the members of a certain football team constitute a finite population and so do the profits reported by 25 corporations in 1962, the I.Q.'s of the children attending a certain school, and the daily low humidity readings in Phoenix for the month of August, 1962.

If the selection is *without replacement,* $\mathbf{x}_1$ is the first number selected, $\mathbf{x}_2$ is the second number selected, . . ., and $\mathbf{x}_n$ is the nth number selected, the values selected are referred to as a *random sample of size n from the finite population* provided that

$$f(x_1, x_2, \ldots, x_n) = \frac{1}{N(N-1) \cdot \ldots \cdot (N-n+1)} \qquad (7.4.13)$$

for each ordered n-tuple selected from the finite population. In other words, the selection must be such that each ordered n-tuple $(x_1, x_2, \ldots, x_n)$, that is, each element of the n-dimensional sample space, has the same probability.

Under these assumptions, the marginal distribution of any one of the random variables $\mathbf{x}_r$ is given by

$$f(x_r) = 1/N \qquad \text{for} \quad x_r = c_1, c_2, \ldots, c_N \tag{7.4.14}$$

and the joint marginal distribution of any two of the random variables $\mathbf{x}_r$ and $\mathbf{x}_s$ is given by

$$f(x_r, x_s) = \frac{1}{N(N-1)} \tag{7.4.15}$$

for each ordered pair selected from the finite population. It follows that

$$E(\mathbf{x}_r) = \sum_{i=1}^{N} \frac{c_i}{N} = \mu \tag{7.4.16}$$

$$\text{var}(\mathbf{x}_r) = \sum_{i=1}^{N} \frac{(c_i - \mu)^2}{N} = \sigma^2 \tag{7.4.17}$$

$$\text{cov}(\mathbf{x}_r, \mathbf{x}_s) = \sum_{i=1}^{N} \sum_{\substack{j=1 \\ i \neq j}}^{N} \frac{(c_i - \mu)(c_j - \mu)}{N(N-1)} \tag{7.4.18}$$

and it is customary to refer to μ and σ^2 as *the mean and the variance of the finite population.*

Leaving it to the reader to verify in Exercise 1 below that

$$\sum_{i=1}^{N} c_i = \mu N \qquad \sum_{i=1}^{N} c_i^2 = N(\sigma^2 + \mu^2),$$

and, hence, that

$$\text{cov}(\mathbf{x}_r, \mathbf{x}_s) = \frac{\left(\sum_{i=1}^{N} c_i\right)^2 - \sum_{i=1}^{N} c_i^2}{N(N-1)} - \mu^2 = -\frac{\sigma^2}{N-1}$$

let us now prove the following theorem:

THEOREM 7.7:

If $\bar{x}$ is the mean of a random sample of size n selected from a finite population of size N, whose mean is μ and whose variance is σ^2, *then*

$$E(\bar{\mathbf{x}}) = \mu \tag{7.4.19}$$

and

$$\text{var}(\bar{\mathbf{x}}) = \frac{\sigma^2}{n} \cdot \frac{N - n}{N - 1} \tag{7.4.20}$$

To prove this theorem we have only to substitute $a_i = 1/n$, $\text{var}(\mathbf{x}_i) = \sigma^2$, and $\text{cov}(\mathbf{x}_i, \mathbf{x}_j) = -\sigma^2/(N - 1)$ into (7.4.1) and (7.4.2) on page 174. The details will again be left to the reader (see Exercise 2 below).

It is interesting to note that the two formulas which we obtained for $\text{var}(\bar{\mathbf{x}})$, the one of Theorem 7.4 which applies to the mean of values assumed by independent random variables (or sampling *with replacement* from a finite population, see Exercise 3 below) and the one of Theorem 7.7 which applies to sampling *without replacement* from a finite population, differ only by the factor $(N - n)/(N - 1)$. If N, the size of the population, is large compared to n, the size of the sample, the difference between the two formulas becomes negligible. Indeed, the formula $\sigma_{\bar{\mathbf{x}}} = \sigma/\sqrt{n}$ is frequently used as an approximation for the standard deviation of the distribution of $\bar{\mathbf{x}}$ for samples obtained without replacement from sufficiently large finite populations.

7.4.4 *The distribution of rank sums*

If the assumptions which underlie so-called standard statistical techniques cannot be met, it is sometimes possible to substitute alternate techniques based on the *ranks* of the measurements or observations within the sample. Several such tests based on ranks will be treated later in Chapter 12.

In this section we shall study some distribution theory connected with rank sums; specifically, we shall obtain expressions for the mean and the variance of the distribution of $\mathbf{y}$, where $\mathbf{y}$ is the sum of n integers selected at random from among the first N positive integers.

Using the result obtained in the Appendix on page 352, we find that the mean and the variance of a finite population consisting of the first N positive integers are

$$\mu = \frac{N + 1}{2}$$

and

$$\sigma^2 = \frac{(N+1)(2N+1)}{6} - \left(\frac{N+1}{2}\right)^2 = \frac{(N+1)(N-1)}{12}$$

Substituting these expressions for μ and σ^2 into (7.4.19) and (7.4.20), we find that

$$E(\bar{\mathbf{x}}) = \frac{N+1}{2}$$

and

$$\operatorname{var}(\bar{\mathbf{x}}) = \frac{(N+1)(N-1)}{12n} \cdot \frac{N-n}{N-1} = \frac{(N+1)(N-n)}{12n}$$

where $\bar{\mathbf{x}}$ is the mean of n integers selected at random from among the first N positive integers. To obtain the corresponding moments of $\mathbf{y}$, the *sum* of the ranks rather than their mean, we have only to multiply $E(\bar{\mathbf{x}})$ by n, $\operatorname{var}(\bar{\mathbf{x}})$ by n^2, getting thus

THEOREM 7.8:

If $\mathbf{y}$ *is the sum of* n *integers selected at random from among the first* N *positive integers, then*

$$E(\mathbf{y}) = \frac{n(N+1)}{2} \tag{7.4.21}$$

and

$$\operatorname{var}(\mathbf{y}) = \frac{n(N+1)(N-n)}{12} \tag{7.4.22}$$

EXERCISES

1. Using (7.4.16), (7.4.17), and (7.4.18) show that

(a) $\sum_{i=1}^{N} c_i = \mu N$ (b) $\sum_{i=1}^{N} c_i^2 = N(\sigma^2 + \mu^2)$

(c) $\operatorname{cov}(\mathbf{x}_r, \mathbf{x}_s) = -\dfrac{\sigma^2}{N-1}$

as indicated on page 182. [*Hint*: to prove (c) refer to rule A.10 in the Appendix.]

2. Prove Theorem 7.7, following the suggestions on page 183.

3. Explain why Theorem 7.4 rather than Theorem 7.7 applies when we sample *with replacement* from a finite population.

4. Sampling with and without replacement was first mentioned in connection with the binomial and hypergeometric distributions. Show that if we let $a + b = N$ and $\theta = a/(a + b)$, the variance of the hypergeometric distribution equals that of the binomial distribution multiplied by the factor $(N - n)/(N - 1)$.

7.5 The Central Limit Theorem

The theorem which we shall study in this section is one of the most important theorems of statistics. Essentially, the *Central Limit Theorem,* as Theorem 7.9 is called, concerns the limiting distribution of the *standardized mean* of n random variables when $n \to \infty$. We shall prove it here for the case where the random variables $\mathbf{x}_1$, $\mathbf{x}_2$, $\ldots$, and $\mathbf{x}_n$ have identical distributions whose moment generating function exists. More general conditions are given in Exercises 1 and 2 on page 187, and the most general conditions are referred to in the Bibliography on page 188.

THEOREM 7.9:

If $\mathbf{x}_1$, $\mathbf{x}_2$, $\ldots$, and $\mathbf{x}_n$ are independent random variables having the same distribution with the mean μ, the variance σ^2, and the moment generating function $M_{\mathbf{x}}(t)$, then if $n \to \infty$ the limiting distribution of

$$\mathbf{z} = \frac{\bar{\mathbf{x}} - \mu}{\sigma/\sqrt{n}}$$

is the standard normal distribution.

Note that $\mathbf{z}$ is the *standardized mean* of the random variables $\mathbf{x}_1$, $\mathbf{x}_2$, $\ldots$, and $\mathbf{x}_n$.

To prove this theorem, let us first write $\mathbf{z}$ as $(\mathbf{y} - n\mu)/\sigma\sqrt{n}$, where $\mathbf{y} = \mathbf{x}_1 + \mathbf{x}_2 + \ldots + \mathbf{x}_n$. Using Theorems 7.1 and (6.4.4) we then get

$$M_{\mathbf{y}}(t) = [M_{\mathbf{x}}(t)]^n$$

$$M_{\mathbf{z}}(t) = e^{-\frac{\mu\sqrt{n}t}{\sigma}}\left[M_{\mathbf{x}}\left(\frac{t}{\sigma\sqrt{n}}\right)\right]^n$$

and, hence,

$$\ln M_{\mathbf{z}}(t) = -\frac{\mu\sqrt{n}}{\sigma}t + n\cdot\ln M_{\mathbf{x}}\left(\frac{t}{\sigma\sqrt{n}}\right)$$

Expanding $M_{\mathbf{x}}(t/\sigma\sqrt{n})$ as a power series in t we get

$$\ln M_{\mathbf{z}}(t) = -\frac{\mu\sqrt{n}}{\sigma}\cdot t + n\cdot\ln\left[1 + \mu_1'\frac{t}{\sigma\sqrt{n}} + \mu_2'\frac{t^2}{2\sigma^2 n} + \mu_3'\frac{t^3}{6\sigma^3 n\sqrt{n}} + \ldots\right]$$

where μ_r' are the moments of the distribution common to the original random variables $\mathbf{x}_i$. If n is sufficiently large, we can then expand $\ln(1 + x)$ as on page 158, getting

$$\begin{aligned}\ln M_{\mathbf{z}}(t) = -\frac{\mu\sqrt{n}}{\sigma}t + n\Bigg\{&\left[\mu_1'\frac{t}{\sigma\sqrt{n}} + \mu_2'\frac{t^2}{2\sigma^2 n} + \mu_3'\frac{t^3}{6\sigma^3 n\sqrt{n}} + \ldots\right] \\ &- \frac{1}{2}\left[\mu_1'\frac{t}{\sigma\sqrt{n}} + \mu_2'\frac{t^2}{2\sigma^2 n} + \mu_3'\frac{t^3}{6\sigma^3 n\sqrt{n}} + \ldots\right]^2 \\ &+ \frac{1}{3}\left[\mu_1'\frac{t}{\sigma\sqrt{n}} + \mu_2'\frac{t^2}{2\sigma^2 n} + \mu_3'\frac{t^3}{6\sigma^3 n\sqrt{n}} + \ldots\right]^3 \\ &- \cdots\cdots\cdots\cdots\Bigg\}\end{aligned}$$

Collecting powers of t we then obtain

$$\ln M_{\mathbf{z}}(t) = \left(-\frac{\mu\sqrt{n}}{\sigma} + \frac{\mu_1'\sqrt{n}}{\sigma}\right)t + \left(\frac{\mu_2'}{2\sigma^2} - \frac{\mu_1'^2}{2\sigma^2}\right)t^2 + \left(\frac{\mu_3'}{6\sigma^3\sqrt{n}} - \frac{\mu_1'\mu_2'}{2\sigma^3\sqrt{n}} + \frac{\mu_1'^3}{3\sigma^3\sqrt{n}}\right)t^3 + \ldots$$

and since $\mu_1' = \mu$ and $\mu_2' - \mu_1'^2 = \sigma^2$, this reduces to

$$\ln M_{\mathbf{z}}(t) = \tfrac{1}{2}t^2 + \left(\frac{\mu_3'}{6} - \frac{\mu_1'\mu_2'}{2} + \frac{\mu_1'^3}{3}\right)\frac{t^3}{\sigma^3\sqrt{n}} + \ldots$$

Noting that the coefficient of t^3 is a constant times $1/\sqrt{n}$ and, in general, the coefficient of t^r is a constant times $n^{(2-r)/2}$, we finally get

$$\lim_{n\to\infty} \ln M_{\mathbf{z}}(t) = \tfrac{1}{2}t^2$$

and, hence,

$$\lim_{n\to\infty} M_{\mathbf{z}}(t) = e^{(1/2)t^2}$$

using the same argument as on page 159. Referring again to the uniqueness theorem for moment generating functions, this completes the proof of Theorem 7.9; the limiting moment generating function is that of the standard normal distribution.

Sometimes the Central Limit Theorem is interpreted incorrectly as saying that the distribution of $\bar{\mathbf{x}}$ approaches a normal distribution when $n \to \infty$. This is incorrect, inasmuch as under the conditions of Theorem 7.9 the variance of $\bar{\mathbf{x}}$ approaches 0 when $n \to \infty$. On the other hand, the Central Limit Theorem justifies *approximating* the distribution of $\bar{\mathbf{x}}$ with a normal distribution whose mean is μ and whose variance is σ^2/n, when n is sufficiently large. It is of interest to note that if the common distribution of the random variables $\mathbf{x}_i$ is normal, the distribution of $\bar{\mathbf{x}}$ *is* the normal distribution $N(\bar{x};\, \mu,\, \sigma^2/n)$ for any n.

We shall prove this in Section 8.2.

EXERCISES

1. The following is a *sufficient* condition for the Central Limit Theorem: *If the random variables $\mathbf{x}_1, \mathbf{x}_2, \ldots,$ and $\mathbf{x}_n$ are independent and uniformly bounded (that is, there is a positive constant k such that the probability that any one of the $\mathbf{x}_i$ assumes a value greater than k or less than $-k$ is 0), then if the variance of $\mathbf{y}_n = \mathbf{x}_1 + \mathbf{x}_2 + \ldots + \mathbf{x}_n$ becomes infinite when $n \to \infty$, the distribution of the standardized mean of the $\mathbf{x}_i$ approaches the standard normal distribution.*

Show that this sufficient condition holds for a sequence of independent random variables whose distributions are

$$f_i(x_i) = \begin{cases} \dfrac{1}{2} & \text{for } x_i = 1 - \left(\dfrac{1}{2}\right)^i \\[2ex] \dfrac{1}{2} & \text{for } x_i = \left(\dfrac{1}{2}\right)^i - 1 \end{cases}$$

2. The following is a sufficient condition, the *Laplace-Liapounoff* condition, for the Central Limit Theorem:

If $\mathbf{x}_1, \mathbf{x}_2, \mathbf{x}_3, \ldots,$ is a sequence of independent random variables, each having an absolute third moment

$$c_i = E(|\mathbf{x}_i - \mu_i|^3)$$

and if

$$\lim_{n\to\infty} [\text{var}(\mathbf{y}_n)]^{-(3/2)} \sum_{i=1}^{n} c_i = 0$$

where $\mathbf{y}_n = \mathbf{x}_1 + \mathbf{x}_2 + \ldots + \mathbf{x}_n$, *then the distribution of the standardized mean of the* $\mathbf{x}_i$ *approaches the standard normal distribution when* $n \to \infty$.

Use this condition to show that the Central Limit Theorem holds for the sequence of random variables of Exercise 1.

3. If $\mathbf{x}_1, \mathbf{x}_2, \mathbf{x}_3, \ldots,$ is a sequence of independent random variables having the uniform densities

$$f_i(x_i) = \begin{cases} \dfrac{1}{2 - \dfrac{1}{i}} & \text{for } 0 < x_i < 2 - \dfrac{1}{i} \\ 0 & \text{elsewhere} \end{cases}$$

show that the Central Limit Theorem holds using

(a) the conditions of Exercise 1

(b) the conditions of Exercise 2.

4. Interpreting the binomial distribution as we did on page 172, use the Central Limit Theorem to show that the standardized binomial distribution approaches the standard normal distribution when $n \to \infty$.

5. Repeat Exercise 7 on page 179, using the Central Limit Theorem rather than Chebyshev's theorem.

6. Repeat Exercise 8 on page 179, using the Central Limit Theorem rather than Chebyshev's theorem.

BIBLIOGRAPHY

Necessary and sufficient conditions for the strongest form of the Central Limit Theorem for independent random variables, the so-called *Lindeberg-Feller* conditions, are given in

Feller, W., *An Introduction to Probability Theory and its Applications, Vol. I,* 2nd ed., New York: John Wiley & Sons, Inc., 1957, Chapter 10.

Munroe, M. E., *Theory of Probability,* New York: McGraw-Hill Book Co., Inc., 1951, Chapter 9.

and, of course, in more advanced texts.

Chapter 8

Sampling Distributions

8.1 Introduction

Given a set of data, a sample, any quantity which can be determined on the basis of the sample values x_1, x_2, . . ., and x_n is called a *statistic*. Thus, the sample mean is a statistic, the proportion of successes in n trials is a statistic, and so are the *sample range* (the largest value minus the smallest) and the *sample median* (a number which is exceeded by as many of the sample values as it exceeds). Another important statistic is the *sample variance*

$$s^2 = \frac{\sum_{i=1}^{n} (x_i - \bar{x})^2}{n - 1} \tag{8.1.1}$$

which is the most widely used measure of the variability of a sample. Its positive square root, s, is called the *sample standard deviation*. Note that (8.1.1) differs from (7.4.17), which defined the variance of a finite population, only inasmuch as division is by $n - 1$ instead of n. The reason for this will be explained in Chapter 9, where we shall use s^2 to estimate σ^2, the variance of the "population" from which the sample was obtained.

As we have defined the term "statistic," a statistic is a value assumed by a random variable; a sample mean is a value assumed by the random variable $\bar{\mathbf{x}}$ and a sample variance is a value assumed by the random variable $\mathbf{s}^2$. In other words, $\bar{\mathbf{x}}$ assumes the value

$$\sum_{i=1}^{n} x_i/n$$

and $\mathbf{s}^2$ assumes the value

$$\frac{\sum_{i=1}^{n} (x_i - \bar{x})^2}{n - 1}$$

at the point $(x_1, x_2, \ldots, x_n)$ of the sample space.

It is customary to refer to the distributions of $\bar{\mathbf{x}}$ and $\mathbf{s}^2$, as well as those of random variables corresponding to other statistics, as *sampling distributions*. Logically speaking, the distribution of any random variable could be called a sampling distribution, but the term is usually reserved for distributions of random variables corresponding to statistics such as $\bar{x}$ and s^2, which play important roles in applied statistics. In this chapter we shall study a number of special sampling distributions.

8.2 Sampling from Normal Populations

To distinguish between the two kinds of random samples defined in Sections 7.4.3 and 7.4.1, it is customary to refer to them, respectively, as samples from *finite* and *infinite* populations. When sampling from a finite population, the sample size cannot exceed N, the size of the population; when sampling from an infinite population, the sample size can be made as large as we want. Note that if we sample *with replacement* from a finite population, the population has, in fact, become infinite; there is no longer any restriction on the possible size of the sample.

In Sections 8.2.1 through 8.2.4 we shall concern ourselves exclusively with random samples from *normal populations*, namely, infinite populations of the form $N(x_i; \mu, \sigma^2)$. This means that the independent random variables, whose values constitute the random sample, have identical normal distributions with the mean μ and the variance σ^2. In particular, we shall investigate distribution theory connected with the statistics $\bar{x}$, s^2, $(\bar{x} - \mu)\sqrt{n}/s$, and s_1^2/s_2^2, where s_1^2 and s_2^2 are the variances of independent random samples from two normal populations.

8.2.1 *The distribution of* $\bar{\mathbf{x}}$

Having shown in Section 7.5 that *for large n* sampling distributions of $\bar{\mathbf{x}}$ can (under very general conditions) be approximated with normal distributions, let us now show that for random samples from normal populations the distribution of $\bar{\mathbf{x}}$ *is* a normal distribution *regardless of the size of the sample.* To prove this we have only to substitute into

$$M_{\bar{\mathbf{x}}}(t) = \left[M_{\mathbf{x}}\left(\frac{t}{n}\right)\right]^n \qquad (8.2.1)$$

which follows immediately from Theorems 6.6 and 7.1 or as a special case of Exercise 5 on page 173. (The reader will be asked to verify this in Exercise 1 on page 192.) Since the moment generating function of the normal distribution $N(x;\ \mu,\ \sigma^2)$ is given by

$$M_{\mathbf{x}}(t) = e^{\mu t+(1/2)t^2\sigma^2}$$

see Theorem 6.9, substitution into (8.2.1) yields

$$M_{\bar{\mathbf{x}}}(t) = \left[e^{\mu(t/n)+(1/2)(t/n)^2\sigma^2}\right]^n$$
$$= e^{\mu t+(1/2)t^2(\sigma^2/n)}$$

namely, the moment generating function of a normal distribution with the mean μ and the variance σ^2/n. Referring again to the uniqueness of the correspondence between moment generating functions and probability densities or distributions, we have thus proved

THEOREM 8.1:
If $\bar{x}$ is the mean of a random sample of size n from the normal population $N(x;\ \mu,\ \sigma^2)$, then the sampling distribution of $\bar{\mathbf{x}}$ is the normal distribution $N(\bar{x};\ \mu,\ \sigma^2/n)$.

Many applications of this important theorem will be taken up later on; for the moment, let us consider the following illustration: a production process which turns out thousands of compression springs each day is *under control* if the free lengths of these springs (in centimeters) may be looked upon as a normal population with $\mu = 4$ and $\sigma^2 = 0.0025$. (In other words, the process is under control if the free length of any one of the springs (selected at random) may be looked upon as a value assumed by a random variable having the normal distribution $N(x;\ 4,\ 0.0025.)$ To check whether the process is under control, 25 springs are randomly selected from each day's production, and the process is considered to be under control if the mean of their lengths falls between 3.985 and 4.015 cm. What is the probability that a sample will fail to meet this criterion even though the process is under control?

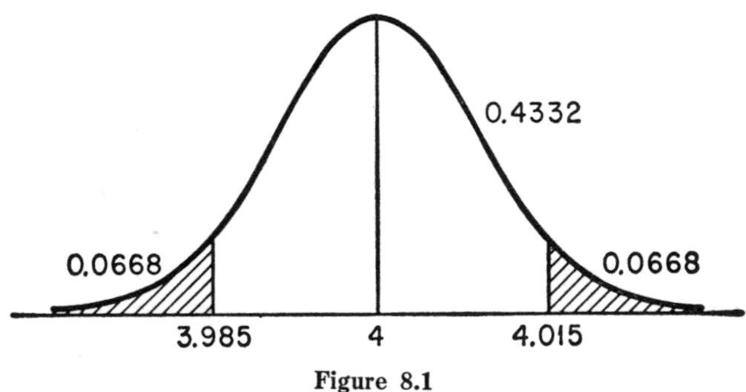

Figure 8.1

The answer to this question is given by the shaded area of Figure 8.1, representing the probability that a random variable having the normal distribution $N(\bar{x}; 4, 0.0001)$ assumes a value less than or equal to 3.985 or greater than or equal to 4.015. Proceeding as in the examples of Section 6.3.3, we find that $z = (4.015 - 4)/0.01 = 1.5$ and, hence, that the shaded area in each tail of the distribution of Figure 8.1 represents a probability of $0.5000 - 0.4332 = 0.0668$. The probability that the production process is *mistakenly* said to be out of control is, thus, 0.1336.

EXERCISES

1. Verify (8.2.1) using (a) Theorems 6.6 and 7.1, and (b) Exercise 5 on page 173.

2. Differentiating the function given by (8.2.1) twice with respect to t and evaluating these derivatives at $t = 0$, prove Theorem 7.4.

3. A random sample of size 36 is to be taken from a normal population with $\mu = 43.2$ and $\sigma^2 = 39.69$. Find the probability that the mean of this sample will fall between 42.0 and 45.0.

4. A random sample of size 100 is to be taken from a normal population with $\mu = 80$ and $\sigma^2 = 400$. What is the probability that the sample mean will differ from the mean of the population by 3 or more?

5. If $\mathbf{x}$ and $\mathbf{y}$ are independent random variables having the normal distributions $N(x;\,\mu_1,\,\sigma_1^2)$ and $N(y;\,\mu_2,\,\sigma_2^2)$, show that $\mathbf{x} - \mathbf{y}$ has a normal distribution with the mean $\mu_1 - \mu_2$ and the variance $\sigma_1^2 + \sigma_2^2$.

6. If $\bar{x}_1$ and $\bar{x}_2$ are the means of independent random samples of size n_1 and n_2 from normal populations having the means μ_1 and μ_2 and the variances σ_1^2 and σ_2^2, show that $\bar{\mathbf{x}}_1 - \bar{\mathbf{x}}_2$ has a normal distribution. What are the mean and the variance of this distribution?

7. Independent random samples of size 100 are taken from two normal populations having equal means and the variances $\sigma_1^2 = 50$ and $\sigma_2^2 = 40$. What is the probability that the (absolute) difference between the sample means will exceed 2? (*Hint*: refer to the result of Exercise 6 and Theorem 7.6.)

8. Independent random samples of size $n_1 = 40$ and $n_2 = 50$ are taken from normal populations having the means $\mu_1 = 68$ and $\mu_2 = 66$ and the variances $\sigma_1^2 = 120$ and $\sigma_2^2 = 150$. What is the probability that the mean of the first sample will exceed that of the second sample by at least 4?

8.2.2 *The chi-square distribution and the distribution of* $\mathbf{s}^2$

In Section 5.4 we showed that if $\mathbf{x}$ has the standard normal distribution, then $\mathbf{x}^2$ has a gamma distribution with $\alpha = \frac{1}{2}$ and $\beta = 2$. In view of this relationship, the gamma distribution plays an important role in sampling theory connected with normal populations; particularly, the gamma distribution with the parameters $\alpha = \nu/2$ and $\beta = 2$, which is given by

$$f(x) = \begin{cases} \dfrac{1}{2^{\nu/2}\Gamma(\nu/2)}\, x^{(\nu-2)/2}e^{-(x/2)} & \text{for } x > 0 \\ 0 & \text{elsewhere} \end{cases} \tag{8.2.2}$$

(see page 127). We shall refer to this density as the *chi-square distribution* (also written χ^2 *distribution*) *with* ν *degrees of freedom*; its parameter, ν (*nu*), is called the *number of degrees of freedom*. Since the chi-square distribution is not really new, we know from (6.4.6) that its moment generating function is given by

$$M_{\mathbf{x}}(t) = (1 - 2t)^{-(\nu/2)} \tag{8.2.3}$$

and from (6.3.4) that its mean and variance are, respectively, ν and 2ν.

The chi-square distribution has a number of important mathematical properties, which are expressed in Theorems 8.2 through 8.5 below. First, let us restate the result obtained in Section 5.4 as follows:

THEOREM 8.2:

If $\mathbf{x}$ *has the standard normal distribution, then* $\mathbf{x}^2$ *has the chi-square distribution with* 1 *degree of freedom.*

More generally, we have

THEOREM 8.3:

If $\mathbf{x}_1, \mathbf{x}_2, \ldots,$ *and* $\mathbf{x}_n$ *are independent random variables having standard normal distrubtions, then*

$$\mathbf{y} = \sum_{i=1}^{n} \mathbf{x}_i^2$$

has the chi-square distribution with n degrees of freedom.

To prove this theorem, we have only to refer to (7.3.1) and Theorem 8.2, according to which $M_{\mathbf{x}_i^2}(t) = (1 - 2t)^{-(1/2)}$. We, thus, get

$$M_{\mathbf{y}}(t) = \prod_{i=1}^{n} (1 - 2t)^{-1/2} = (1 - 2t)^{-n/2}$$

and it can be seen by inspection that this gives the moment generating function of the chi-square distribution with n degrees of freedom.

Two further properties of the chi-square distribution are given in the following two theorems, whose proof will be left to the reader (see Exercises 1 and 2 on page 197):

THEOREM 8.4:

If $\mathbf{x}_1, \mathbf{x}_2, \ldots,$ *and* $\mathbf{x}_n$ *are independent random variables having chi-square distributions with* $\nu_1, \nu_2, \ldots,$ *and* ν_n *degrees of freedom, then*

$$\mathbf{y} = \sum_{i=1}^{n} \mathbf{x}_i$$

has the chi-square distribution with

$$\nu = \sum_{i=1}^{n} \nu_i$$

degrees of freedom.

THEOREM 8.5:

If $\mathbf{x}_1$ *and* $\mathbf{x}_2$ *are independent random variables,* $\mathbf{x}_1$ *has a chi-square distribution with* ν_1 *degrees of freedom, and* $\mathbf{x}_1 + \mathbf{x}_2$ *has a chi-square distribution with* $\nu > \nu_1$ *degrees of freedom, then* $\mathbf{x}_2$ *has a chi-square distribution with* $\nu - \nu_1$ *degrees of freedom.*

The chi-square distribution has many important applications, some of which will be discussed in Chapters 9 through 12. Foremost, there are those based, directly or indirectly, on the following theorem:

THEOREM 8.6:

If $\mathbf{s}^2$ *is the variance of a random sample of size n from the normal population* $N(x; \mu, \sigma^2)$, *then* $(n - 1)\mathbf{s}^2/\sigma^2$ *has a chi-square distribution with* $n - 1$ *degrees of freedom.*

We shall not be able to give a complete proof of this theorem, since one step requires use of a theorem, which is of a somewhat more advanced nature. Nevertheless, let us observe that for a random sample of size n from the normal population $N(x; \mu, \sigma^2)$

$$\sum_{i=1}^{n} \left(\frac{x_i - \mu}{\sigma}\right)^2 = \frac{1}{\sigma^2} \sum_{i=1}^{n} (x_i - \mu)^2 \qquad (8.2.4)$$

is a value assumed by a random variable having the chi-square distribution with n degrees of freedom (see Theorem 8.3). Note that (8.2.4) differs from

$$\frac{(n - 1)s^2}{\sigma^2} = \frac{1}{\sigma^2} \sum_{i=1}^{n} (x_i - \bar{x})^2 \qquad (8.2.5)$$

only inasmuch as the quantities squared are deviations from μ instead of deviations from $\bar{x}$. In fact, the exact relationship between

(8.2.4) and (8.2.5) is given by the identity

$$\frac{1}{\sigma^2}\sum_{i=1}^{n}(x_i - \mu)^2 = \left(\frac{\bar{x} - \mu}{\sigma/\sqrt{n}}\right)^2 + \frac{(n-1)s^2}{\sigma^2} \tag{8.2.6}$$

which the reader will be asked to verify in Exercise 3 on page 197.

Since, under the given assumptions, $[(\bar{\mathbf{x}} - \mu)/(\sigma/\sqrt{n})]^2$ has a chi-square distribution with 1 degree of freedom (see Theorem 8.2), Theorem 8.5 *would* lead to the result that $(n - 1)\mathbf{s}^2/\sigma^2$ has a chi-square distribution with $n - 1$ degrees of freedom *provided that the two terms on the righthand side of* (8.2.6) *are values assumed by independent random variables.* A proof of this independence is referred to in the Bibliography on page 208; in Exercise 4 on page 197 the reader will be asked to prove it for the special case where $n = 2$. Note also that s^2 is expressed in terms of the deviations from the mean $x_i - \bar{x}$ and that we showed in Section 7.4.1 that the covariance of $\mathbf{x}_i - \bar{\mathbf{x}}$ and $\bar{\mathbf{x}}$ is equal to 0. The fact that the covariance of two random variables is zero does *not* imply that they are independent, although it does serve as some indication of how they "vary together" (see discussion on page 112). In Chapter 13 we shall be able to show that a covariance of zero *does* imply independence in the case where the two random variables have the bivariate normal distribution.

To simplify the many applications of the chi-square distribution, this distribution has been extensively tabulated. Table V contains the values of $\chi^2_{\alpha,\nu}$, where

$$\int_{\chi^2_{\alpha,\nu}}^{\infty} f(x)\,dx = \alpha \tag{8.2.7}$$

and $f(x)$ is given by (8.2.2), for $\alpha = 0.995, 0.99, 0.975, 0.95, 0.05, 0.025, 0.01, 0.005$, and $\nu = 1, 2, \ldots, 30$ (see Figure 8.2). When ν is

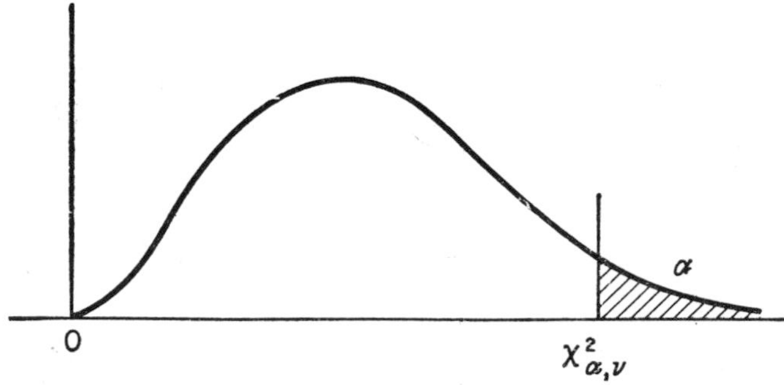

Figure 8.2

greater than 30, the chi-square distribution is usually approximated with a normal distribution (see Exercises 9 and 10 below).

To give a numerical illustration in which Theorem 8.6 is applied, suppose that the specifications for a certain kind of optical glass require, among other things, that the index of refraction be uniform to the extent that σ must not exceed 0.0075. A random sample of 10 pieces of this glass is taken from each (large) shipment and the shipment is rejected as unsatisfactory if the sample variance is too large; specifically, if the probability of obtaining such a large value of s^2 *even though* $\sigma = 0.0075$ is less than or equal to 0.01. What is to be done with a shipment of this glass for which the sample variance of the indices of refraction equalled 0.000182?

Translating this criterion into the language used above, we can say that the shipment is to be rejected if $(n - 1)s^2/\sigma^2$ with $\sigma = 0.0075$ exceeds $\chi^2_{.01,9}$. Since

$$\frac{(n - 1)s^2}{\sigma^2} = \frac{9(0.000182)}{(0.0075)^2} = 29.12$$

and $\chi^2_{.01,9} = 21.666$ according to Table V, it follows that the shipment will have to be rejected.

EXERCISES

1. Prove Theorem 8.4.

2. Prove Theorem 8.5. Why is it necessary to assume that ν is greater than ν_1?

3. Verify the identity (8.2.6) on page 196.

4. Given the independent random variables $\mathbf{x}_1$ and $\mathbf{x}_2$ having standard normal distributions, show that

(a) $s^2 = \frac{1}{2}(x_1 - x_2)^2 = 2(x_1 - \bar{x})^2$, where x_1 and x_2 are values assumed by $\mathbf{x}_1$ and $\mathbf{x}_2$, and $\bar{x}$ and s^2 are their mean and their variance,

(b) the joint density of $\mathbf{x}_1$ and $\bar{\mathbf{x}}$ is given by

$$f(x_1, \bar{x}) = \frac{1}{\pi} e^{-\bar{x}^2} e^{-(x_1 - \bar{x})^2}$$

for $-\infty < x_1 < \infty$ and $-\infty < \bar{x} < \infty$,

(c) the joint density of $\mathbf{s}^2$ and $\bar{\mathbf{x}}$ is given by

$$g(s^2, \bar{x}) = \frac{1}{\sqrt{\pi}} e^{-\bar{x}^2} \cdot \frac{1}{\sqrt{2\pi}} s^{-1} e^{-(s^2/2)}$$

for $s^2 > 0$ and $-\infty < \bar{x} < \infty$ and, hence, that $\mathbf{s}^2$ and $\bar{\mathbf{x}}$ are independent.

5. Derive the following computing formula for the sample variance:

$$s^2 = \frac{n \sum_{i=1}^{n} x_i^2 - \left(\sum_{i=1}^{n} x_i\right)^2}{n(n-1)}$$

6. Using (8.2.2), find the probability that the variance of a random sample of size 5 taken from a normal population with $\sigma^2 = 36$ falls between 35 and 37.

7. Using (8.2.2), find the probability that the variance of a random sample of size 3 taken from a normal population with $\sigma^2 = 64$ exceeds 78.

8. The hypothesis that the variance of a normal population is $\sigma^2 = 100$ is rejected if the variance of a random sample of size 5 exceeds 237.2 or is less than 17.775. What is the probability that this hypothesis will be rejected even though $\sigma^2 = 100$?

9. (a) Given a random variable $\mathbf{x}$ whose range is the positive real numbers, show that the probability that the random variable $\sqrt{2\mathbf{x}} - \sqrt{2n}$ assumes a value less than k equals the probability that the random variable $(\mathbf{x} - n)/\sqrt{2n}$ assumes a value less than $k + k^2/(2\sqrt{2n})$.

(b) Using the result of (a), show that if $\mathbf{x}$ has a chi-square distribution with n degrees of freedom, then for large n the distribution of $\sqrt{2\mathbf{x}} - \sqrt{2n}$ can be approximated with the standard normal distribution.

10. Find approximate values for the probability that a random variable $\mathbf{x}$ having the chi-square distribution with 50 degrees of freedom assumes a value greater than 72 treating (a) $(\mathbf{x} - \nu)/\sqrt{2\nu}$ and (b) $\sqrt{2\mathbf{x}} - \sqrt{2\nu}$ as random variables having standard normal distributions. (According to the BIOMETRIKA table referred to in the Bibliography on page 208, the correct value for this probability is 0.02245.)

8.2.3 *The F distribution*

Another distribution which plays an important role in sampling theory connected with normal populations is the F *distribution*, which we shall derive by means of a transformation from the beta distribution (see Exercise 6 on page 130). Writing the equation for the beta distribution with the parameters $\alpha = \nu_1/2$ and $\beta = \nu_2/2$ as

$$f(x) = \begin{cases} k \cdot x^{(\nu_1/2)-1}(1 - x)^{(\nu_2/2)-1} & \text{for } 0 < x < 1 \\ 0 & \text{elsewhere} \end{cases} \tag{8.2.8}$$

where

$$k = \frac{\Gamma\left(\frac{\nu_1 + \nu_2}{2}\right)}{\Gamma\left(\frac{\nu_1}{2}\right)\Gamma\left(\frac{\nu_2}{2}\right)}$$

let us find the probability density of the random variable **y**, where

$$y = \frac{\nu_2 x}{\nu_1(1 - x)}$$

According to Theorem 5.1 we have

$$g(y) = f(x) \cdot \left| \frac{dx}{dy} \right| \tag{8.2.9}$$

and since

$$\frac{dx}{dy} = \frac{\nu_1 \nu_2}{(\nu_2 + \nu_1 y)^2}$$

substitution into (8.2.9) yields

$$g(y) = \begin{cases} \dfrac{c \cdot y^{(\nu_1/2)-1}}{\left(1 + \dfrac{\nu_1}{\nu_2} y\right)^{(\nu_1+\nu_2)/2}} & \text{for } y > 0 \\ 0 & \text{elsewhere} \end{cases} \tag{8.2.10}$$

where

$$c = \frac{\Gamma\left(\frac{\nu_1 + \nu_2}{2}\right)}{\Gamma\left(\frac{\nu_1}{2}\right)\Gamma\left(\frac{\nu_2}{2}\right)} (\nu_1/\nu_2)^{(\nu_1/2)}$$

The distribution given by (8.2.10) is called the *F distribution with ν_1 and ν_2 degrees of freedom.* In view of its importance, it has been tabulated extensively; Table VI contains the values of F_{α,ν_1,ν_2}, where

$$\int_{F_{\alpha,\nu_1,\nu_2}}^{\infty} g(y)\,dy = \alpha \tag{8.2.11}$$

and $g(y)$ is given by (8.2.10), for $\alpha = 0.05$ and 0.01, and various values of ν_1 and ν_2 (see Figure 8.3).

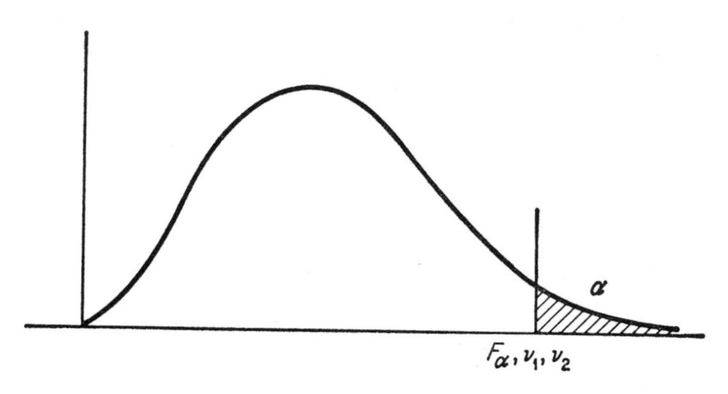

Figure 8.3

The importance of the F distribution in applied statistics rests mainly in the following theorem:

THEOREM 8.7:

If $\mathbf{x}_1$ and $\mathbf{x}_2$ are independent random variables having chi-square distributions with ν_1 and ν_2 degrees of freedom, then

$$\mathbf{y} = \frac{\mathbf{x}_1/\nu_1}{\mathbf{x}_2/\nu_2}$$

has an F distribution with ν_1 and ν_2 degrees of freedom.

The details of the proof of this theorem will be left to the reader (see Exercise 3 on page 203); essentially, it consists of beginning with the joint density of $\mathbf{x}_1$ and $\mathbf{x}_2$, performing a transformation to get the joint density of $\mathbf{y}$ and $\mathbf{x}_2$, and then integrating out x_2 to obtain the marginal density of $\mathbf{y}$.

One application of Theorem 8.7 arises in problems in which we are interested in comparing the variances of two normal populations; for example, in testing the hypothesis that $\sigma_1^2 = \sigma_2^2$. According to

Theorem 8.6 we know that

$$\frac{(n_1 - 1)s_1^2}{\sigma_1^2} \quad \text{and} \quad \frac{(n_2 - 1)s_2^2}{\sigma_2^2}$$

are independent random variables having chi-square distributions with $n_1 - 1$ and $n_2 - 1$ degrees of freedom, assuming, of course, that we are dealing with independent random samples from the two normal populations. Under the assumption that $\sigma_1^2 = \sigma_2^2$ we, thus, find that s_1^2/s_2^2 has an F distribution with $n_1 - 1$ and $n_2 - 1$ degrees of freedom, and we can base our decision on the value which we obtain for the *ratio* of the two sample variances (see Section 12.3).

8.2.4 *The t distribution*

Earlier in this chapter we showed that for random samples from normal populations the sampling distribution of $(\bar{x} - \mu)\sqrt{n}/\sigma$ is the standard normal distribution. One difficulty in applying this theory is that in actual practice σ is usually unknown, which makes it necessary to replace it with an estimate. The theory which follows leads to the *exact* sampling distribution of $(\bar{x} - \mu)\sqrt{n}/s$ for random samples from normal populations.

To derive this sampling distribution, let us first study the more general problem of obtaining the probability density of the random variable $t = x/\sqrt{y/\nu}$, where x and y are independent, x has the standard normal distribution, and y has the chi-square distribution with ν degrees of freedom. The joint density of x and y is thus given by

$$f(x, y) = \begin{cases} \dfrac{1}{\sqrt{2\pi}} e^{-(1/2)x^2} \dfrac{1}{\Gamma(\nu/2)2^{\nu/2}} y^{(\nu/2)-1}e^{-(y/2)} & \text{for } -\infty < x < \infty \text{ and } y > 0 \\ 0 & \text{elsewhere} \end{cases}$$

and the method of Section 5.4 leads to

$$g(t, y) = f(x, y) \cdot \left| \frac{dx}{dt} \right|$$

$$= \begin{cases} \dfrac{1}{\sqrt{2\pi\nu}\,\Gamma(\nu/2)2^{\nu/2}} y^{(\nu-1)/2}e^{-\frac{y}{2}\left(1+\frac{t^2}{\nu}\right)} & \text{for } -\infty < t < \infty \text{ and } y > 0 \\ 0 & \text{elsewhere} \end{cases}$$

since $t = x/\sqrt{y/\nu}$ and, hence, $dx/dt = \sqrt{y/\nu}$ keeping y fixed. Finally, integrating out y with the aid of the substitution

$$z = \frac{y}{2}\left(1 + \frac{t^2}{\nu}\right)$$

we get

$$f(t) = \frac{\Gamma\left(\frac{\nu+1}{2}\right)}{\sqrt{\nu}\sqrt{\pi}\Gamma\left(\frac{\nu}{2}\right)}\left(1 + \frac{t^2}{\nu}\right)^{-(\nu+1)/2} \quad \text{for } -\infty < t < \infty \tag{8.2.12}$$

This distribution is called the *t distribution* (or the *Student-t distribution*) *with ν degrees of freedom*. It was first obtained by W. S. Gosset, who at the time was employed by a well-known Irish brewery. Since this brewery did not permit the publication of research done by its staff, Gosset chose the pen name "Student"; hence, the name "Student-t distribution."

In view of its importance, the t distribution has been tabulated extensively (see Bibliography on page 208). Table IV contains the values of $t_{\alpha,\nu}$, where

$$\int_{t_{\alpha,\nu}}^{\infty} f(t)\, dt = \alpha$$

and $f(t)$ is given by (8.2.12), for $\alpha = 0.10, 0.05, 0.025, 0.01, 0.005$, and $\nu = 1, 2, \ldots, 30$. Note that in view of the symmetry of the t distribution $t_{1-\alpha,\nu} = -t_{\alpha,\nu}$. When ν exceeds 30, the t distribution, or better the distribution of $t\sqrt{(\nu-2)/\nu}$ can be approximated with the standard normal distribution (see Exercises 8 and 10 below).

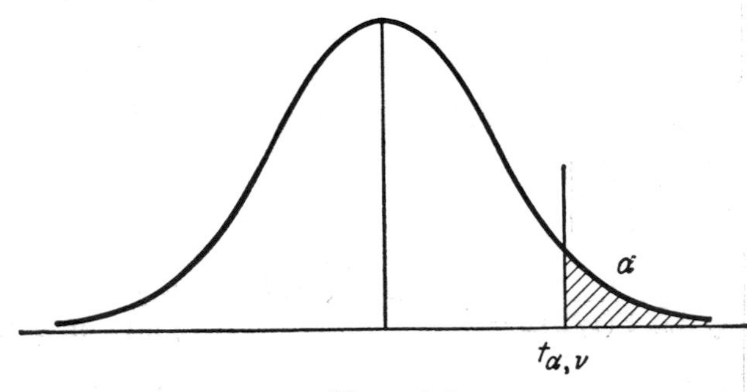

Figure 8.4

Although the t distribution has many other applications, some of which will be treated in Chapter 12, its major application is based on the following theorem:

THEOREM 8.8:
If $\bar{x}$ and s are the mean and the standard deviation of a random sample of size n from the normal population $N(x;\ \mu,\ \sigma^2)$, then $(\bar{\mathbf{x}} - \mu)\sqrt{n}/\mathbf{s}$ has the t distribution with $n - 1$ degrees of freedom.

To prove this theorem, we have only to make use of the fact that for random samples from normal populations $(\bar{\mathbf{x}} - \mu)/(\sigma/\sqrt{n})$ has the standard normal distribution, $(n - 1)\mathbf{s}^2/\sigma^2$ has a chi-square distribution with $n - 1$ degrees of freedom, and the two random variables are independent.

To illustrate the use of Theorem 8.8, suppose that we want to check whether the mean of a given normal population is $\mu = 100$, if a random sample of size 16 had a mean of 108 and a variance of 9. We thus get

$$t = \frac{\bar{x} - \mu}{s/\sqrt{n}} = \frac{108 - 100}{3/\sqrt{16}} = 10.67$$

and since Table IV shows that the probability of getting a value of t greater than 2.947 is 0.005 for 15 degrees of freedom, *the probability of getting a value as large as* 10.67 *is exceedingly small.* Basing our decision on the value thus obtained for the *t statistic*, it would seem reasonable to reject the hypothesis that the sample came from a normal population whose mean is $\mu = 100$.

EXERCISES

1. If the random variable $\mathbf{x}$ has an F distribution with ν_1 and ν_2 degrees of freedom, show that the random variable $\mathbf{y} = 1/\mathbf{x}$ has an F distribution with ν_2 and ν_1 degrees of freedom.

2. Using the result of Exercise 1, show that

$$F_{1-\alpha,\nu_1,\nu_2} = \frac{1}{F_{\alpha,\nu_2,\nu_1}}$$

3. Give a detailed proof of Theorem 8.7.

4. Show that for $\nu_2 > 2$ the mean of the F distribution is $\nu_2/(\nu_2 - 2)$.

5. If $\mathbf{x}$ has an F distribution with ν_1 and ν_2 degrees of freedom, show that when $\nu_2 \to \infty$ the distribution of $\nu_1\mathbf{x}$ approaches the chi-square distribution with ν_1 degrees of freedom.

6. If s_1^2 and s_2^2 are the variances of independent random samples of size $n_1 = 5$ and $n_2 = 3$ from two normal populations having the same variance σ^2, find the probability that $\mathbf{s}_1^2/\mathbf{s}_2^2$ assumes a value less than $\frac{1}{2}$ or greater than 2. (*Hint*: integrate the function which gives the appropriate F distribution from 0 to $\frac{1}{2}$ and from 2 to ∞.)

7. If independent random samples of size 5 are taken from two normal populations having the same variance, find the probability that $\mathbf{s}_1^2/\mathbf{s}_2^2$ will assume a value less than $\frac{1}{3}$ or greater than 3.

8. Show that the variance of the t distribution with ν degrees of freedom is $\nu/(\nu - 2)$.

9. Show that if $\mathbf{x}$ has the t distribution with ν degrees of freedom, then $\mathbf{x}^2$ has the F distribution with 1 and ν degrees of freedom.

10. Using Stirling's approximation (see Exercise 23 on page 30), show that when $\nu \to \infty$ the t-distribution approaches the standard normal distribution.

11. A random sample of size 25 from a normal population has a mean of 63 and a variance of 36. Basing your decision on the value of the t statistic, is it reasonable to say that this information supports the hypothesis that the mean of the population is 58?

12. A random sample of size 9 from a normal population has a mean of 39.2 and a variance of 3.24. Basing your decision on the value of the t statistic, is it reasonable to say that this evidence supports the hypothesis that the mean of the population is 40.0?

8.3 Sampling Distributions of Order Statistics

If $x_1, x_2, \ldots,$ and x_n is a random sample of size n from a *continuous* population, the rth largest of these sample values is called the *r'th order statistic* and it is written as $\mathbf{u}_r$. Thus, the smallest sample value is u_1 and the largest is u_n. (In the discrete case, where there is a non-zero probability that two or more of the sample values are equal, u_r is defined as the sample value which is such that $r - 1$ of the x's are less than or equal to u_r and $n - r$ of the x's are greater than or equal to u_r.)

To find the probability density of $\mathbf{u}_r$, let us consider the following argument: suppose that the real axis is divided into three parts, one going from $-\infty$ to u_r, a second going from u_r to $u_r + h$, where h is a positive constant, and the third going from $u_r + h$ to ∞. If the common probability density of the random variables x_i is given by $f(x)$, the probability that $r - 1$ of the sample values fall into the first interval, one falls into the second interval, and $n - r$ fall into the third interval is

$$\frac{n!}{(r-1)!(n-r)!}\left[\int_{-\infty}^{u_r} f(x)\,dx\right]^{r-1}\left[\int_{u_r}^{u_r+h} f(x)\,dx\right]\left[\int_{u_r+h}^{\infty} f(x)\,dx\right]^{n-r}$$

according to (3.3.6). Using the *law of the mean* we have

$$\int_{u_r}^{u_r+h} f(x)\,dx = f(\xi)h \qquad \text{with} \quad u_r \leq \xi \leq u_r + h$$

and if we now let $h \to 0$, the *probability density* of $\mathbf{u}_r$, the random variable whose value is the rth order statistic, becomes

$$g(u_r) = \frac{n!}{(r-1)!(n-r)!}\left[\int_{-\infty}^{u_r} f(x)\,dx\right]^{r-1} f(u_r)\left[\int_{u_r}^{\infty} f(x)\,dx\right]^{n-r}$$

$$\text{for} \quad -\infty < u_r < \infty \tag{8.3.1}$$

In particular, the distribution of $\mathbf{u}_1$, the *smallest value* in a random sample of size n, is given by

$$g_1(u_1) = nf(u_1)\left[\int_{u_1}^{\infty} f(x)\,dx\right]^{n-1} \qquad \text{for} \quad -\infty < u_1 < \infty \tag{8.3.2}$$

while the distribution of $\mathbf{u}_n$, the *largest value* in a random sample of size n, is given by

$$g_n(u_n) = nf(u_n)\left[\int_{-\infty}^{u_n} f(x)\,dx\right]^{n-1} \qquad \text{for} \quad -\infty < u_n < \infty \tag{8.3.3}$$

In a random sample of size $n = 2m + 1$ the *sample median* is u_{m+1} and in a random sample of size $n = 2m$ it is the mean of u_m and u_{m+1}. Writing the sample median as $\tilde{x}$, we find that for random samples of size $n = 2m + 1$ the sampling distribution of $\tilde{\mathbf{x}}$ is given by

$$h(\tilde{x}) = \frac{(2m+1)!}{m!m!}\left[\int_{-\infty}^{\tilde{x}} f(x)\,dx\right]^{m} f(\tilde{x})\left[\int_{\tilde{x}}^{\infty} f(x)\,dx\right]^{m}$$

$$\text{for} \quad -\infty < \tilde{x} < \infty \tag{8.3.4}$$

In some instances it is possible to find expressions for the integrals in (8.3.2), (8.3.3), and (8.3.4); for other populations there may be no choice but to approximate these integrals with numerical methods. It will be left to the reader to show in Exercise 1 below that for random samples of size n from the exponential population

$$f(x) = \begin{cases} \frac{1}{\theta} e^{-(x/\theta)} & \text{for } x > 0 \\ 0 & \text{elsewhere} \end{cases}$$

the sampling distributions of $\mathbf{u}_1$, $\mathbf{u}_n$, and $\tilde{\mathbf{x}}$ are given by

$$g_1(u_1) = \frac{n}{\theta} e^{-(nu_1/\theta)} \qquad \text{for } u_1 > 0$$

$$g_n(u_n) = \frac{n}{\theta} e^{-(u_n/\theta)}[1 - e^{-(u_n/\theta)}]^{n-1} \qquad \text{for } u_n > 0 \tag{8.3.3}$$

and

$$h(\tilde{x}) = \frac{(2m+1)!}{m!m!\theta} e^{-\tilde{x}(m+1)/\theta}[1 - e^{-(\tilde{x}/\theta)}]^m \qquad \text{for } \tilde{x} > 0$$

where $\tilde{x}$ is the median of a random sample of size $n = 2m + 1$.

The following is an interesting result about the sampling distribution of $\tilde{\mathbf{x}}$, which holds when $f(x)$ is continuous at $\tilde{\mu}$ and $f(\tilde{\mu}) \neq 0$, where $\tilde{\mu}$, the *population median*, is such that

$$\int_{-\infty}^{\tilde{\mu}} f(x)\, dx = \int_{\tilde{\mu}}^{\infty} f(x)\, dx$$

THEOREM 8.9:

For large n, the sampling distribution of $\tilde{\mathbf{x}}$ *for random samples of size* $2n + 1$ *is approximately normal with the mean* $\tilde{\mu}$ *and the variance*

$$\frac{1}{8[f(\tilde{\mu})]^2 n} \tag{8.3.5}$$

A proof of this theorem is referred to in the Bibliography on page 208. Note that for random samples of size $2n + 1$ from a normal population, where $f(\tilde{\mu}) = f(\mu) = 1/(\sqrt{2\pi}\sigma)$, the variance of $\tilde{\mathbf{x}}$ is approximately $\pi\sigma^2/4n$. Comparing this with the variance of $\bar{\mathbf{x}}$, which for random samples of size $2n + 1$ is $\sigma^2/(2n + 1)$, we find that for large samples from normal populations the mean is *more reliable* than the median, that is, the mean is subject to less chance variation than the median.

EXERCISES

1. Verify the results given in the text for the sampling distributions of $\mathbf{u}_1$, $\mathbf{u}_n$, and $\tilde{\mathbf{x}}$ for random samples from exponential populations.

2. Find the sampling distributions of $\mathbf{u}_1$ and $\mathbf{u}_n$ for random samples of size n from the *uniform population* given by (5.3.1) on page 126. Also find the sampling distribution of $\tilde{\mathbf{x}}$ for random samples of size $2m + 1$ from this population.

3. Find the mean of the sampling distribution of $\mathbf{u}_1$ for random samples of size 5 from the population of Exercise 2.

4. If a random sample of size 2 is taken *with replacement* from the first five positive integers, find the sampling distribution of the smallest value obtained in such a sample. (*Hint*: enumerate all possibilities.)

5. (a) Duplicating the method used on page 205, find an expression for the joint density of $\mathbf{u}_r$ and $\mathbf{u}_s$ with $r < s$.

(b) Using the result obtained in (a), show that the joint density of $\mathbf{u}_1$ and $\mathbf{u}_n$ is given by

$$g(u_1, u_n) = n(n - 1)f(u_1)f(u_n)\left[\int_{u_1}^{u_n} f(x)\, dx\right]^{n-2}$$

for $-\infty < u_1 < u_n < \infty$.

(c) Using the result obtained in (b), find an expression for the joint density of $\mathbf{u}_1$ and $\mathbf{u}_n$ for random samples of size n from the exponential population given on page 206.

6. Defining the *sample range* as $R = u_n - u_1$, use the result obtained in (b) of Exercise 5 to show that the joint density of $\mathbf{u}_1$ and $\mathbf{R}$ is given by

$$h(u_1, R) = n(n - 1)f(u_1)f(u_1 + R)\left[\int_{u_1}^{u_1+R} f(x)\, dx\right]^{n-2}$$

with the domain of this function depending on the range of the random variable whose density is given by $f(x)$.

7. Using the result of Exercise 6 and integrating out u_1, show that for the exponential population on page 206 the sampling distribution of **R** is given by

$$g(R) = \frac{n-1}{\theta} e^{-(R/\theta)}[1 - e^{-(R/\theta)}]^{n-2} \qquad \text{for } R > 0$$

8. Using the result of Exercise 6 and integrating out u_1, find an expression for the sampling distribution of **R** for random samples of size n from the uniform population given by (5.3.1) on page 126 (*Hint*: watch the limits of integration.)

BIBLIOGRAPHY

Extensive tables of the normal, chi-square, F, and t distributions may be found in

Pearson, E. S., and H. O. Hartley, *Biometrika Tables for Statisticians, Volume I*, New York: Cambridge University Press, 1954.

Proofs of the independence of $\bar{x}$ and s^2 for random samples from normal populations are given in many advanced texts on mathematical statistics. A proof based on moment generating functions may be found in

Mood, A. M., *Introduction to the Theory of Statistics*, New York: McGraw-Hill Book Co., Inc., 1950, Section 10.4.

and a proof based on transformations is given in

Anderson, R. L., and T. A. Bancroft, *Statistical Theory in Research*, New York: McGraw-Hill Book Co., Inc., 1952, Section 7.9.

For a proof of Theorem 8.9 see

Wilks, S. S., *Mathematical Statistics*, Princeton, N. J.: Princeton University Press, 1947, Chapter 4.

Chapter 9

Point Estimation

9.1 Statistical Inference and Decision Theory

Statistical inference is the process of arriving at conclusions or decisions concerning the parameters of populations on the basis of information contained in samples. We, thus, make a statistical inference when we *estimate* the "true" average lifetime of a certain kind of television tube as 5000 hours, when we *decide* (on the basis of appropriate experiments) that one variety of corn has a higher yield than another, and when we *claim* (on the basis of certain tests) that a new drug is not effective. Assuming that the lifetimes of the television tubes may be looked upon as values assumed by random variables having exponential distributions with the parameter θ, the "true" average lifetime we are trying to estimate is, in fact, the parameter θ. Similarly, if the measurements of the yield of the two varieties of corn may be looked upon as random samples from populations with the means μ_1 and μ_2, the decision we are trying to reach is whether $\mu_1 > \mu_2$, $\mu_1 = \mu_2$, or $\mu_1 < \mu_2$; finally, if the number of patients cured with the new drug may be looked upon as a value assumed by a random variable having a binomial distribution, we want to determine whether the parameter θ is greater than some constant k.

Traditionally, problems of statistical inference have been classified into *problems of estimation* and *problems of testing hypotheses*. Like the first example of the preceding paragraph, problems of estimation require that we provide values for unknown parameters of distributions; like the other two examples, hypothesis testing deals with reaching conclusions or decisions concerning assumed values of the parameters. Although we shall maintain this distinction in this book, the whole problem of statistical inference can be approached in a more unified fashion from the view point of *decision theory.*

To give a brief introduction to the basic concepts of decision theory, let us define a *decision function* δ as a function defined on the sample space (of the experiment with which we are concerned), whose range consists of the various actions that can be taken as a result of the experiment. For instance, if we want to estimate the mean of a normal population on the basis of a random sample of size three, we could use the decision function which assigns to each point (x_1, x_2, x_3) of the sample space the action of estimating μ as $x = (x_1 + x_2 + x_3)/3$; another decision function which we could use is the one which assigns to each point of the sample space the action of estimating μ as the median of x_1, x_2, and x_3. To give another example, suppose that we want to test whether the mean of a certain population is $\mu = 0$ on the basis of a random sample of size 2. A possible decision function for this experiment is shown graphically in Figure 9.1, where the action a_1, to accept the hypothesis $\mu = 0$, is assigned to each sample point falling between the two lines, while the action a_2, to reject the hypothesis $\mu = 0$, is assigned to all other points of the sample space.

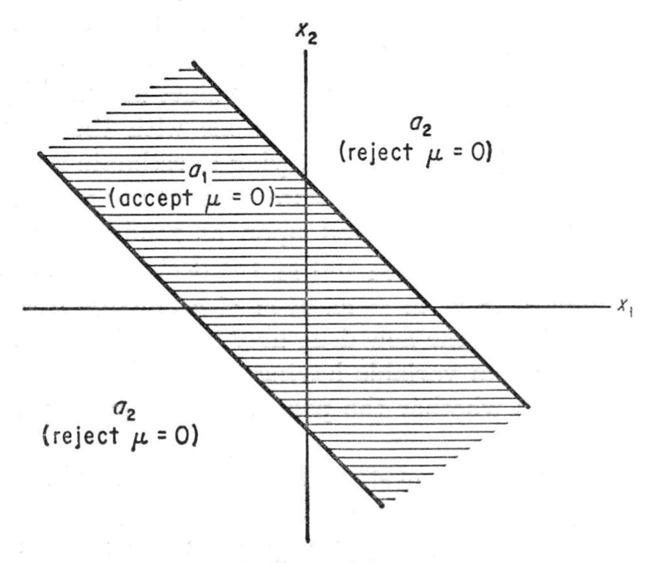

Figure 9.1

Generally speaking, the basic problem which we must solve, when approaching problems of statistical inference from the viewpoint of decision theory, is that of selecting a decision function whose properties are, in some sense, most desirable. To this end, we usually take into account the various consequences, rewards for making correct decisions and penalties for making incorrect decisions, to which we are exposed in a given experiment. More precisely, we base the selection on a *loss function* which assigns a numerical value $L(\theta, a)$ to each pair of values of θ and a, where θ is the parameter with which we are concerned and a is an element of the set of all possible actions. Using this loss function, we can then determine the *risk function*, whose values $\rho(\theta, \delta)$ give the average (expected) loss to which we are exposed by using the decision function δ when the value of the parameter is θ.

To illustrate these ideas, suppose that an urn contains 2 balls of which θ are white, and that we want to decide on the basis of a random sample of size 2, taken *with replacement*, whether θ is 0, 1, or 2. The penalty which we have to pay for making an incorrect decision equals (in dollars) the actual size of our error. If $\theta = 1$ and we decide erroneously that it equals 2, the penalty is $|1 - 2| = 1$. In general, if $a = 0, 1$, and 2 means that we decide that θ is 0, 1, or 2, this loss function is given by $L(\theta, a) = |\theta - a|$. Although there are many other possibilities (see Exercises 1 and 3 below), let us consider the decision function δ_1 for which $a = x$, where x is the number of white balls obtained in the sample. In other words, we decide that θ is 0, 1, or 2 when the respective number of white balls in the sample is 0, 1, or 2.

It is easy to see that $\rho(0, \delta_1) = 0$ and $\rho(2, \delta_1) = 0$ since our decision will have to be correct when all or none of the balls are white. However, when $\theta = 1$, the probabilities of getting 0, 1, and 2 white balls are, respectively, $\frac{1}{4}$, $\frac{1}{2}$, and $\frac{1}{4}$, and

$$\rho(1, \delta_1) = \tfrac{1}{4}(1) + \tfrac{1}{2}(0) + \tfrac{1}{4}(1) = \tfrac{1}{2}.$$

Hence, the risk function for δ_1 is given by

$$\rho(\theta, \delta_1) = \begin{cases} 0 & \text{for } \theta = 0 \\ \frac{1}{2} & \text{for } \theta = 1 \\ 0 & \text{for } \theta = 2 \end{cases}$$

In Exercises 2 and 4 below, the reader will be asked to compare this risk function with those of two other decision functions. Using two criteria, the *minimax criterion* and the *Bayes criterion*, the reader can then select the decision function which has the most desirable properties.

One of the main difficulties in applying the methods of decision theory to practical situations is that of defining appropriate loss functions. For instance, if we had to decide on the basis of an experiment whether a new drug is really effective, how could we put cash values on the lives that might be lost if we erroneously decide not to release the new drug. Similarly, if we decide on the basis of a sample that a shipment of steel to be used in the construction of a bridge is satisfactory, how can we foresee all the consequences which might conceivably be involved?

EXERCISES

1. Referring to the example in the text, find the risk function which corresponds to the decision function δ_2, according to which we decide that θ is 1 regardless of the outcome of the experiment.

2. (*The minimax criterion*) According to the *minimax criterion* we select the decision function for which $\max_{\theta} \rho(\theta, \delta)$ is a minimum. In other words, we check for each decision function which value of θ makes $\rho(\theta, \delta)$ a maximum; then we select the decision function for which this maximum is as small as possible. With reference to the example in the text and Exercise 1, does this criterion select δ_1 or δ_2?

3. Referring to the example in the text, suppose that when x, the number of white balls in the sample, is 0 we flip a balanced coin, heads we decide that θ is 0 and tails we decide that θ is 1; when $x = 1$ we decide that θ is 1; and when $x = 2$ we again flip a balanced coin, heads we decide that θ is 2 and tails we decide that θ is 1. Find the risk function which corresponds to this decision function δ_3.

4. (*The Bayes criterion*) Treating the parameter under consideration as a random variable whose probability distribution or density is given by $f(\theta)$, the *Bayes risk* associated with the decision function δ is defined as $\sum \rho(\theta, \delta) f(\theta)$, with the summation extending over all values within the range of θ, or as $\int \rho(\theta, \delta) f(\theta)\, d\theta$. According to the *Bayes criterion* we then select the decision function whose Bayes risk is a minimum.

(a) Referring to the example in the text and the decision functions of Exercises 1 and 3, use the Bayes criterion to choose between δ_1, δ_2, and δ_3 given that

$$f(\theta) = \begin{cases} 0.20 & \text{for } \theta = 0 \\ 0.60 & \text{for } \theta = 1 \\ 0.20 & \text{for } \theta = 2 \end{cases}$$

(b) Which of the three decision functions would be selected by the Bayes criterion if

$$f(\theta) = \begin{cases} 0.10 & \text{for } \theta = 0 \\ 0.80 & \text{for } \theta = 1 \\ 0.10 & \text{for } \theta = 2 \end{cases}$$

5. (*Minimax estimation*) Suppose we want to estimate the parameter θ of a binomial population by means of an expression of the form $\alpha x + \beta$, where x is the number of successes obtained in n trials and α and β are constants. The loss function is given by $L(\alpha x + \beta, \theta) = k(\alpha x + \beta - \theta)^2$, where k is a positive constant. (In other words, the loss is proportional to the square of the error.)

(a) Evaluating $E[k(\alpha \mathbf{x} + \beta - \theta)^2]$, show that the risk function is given by

$$\rho(\theta, \delta) = k\{\alpha^2[n\theta + n(n-1)\theta^2] + \beta^2 + \theta^2 + 2\alpha\beta n\theta - 2\alpha\theta^2 n - 2\beta\theta\}$$

where δ is the decision function according to which θ is estimated as $\alpha x + \beta$.

(b) Find the value of θ for which the risk function given in (a) is a maximum

(c) Substituting the value obtained for θ in (b) into the expression given for the risk function in (a), show that the values of α and β which minimize $\max_{\theta} \rho(\theta, \delta)$ are

$$\alpha = \frac{1}{\sqrt{n}(\sqrt{n} + 1)} \quad \text{and} \quad \beta = \frac{1}{2(\sqrt{n} + 1)}$$

(d) If a sample from a binomial population yielded 10 successes in 25 trials, use the result of (c) to estimate the parameter θ of this binomial population. This estimate is, appropriately, called a *minimax estimate.* (The logic behind this kind of estimation is that the choice of α and β can be controlled, whereas the choice of θ cannot. Protecting ourselves against the worst that can happen, we thus maximize first with respect to θ before minimizing with respect to α and β.)

6. (*Bayes estimation*) Using the risk function of part (a) of Exercise 5 and the "prior" distribution

$$f(\theta) = \begin{cases} 1 & \text{for } 0 < \theta < 1 \\ 0 & \text{elsewhere} \end{cases}$$

find the corresponding Bayes risk (see Exercise 4) and show that it is minimized when $\alpha = 1/(n+2)$ and $\beta = 1/(n+2)$.

9.2 Point Estimation and Interval Estimation

If we use a sample mean to estimate the mean of a population, a sample proportion to estimate the probability of success on an individual trial, or a sample variance to estimate the variance of a population, we are in each case using a *point estimate* of the parameter in question. These estimates are called *point estimates* since they are single numbers, single points, used, respectively, to estimate μ, θ, and σ^2.

Since we can hardly expect that point estimates based on samples always hit the parameters they are supposed to estimate *exactly "on the nose,"* it is often desirable to give an interval rather than a single number. We can then assert with a certain probability (or degree of confidence) that such an interval contains the parameter it is intended to estimate. For instance, when estimating the average I.Q. of all college students in the United States, we might arrive at a *point estimate* of 117, or we might arrive at an *interval estimate* to the effect that the interval from 113 to 121 contains the "true" average I.Q. of all college students in the United States.

In the next few sections we shall study some basic problems of point estimation; problems of interval estimation and specific applications will be taken up in Chapter 10.

9.3 Properties of Point Estimators

If we use the mean of a sample to estimate the mean of a population, we refer to the random variable $\mathbf{\bar{x}}$ as an *estimator* of μ and to the actual value which we obtain, say, $\bar{x} = 15.3$, as an *estimate* of μ. More generally, we refer to the statistic which we use to estimate a parameter as an *estimate,* reserving the term *estimator* for the corresponding random variable.

Defining estimators, thus, as random variables, one of the key problems of point estimation is to study the statistical properties of these random variables. For instance, when estimating the variance of a population, we know that the sample variance will not always hit σ^2 exactly "on the nose"; however, it would be assuring to know that this will happen at least on the average, namely, that $E(\mathbf{s}^2) = \sigma^2$. Similarly, if we must decide whether to estimate the mean of a population with the sample mean or the sample median, it would be important to know whether $\mathbf{\bar{x}}$ or $\mathbf{\tilde{x}}$ is more likely to yield a value that is actually close to the mean of the population.

Statistical properties of estimators may, thus, be used to decide which estimator is most appropriate in a given situation, which is most apt to give us a desired result, which exposes us to the smallest risks, which will give us the most information at the lowest cost, and so forth. In Sections 9.3.1 through 9.3.4 we shall discuss four of the most important statistical properties of estimators; they are the properties of *unbiasedness, consistency, relative efficiency,* and *sufficiency.*

9.3.1 *Unbiased estimators*

When estimating the parameter of a population, it would seem desirable that if the experiment were repeated over and over again, the values obtained for the estimator should *on the average* equal the parameter which they are supposed to estimate. In other words, it is desirable that the expected value of an estimator equals the parameter it is supposed to estimate, in which case the estimator is said to be *unbiased.* If the expected value of an estimator is not equal to the parameter it is intended to estimate it is said to be *biased.*

Using this definition, we find that $\mathbf{\bar{x}}$ is an unbiased estimator of μ since $E(\mathbf{\bar{x}}) = \mu$ whenever μ exists. Similarly, it is easy to show that

$\mathbf{x}/n$, where $\mathbf{x}$ is the number of successes in n trials, is an unbiased estimator of the parameter θ of a binomial population. Using the fact that the mean of the binomial distribution is $E(\mathbf{x}) = n\theta$, we get

$$E(\mathbf{x}/n) = \frac{1}{n} E(\mathbf{x}) = \theta$$

Note that the estimators of the parameter θ of the binomial distribution which were obtained in Exercises 5 and 6 on page 213 are *biased*. The one of Exercise 6 may be written in the form $(\mathbf{x} + 1)/(n + 2)$ and we find that

$$E\left(\frac{\mathbf{x} + 1}{n + 2}\right) = \frac{E(\mathbf{x} + 1)}{n + 2} = \frac{n\theta + 1}{n + 2} \neq \theta$$

This illustrates the very important point that *questions of unbiasedness may be outweighed by other considerations.* Under the conditions of Exercise 6 on page 214, $(\mathbf{x} + 1)/(n + 2)$ is a *better* estimator than $\mathbf{x}/n$ even though it is biased.

Let us now show why we divided by $n - 1$ and not by n when we defined the sample variance on page 189—*it makes* $\mathbf{s}^2$ *an unbiased estimator of* σ^2 *for random samples from infinite populations.* To prove this we have only to write

$$\begin{aligned} E(\mathbf{s}^2) &= E\left[\frac{1}{n - 1} \sum_{i=1}^{n} (\mathbf{x}_i - \bar{\mathbf{x}})^2\right] \\ &= \frac{1}{n - 1} E\left[\sum_{i=1}^{n} \{(\mathbf{x}_i - \mu) - (\bar{\mathbf{x}} - \mu)\}^2\right] \\ &= \frac{1}{n - 1} \left\{\sum_{i=1}^{n} E[(\mathbf{x}_i - \mu)^2] - nE[(\bar{\mathbf{x}} - \mu)^2]\right\} \end{aligned}$$

Using the fact that $E[(\mathbf{x}_i - \mu)^2] = \sigma^2$ by definition and $E[(\bar{\mathbf{x}} - \mu)^2] = \sigma^2/n$ according to Theorem 7.4, it follows that

$$E(\mathbf{s}^2) = \frac{1}{n - 1}\left(\sum_{i=1}^{n} \sigma^2 - n\frac{\sigma^2}{n}\right) = \sigma^2 \qquad (9.3.1)$$

Note that $\mathbf{s}^2$ is *not* an unbiased estimator of the variance of a finite population as we defined it Section 7.4.3 and that in either case $\mathbf{s}$ is *not* an unbiased estimator of σ.

9.3.2 *Consistency*

Although unbiasedness is a desirable property, it implies only that the values of an estimator will on the average equal the parameter they are supposed to estimate; it does not imply that any of these values must necessarily be close. Perhaps, the reader will recall that we already touched upon questions concerning the "closeness" of estimates in Sections 4.3.1 and 7.4.1. Basing our argument on Chebyshev's theorem, we showed in Section 4.3.1 that *when* $n \to \infty$ *the probability that* $\mathbf{x}/n$ *assumes a value which differs from* θ *by more than any arbitrary constant c approaches* 0. (Here $\mathbf{x}/n$ is the proportion of successes in n trials and θ is the parameter of the corresponding binomial population.) Also using Chebyshev's theorem, we showed in Section 7.4.1 that *when* $n \to \infty$ *the probability that* $\bar{\mathbf{x}}$ *assumes a value which differs from* μ *by more than any arbitrary constant c approaches* 0. (Here $\bar{\mathbf{x}}$ is the mean of a random sample of size n from an infinite population having the mean μ and the finite variance σ^2.) Note that in these two examples we are *practically assured*, at least for sufficiently large n, that the estimators will assume values which are very close to the parameters they are intended to estimate.

In general, if $\hat{\boldsymbol{\theta}}$ is an estimator of the parameter θ of a given population, *this estimator is said to be consistent if the probability that* $\hat{\boldsymbol{\theta}}$ *assumes a value which differs from* θ *by more than any arbitrary constant c approaches* 0 *when* $n \to \infty$. We have, thus, shown in Sections 4.3.1 and 7.4.1 that $\mathbf{x}/n$ is a *consistent* estimator of the parameter θ of a binomial population and that $\bar{\mathbf{x}}$ is a *consistent* estimator of μ. Note that consistency is a *limiting property* (or *asymptotic property*) of an estimator; informally it says that if n is sufficiently large we can be *practically certain* that the error made with a consistent estimator will be less than any small preassigned constant. (By "error" we mean the absolute difference between the value assumed by the estimator and the parameter.)

When we showed that $\mathbf{x}/n$ is a consistent estimator of the parameter θ of a binomial population in Section 4.3.1, we made use of Chebyshev's Theorem, the fact that $E(\mathbf{x}/n) = \theta$, and the fact that $\text{var}(\mathbf{x}/n)$, which equals $\theta(1 - \theta)/n$, approaches 0 when $n \to \infty$. Similarly, in Section 7.4.1 we showed that $\bar{\mathbf{x}}$ is a consistent estimator of μ by making use of Chebyshev's Theorem, the fact that $E(\bar{\mathbf{x}}) = \mu$, and the fact that $\text{var}(\bar{\mathbf{x}})$, which equals σ^2/n, approaches

0 when $n \to \infty$. In general, we often show that an estimator is consistent by using the following *sufficient*, though *not necessary*, conditions, which may be obtained as an immediate consequence of Chebyshev's Theorem:

THEOREM 9.1:

$\hat{\theta}$ is a consistent estimator of the parameter θ of a given population if

(a) *$\hat{\theta}$ is unbiased*

(b) *$var(\hat{\theta}) \to 0$ when $n \to \infty$*

It is of interest to note that an estimator can be consistent without being unbiased. It will be left to the reader to show that $(\mathbf{x} + 1)/(n + 2)$, the estimator of Exercise 6 on page 214, is a consistent estimator of the parameter θ of a binomial population.

To illustrate the use of Theorem 9.1, let us show that $\mathbf{s}^2$ is a consistent estimator of σ^2 for random samples of size n from a normal population. Having shown on page 216 that $\mathbf{s}^2$ is unbiased, it remains to be seen whether the variance of its distribution approaches 0 when $n \to \infty$. According to Theorem 8.6 we know that $(n - 1)\mathbf{s}^2/\sigma^2$ has a chi-square distribution with $n - 1$ degrees of freedom and, hence, the variance $2(n - 1)$. It follows that the variance of $\mathbf{s}^2$ equals

$$2(n-1)\left(\frac{\sigma^2}{n-1}\right)^2 = \frac{2\sigma^4}{n-1}$$

and that $\mathbf{s}^2$ is a consistent estimator of σ^2.

9.3.3 *Relative efficiency*

If we have to select one of several unbiased consistent estimators, it is customary to base the choice on their *relative efficiency*. If $\hat{\theta}_1$ and $\hat{\theta}_2$ are two unbiased estimators of θ, $\hat{\theta}_1$ is said to be *relatively more efficient* than $\hat{\theta}_2$ if $\text{var}(\hat{\theta}_1)$ is less than $\text{var}(\hat{\theta}_2)$. An actual measure of the *relative efficiency of $\hat{\theta}_1$ with respect to $\hat{\theta}_2$* is given by the ratio

$$\frac{\text{var}(\hat{\theta}_2)}{\text{var}(\hat{\theta}_1)} \tag{9.3.2}$$

An unbiased estimator is, thus, particularly desirable if the variance of its distribution is small, that is, if the area under its density or distribution is concentrated closely about the mean.

To give a concrete example, suppose that we want to estimate the mean of a normal population on the basis of a random sample of size n and that we can use either the median or the mean. From Theorem 7.4 we know that $\bar{\mathbf{x}}$ is unbiased and that $\text{var}(\bar{\mathbf{x}}) = \sigma^2/n$; from Theorem 8.9 we know that the variance of the median, which is also unbiased, is approximately, $\pi\sigma^2/2n$. Hence, the sample mean is relatively more efficient than the sample median for estimating the mean of a normal population; the relative efficiency is $\pi/2$. The following is a somewhat more intuitive way of stating this result: since σ^2/n for $n = 64$ is approximately equal to $\pi\sigma^2/2n$ for $n = 100$, we can say that *a sample mean based on 64 observations is "as reliable" as a sample median based on 100 observations.*

It should be noted that we restricted our definition of relative efficiency to unbiased estimators. Otherwise, we could estimate any parameter by simply guessing that it equals some constant k. The variance of this "estimator" would be 0 and it would, thus, be ideal from the view point of relative efficiency. When dealing with biased estimators it is, thus, preferable to base efficiency comparisons on $E[(\hat{\boldsymbol{\theta}} - \theta)^2]$ instead of $\text{var}(\hat{\boldsymbol{\theta}})$.

An estimator $\hat{\boldsymbol{\theta}}$ is said to be a *best unbiased* (or *most efficient*) estimator of the parameter θ if it is unbiased and its variance is *at least as small* as that of any other unbiased estimator of θ. A method of finding best unbiased estimators (when they exist) will be discussed in Section 9.4.2; a method of checking whether a given estimator is a best unbiased estimator is given in Exercise 7 on page 221.

9.3.4 *Sufficiency*

An estimator $\hat{\boldsymbol{\theta}}$ is said to be *sufficient* if it utilizes all the information (relevant to the estimation of θ) that is contained in a sample. There are several ways in which this criterion can be formulated in a more rigorous fashion; let us state it as follows: *$\hat{\boldsymbol{\theta}}$ is a sufficient estimator of θ if $f(x_1, x_2, \ldots, x_n \mid \hat{\theta})$ does not depend on the actual value of θ.* Here $f(x_1, x_2, \ldots, x_n \mid \hat{\theta})$ is the conditional joint density of $\mathbf{x}_1, \mathbf{x}_2, \ldots,$ and $\mathbf{x}_n$, given that $\hat{\boldsymbol{\theta}}$ assumes the value $\hat{\theta}$. Intuitively, this means that if we are given the value of a sufficient estimator, the sample values $x_1, x_2, \ldots$, and x_n, themselves, do not provide any further information about the parameter θ.

To illustrate this criterion, suppose that a random sample from a binomial population with the parameter θ yielded x successes in n trials and that a subsequent sample from the same population yielded y successes in m trials. We shall show that $(\mathbf{x} + \mathbf{y})/(n + m)$ is a sufficient estimator of θ or, which is the same, that given the sum $x + y$, the individual values of $\mathbf{x}$ and $\mathbf{y}$ do not provide any additional information about θ. Since

$$f(x, y \mid x + y) = \frac{f(x, y, x + y)}{g(x + y)} = \frac{f(x, y)}{g(x + y)}$$

and

$$f(x, y) = \binom{n}{x}\theta^x(1 - \theta)^{n-x}\binom{m}{y}\theta^y(1 - \theta)^{m-y}$$

$$g(x + y) = \binom{n + m}{x + y}\theta^{x+y}(1 - \theta)^{n+m-x-y}$$

it follows that

$$f(x, y \mid x + y) = \binom{n}{x}\binom{m}{y} \Big/ \binom{n + m}{x + y}$$

Since this does not depend on θ, we have shown that knowledge of $x + y$ is *sufficient* for the estimation of θ, namely, that the individual values of $\mathbf{x}$ and $\mathbf{y}$ do not contain additional information relevant to the estimation of this parameter.

EXERCISES

1. Show that the estimator of Exercise 5 on page 213 is biased.

2. If $x_1, x_2, \ldots$, and x_n is a random sample from the exponential population given by (5.3.2), show that $\bar{\mathbf{x}}$ is an unbiased estimator of the parameter θ.

3. Show that the estimator of Exercise 6 on page 214 is a consistent estimator of θ.

4. If $x_1, x_2, \ldots$, and x_n is a random sample from the population given by

$$f(x) = \begin{cases} 1 & \text{for } \theta - \frac{1}{2} < x < \theta + \frac{1}{2} \\ 0 & \text{elsewhere} \end{cases}$$

show that $\bar{\mathbf{x}}$ is an unbiased as well as a consistent estimator of θ. Also show that for $n = 3$ the variance of $\bar{\mathbf{x}}$ is greater than that of the *mid-range*, that is, $(\mathbf{u}_1 + \mathbf{u}_3)/2$ (see Section 8.3). This result is interesting inasmuch as it demonstrates that the sample mean is not necessarily always the most efficient estimator of the mean of a population.

5. If $\mathbf{x}_1$, $\mathbf{x}_2$, and $\mathbf{x}_3$ are independent random variables having the Poisson distribution with the parameter λ, show that

$$\hat{\lambda}_1 = \frac{\mathbf{x}_1 + 2\mathbf{x}_2 + 3\mathbf{x}_3}{6}$$

is an unbiased estimator of λ. Also compare the efficiency of $\hat{\lambda}_1$ with that of the alternate estimator

$$\hat{\lambda}_2 = \frac{\mathbf{x}_1 + \mathbf{x}_2 + \mathbf{x}_3}{3}$$

6. If $\mathbf{x}$ is the number of successes in n binomial trials, $\hat{\boldsymbol{\theta}}_1 = \mathbf{x}/n$, and $\hat{\boldsymbol{\theta}}_2 = (\mathbf{x} + 1)/(n + 2)$, for what values of θ is $E[(\hat{\boldsymbol{\theta}}_2 - \theta)^2]$ less than $E[(\hat{\boldsymbol{\theta}}_1 - \theta)^2]$?

7. (*Cramer-Rao inequality*) If $\hat{\boldsymbol{\theta}}$ is an unbiased estimator of θ, it can be shown that under very general conditions (see Bibliography on page 226) the variance of $\hat{\boldsymbol{\theta}}$ must satisfy the inequality

$$\text{var}(\hat{\boldsymbol{\theta}}) \geq \frac{1}{n \cdot E\left[\left(\frac{\partial \ln f(\mathbf{x})}{\partial \theta}\right)^2\right]} \tag{9.3.3}$$

where $f(x)$ is the probability density or distribution of the population from which the random sample of size n is obtained. Using (9.3.3), show that for a random sample of size n from a Poisson population with the parameter λ, $\bar{\mathbf{x}}$ is a *minimum variance unbiased estimator* of λ, namely, that for this estimator the equality holds in (9.3.3).

8. Assuming that the conditions underlying (9.3.3) are met, show that $\hat{\boldsymbol{\theta}} = \mathbf{x}/n$ is a *minimum variance unbiased estimator* of the parameter θ of a binomial distribution. [*Hint:* $f(x) = \theta^x(1 - \theta)^{1-x}$ in this case for $x = 0$ or 1.]

9. If $\mathbf{x}_1$ and $\mathbf{x}_2$ are independent random variables having Poisson distributions with the parameter λ, show that their mean is a *sufficient* estimator of λ.

10. Given a random sample of size n from a normal population having the *unknown* mean μ and the *known* variance σ^2, show that $\bar{\mathbf{x}}$ is a sufficient estimator of μ.

9.4 Methods of Point Estimation

Intuitively speaking, it seems natural to estimate the mean of a population with the mean of a sample, the true proportion of defectives, say, among thousands of light bulbs, with the proportion of defectives contained in a sample, and the actual variance, say, of the strength of some kind of ceramic tile, with the variance of a sample. Although there are many instances where such "obvious" estimators are best, we have already seen examples where this is not the case.

Looking at questions of estimation from the viewpoint of decision theory, each problem can be handled individually with reference to an appropriate loss function and a criterion such as minimizing the maximum risk or minimizing the Bayes risk. If we do not approach problems of estimation from the viewpoint of decision theory, which in practice is usually the case, it would seem desirable, at least, to have some *general methods* yielding estimators which have many (perhaps all) of the properties discussed in the preceding sections. In the remainder of this chapter we shall discuss two such methods, the *method of moments* and the *method of maximum likelihood*; another method, the *method of least squares*, will be taken up later.

9.4.1 *The method of moments*

Historically, one of the oldest methods of estimation consists of equating the first few moments of a population distribution with the corresponding moments of a sample, thus getting as many equations as are needed to solve for the unknown parameters. The kth *sample moment* of a set of observations x_1, x_2, . . ., and x_n is defined as

$$m_k' = \frac{\sum_{i=1}^{n} x_i^k}{n} \tag{9.4.1}$$

It is the *average* of the kth powers of the x's, just as the kth moment of a distribution is the *expected value* of the kth power of $\mathbf{x}$. In the *method of moments*, as this method is called, we use as many of the equations

$$m'_k = \mu'_k \tag{9.4.2}$$

for $k = 1, 2, \ldots$, as are needed to solve for the unknown parameters of a distribution.

To illustrate this method, let us find estimates for the two parameters of the gamma distribution given by (5.3.3) on the basis of a random sample of size $n > 1$. The two equations which we shall have to solve are

$$m'_1 = \mu'_1 \qquad \text{and} \qquad m'_2 = \mu'_2$$

and since $\mu'_1 = \alpha\beta$ and $\mu'_2 = \beta^2\alpha(1 + \alpha)$ according to (6.3.3), we get

$$m'_1 = \alpha\beta \qquad \text{and} \qquad m'_2 = \beta^2\alpha(1 + \alpha)$$

Solving these two equations for α and β, we obtain the following estimates of the parameters of the gamma distribution:

$$\hat{\alpha} = \frac{(m'_1)^2}{m'_2 - (m'_1)^2} \qquad \text{and} \qquad \hat{\beta} = \frac{m'_2 - (m'_1)^2}{m'_1}$$

In the above example we estimated the parameters of a *specific* distribution. When the parameters to be estimated are, themselves, the moments of a distribution, the method of moments can be used even without knowledge of the exact functional form of the distribution.

9.4.2 *The method of maximum likelihood*

In two papers published in the early 1920's, R. A. Fisher, one of the foremost statisticians of our time, proposed a general method of estimation, called the *method of maximum likelihood*. At the time he also demonstrated the advantages of this method by showing that (1) it yields sufficient estimators whenever sufficient estimators exist and that (2) for large n, that is, in the limit, maximum likelihood estimators are most efficient.

In principle, *the method of maximum likelihood selects that value of a parameter θ for which the probability (or probability density) of obtaining a given set of sample values is a maximum.* Since the joint probability or probability density of obtaining the sample values is maximized with respect to θ, thus treating this parameter as a variable, there has been some uneasiness about referring to $f(x_1, x_2, \ldots, x_n)$, as it is used here, as a probability or a probability density. Fisher called it the *likelihood* or the *likelihood function* and, hence, the name "method of maximum likelihood."

To illustrate the method of maximum likelihood, let us use it first to estimate the parameter θ of a binomial distribution. If a sample yields x successes in n trials, the likelihood function is given by

$$L = \binom{n}{x}\theta^x(1 - \theta)^{n-x}$$

and we must find the value of θ which maximizes this function. Maximizing $\ln L$ instead of L, which is the same, we obtain

$$\ln L = \ln \binom{n}{x} + x \cdot \ln \theta + (n - x) \cdot \ln (1 - \theta)$$

$$\frac{d(\ln L)}{d\theta} = \frac{x}{\theta} - \frac{n - x}{1 - \theta}$$

and, equating this derivative to 0, we find that the likelihood function has a maximum at $\theta = x/n$. Hence, the maximum likelihood estimator of the parameter θ of the binomial distribution is the sample proportion $\mathbf{x}/n$.

To consider another illustration, suppose that $x_1, x_2, \ldots,$ and x_n is a random sample from a population having the exponential distribution (5.3.2) and that the method of maximum likelihood is to be used to estimate the parameter θ. Since the likelihood function is given by

$$L = \left(\frac{1}{\theta}\right)^n e^{-\frac{1}{\theta}\left(\sum_{i=1}^{n} x_i\right)}$$

differentiating $\ln L$ with respect to θ and putting this derivative equal to 0 gives

$$-\frac{n}{\theta} + \frac{1}{\theta^2}\left(\sum_{i=1}^{n} x_i\right) = 0$$

It follows that the maximum likelihood estimator of the parameter θ of an exponential population is $\bar{\mathbf{x}}$. (In this and the preceding examples it was convenient to maximize $\ln L$ rather than L. Although this is often the case, it is by no means necessary.)

Symbolic Definition of a likelihood function is:

$$L = f(x_1, x_2, \cdots x_n) = f(x_1) \cdot f(x_2) \cdots \cdot f(y_n) = \prod_{i=1}^{n} f(y_i)$$

The method of maximum likelihood can also be used for the simultaneous estimation of several parameters of a given population. To illustrate, let us find simultaneous maximum likelihood estimators for the mean and the variance of a normal population on the basis of a random sample of size n. Since the likelihood function is given by

$$L = \frac{1}{(2\pi)^{n/2}\sigma^n} e^{-\frac{1}{2\sigma^2}\sum_{i=1}^{n}(x_i-\mu)^2}$$

the partial derivatives of $\ln L$ with respect to μ and σ^2 are

$$\frac{\partial(\ln L)}{\partial\mu} = \frac{1}{\sigma^2}\sum_{i=1}^{n}(x_i - \mu)$$

$$\frac{\partial(\ln L)}{\partial\sigma^2} = -\frac{n}{2\sigma^2} + \frac{1}{2\sigma^4}\sum_{i=1}^{n}(x_i - \mu)^2$$

Equating the first of these partial derivatives to 0 gives the maximum likelihood estimate $\hat{\mu} = \bar{x}$; equating the second partial derivative to 0 and solving for σ^2 after substituting $\hat{\mu} = \bar{x}$, gives the maximum likelihood estimate

$$\hat{\sigma}^2 = \sum_{i=1}^{n}(x_i - \bar{x})^2/n.$$

Note that this demonstrates that maximum likelihood estimators are not necessarily unbiased.

The foregoing does not prove that $\hat{\sigma}$ is necessarily also a maximum likelihood estimate of σ. However, maximum likelihood estimators have the *invariance property* that if $\hat{\theta}$ is a maximum likelihood estimator of θ and the function given by $g(\theta)$ is continuous, then $g(\hat{\theta})$ is also a maximum likelihood estimator of $g(\theta)$. From this it follows that $\hat{\sigma}$ is also a maximum likelihood estimate of σ.

EXERCISES

1. If x_1, x_2, ..., and x_n is a random sample from a Poisson population with the parameter λ, find an estimator for λ using (a) the method of moments and (b) the method of maximum likelihood.

2. Given a random sample of size n from a normal population with the *known* mean μ, find the maximum likelihood estimate of σ.

3. Given a random sample of size n from a uniform population whose distribution is given by $f(x) = 1/\theta$ for $0 < x < \theta$ and $f(x) = 0$ elsewhere, find the maximum likelihood estimate of θ.

4. An urn contains N coins among which θ are perfectly balanced (the probabilities for heads and tails are 0.50) and $N - \theta$ have heads on both sides. One coin is drawn at random, it is flipped twice, the result is noted, and the coin is returned to the urn without being otherwise inspected. If n repetitions of this experiment yielded 0, 1, and 2 heads, respectively, with frequencies of n_0, n_1, and n_2, estimate θ using (a) the method of moments and (b) the method of maximum likelihood.

5. Given a random sample of size n from the population

$$f(x) = \begin{cases} \theta x^{\theta-1} & \text{for } 0 < x < 1 \\ 0 & \text{elsewhere} \end{cases}$$

where $\theta > 0$, find the maximum likelihood estimator for θ.

6. Given a random sample of size n from the population

$$f(x) = \begin{cases} \dfrac{1}{\beta} e^{-(x-\alpha)/\beta} & \text{for } \alpha < x < \infty \\ 0 & \text{elsewhere} \end{cases}$$

where $-\infty < \alpha < \infty$ and $0 < \beta < \infty$, find simultaneous maximum likelihood estimators for α and β.

BIBLIOGRAPHY

A derivation of the Cramer-Rao inequality may be found in

Rao, C. R., *Advanced Statistical Methods in Biometric Research*, New York: John Wiley & Sons, Inc., 1952, Chapter 4.

Chapter 10

Interval Estimation

10.1 Confidence Intervals

To introduce the basic idea of interval estimation, that of a *confidence interval*, let us refer again to the distribution of $\mathbf{\bar{x}}$ for random samples from a normal population with the mean μ and the variance σ^2. Letting $z_{\alpha/2}$ be such that the integral of the standard normal density from $z_{\alpha/2}$ to ∞ equals $\alpha/2$, we can assert with a probability of $1 - \alpha$ that the random variable $(\mathbf{\bar{x}} - \mu)\sqrt{n}/\sigma$ will assume a value between $-z_{\alpha/2}$ and $z_{\alpha/2}$. (See Theorem 8.1.) Suppose now that we write

$$-z_{\alpha/2} < \frac{\bar{x} - \mu}{\sigma/\sqrt{n}} < z_{\alpha/2} \tag{10.1.1}$$

or equivalently

$$\bar{x} - z_{\alpha/2}\frac{\sigma}{\sqrt{n}} < \mu < \bar{x} + z_{\alpha/2}\frac{\sigma}{\sqrt{n}} \tag{10.1.2}$$

where $\bar{x}$ is the mean which we actually obtained in a sample. Since σ, n, $z_{\alpha/2}$, and $\bar{x}$ are all constants, the double inequality given by (10.1.2) must be *either true or false*; either μ is contained between $\bar{x} - z_{\alpha/2}\,\sigma/\sqrt{n}$ and $\bar{x} + z_{\alpha/2}\,\sigma/\sqrt{n}$ or it is not.

For instance, if we want to estimate the mean of a normal population having the variance $\sigma^2 = 144$ and a random sample of size $n = 25$ yielded $\bar{x} = 81$, then for $\alpha = 0.05$, and, hence, $z_{.025} = 1.96$, (10.1.2) gives

$$76.3 < \mu < 85.7$$

Although this double inequality can only be true or false, it is difficult to shake the feeling that somehow it is more apt to be true than false. After all did we not let $\alpha = 0.05$ so that there is a probability of 0.95 that $(\bar{\mathbf{x}} - \mu)\sqrt{n}/\sigma$ will assume a value between -1.96 and 1.96?

Although we cannot make probability statements about (10.1.2), we can assert with a probability of $1 - \alpha$ that the *random variables* $\bar{\mathbf{x}} - z_{\alpha/2}\,\sigma/\sqrt{n}$ and $\bar{\mathbf{x}} + z_{\alpha/2}\,\sigma/\sqrt{n}$ will assume values satisfying (10.1.2). In this sense we assign (10.1.2) a "degree of confidence" equal to this probability; *in fact we refer to the interval from* $\bar{x} - z_{\alpha/2}\,\sigma/\sqrt{n}$ *to* $\bar{x} + z_{\alpha/2}\,\sigma/\sqrt{n}$ *as a* $1 - \alpha$ *confidence interval for* μ. The interval from 76.3 to 85.7, which we obtained in the numerical example, is a 0.95 confidence interval for the mean of the population. Although $76.3 < \mu < 85.7$ must be either true or false, fair odds would be 95 to 5 that it is true. We should be willing to give these odds because the method which we used to obtain the interval works, so to speak, 95 per cent of the time.

In general, to obtain a $1 - \alpha$ confidence interval for the parameter θ of a given population, we must find two random variables $\boldsymbol{\theta}_1$ and $\boldsymbol{\theta}_2$ for which $\boldsymbol{\theta}_2$ can never assume a value less than $\boldsymbol{\theta}_1$, and for which we can assert with a probability of $1 - \alpha$ that they will assume values satisfying the double inequality $\theta_1 < \theta < \theta_2$. It is customary to refer to θ_1 and θ_2, the values assumed by $\boldsymbol{\theta}_1$ and $\boldsymbol{\theta}_2$, as the *lower and upper confidence limits for* θ, to $1 - \alpha$ as the *degree of confidence*, and, of course, to the interval from θ_1 to θ_2 as a $1 - \alpha$ *confidence interval for* θ.

The method by which we shall construct confidence intervals in the next few sections consists, essentially, of finding an appropriate random variable whose values can be calculated on the basis of the sample values and the parameter, but whose distribution does not depend on the parameter. In this section we, thus, used the random variable $(\bar{\mathbf{x}} - \mu)\sqrt{n}/\sigma$ which has the standard normal distribution; later we shall use the random variable $(\bar{\mathbf{x}} - \mu)\sqrt{n}/\mathbf{s}$ which has the t distribution with $n - 1$ degrees of freedom and the random variable $(n - 1)\mathbf{s}^2/\sigma^2$ which has the chi-square distribution with $n - 1$ degrees of freedom. Although this method, sometimes called the *pivotal method*, is widely used, there are more general methods, for instance, the one referred to in the Bibilography on page 236.

The fact that confidence intervals for a given parameter are not unique is illustrated by Exercises 2 and 3 below. Note also that instead of (10.1.2) we could have given the $1 - \alpha$ confidence interval

$$\bar{x} - z_{2\alpha/3} \frac{\sigma}{\sqrt{n}} < \mu < \bar{x} + z_{\alpha/3} \frac{\sigma}{\sqrt{n}} \tag{10.1.3}$$

or a confidence interval based on the sampling distribution of the median. As in the case of point estimation, methods of obtaining confidence intervals must, thus, be judged by their various statistical properties.

One desirable property is that the length of the confidence interval be literally *as short as possible* and this is why we would prefer (10.1.2) to (10.1.3), see Exercise 4 below. Another criterion is to have the *expected length*, that is, $E(\boldsymbol{\theta}_2 - \boldsymbol{\theta}_1)$ as small as possible. Further criteria are referred to in the Bibliography on page 236.

EXERCISES

1. If x is a value assumed by a random variable having the exponential distribution given by (5.3.2), find k so that the interval from 0 to kx is a $1 - \alpha$ confidence interval for the parameter θ. (*Hint*: note that $0 < \theta < kx$ is equivalent to $x > \theta/k$, since by definition $\theta > 0$.)

2. If x_1 and x_2 constitute a random sample of size 2 from a population having the uniform density on the interval from 0 to θ, find k so that

$$0 < \theta < k(x_1 + x_2)$$

is a $1 - \alpha$ confidence interval for θ. (*Hint*: refer to the result obtained on page 168.)

3. If x_1 and x_2 constitute a random sample of size 2 from the uniform population of Exercise 2, it can be shown that the distribution of the *sample range* is given by

$$f(R) = \begin{cases} \dfrac{2}{\theta^2}(\theta - R) & \text{for } 0 < R < \theta \\ 0 & \text{elsewhere} \end{cases}$$

(see Exercise 8 on page 208.) Find c so that

$$R < \theta < cR$$

is a $1 - \alpha$ confidence interval for θ.

4. Show that the confidence interval given by (10.1.2) is always shorter than the corresponding confidence interval given by (10.1.3).

10.2 Confidence Intervals for Means

The confidence interval given by (10.1.2) was designed to estimate the mean of a normal population whose variance is known. When dealing with samples which are large enough to justify use of the central limit theorem, (10.1.2) is also used to estimate means of other populations with known variances. In applications like these it is customary to refer to a sample as large if $n \geq 30$.

In order to construct a $1 - \alpha$ confidence interval for μ when σ is unknown, let us make use of the fact that for a random sample of size n from a normal population $(\bar{\mathbf{x}} - \mu)\sqrt{n}/\mathbf{s}$ has a t distribution with $n - 1$ degrees of freedom (see Theorem 8.8.) Hence, we can assert with a probability of $1 - \alpha$ that this random variable will assume a value between $-t_{\alpha/2,n-1}$ and $t_{\alpha/2,n-1}$, and for a given sample we assign a degree of confidence of $1 - \alpha$ to

$$-t_{\alpha/2,n-1} < \frac{\bar{x} - \mu}{s/\sqrt{n}} < t_{\alpha/2,n-1} \tag{10.2.1}$$

or

$$\bar{x} - t_{\alpha/2,n-1}\frac{s}{\sqrt{n}} < \mu < \bar{x} + t_{\alpha/2,n-1}\frac{s}{\sqrt{n}} \tag{10.2.2}$$

This confidence interval for μ can be used only for random samples from normal populations; for other populations, an *approximate large sample confidence interval* for μ may be obtained by substituting s for σ in (10.1.2).

To illustrate the use of (10.2.2), suppose that measurements of the height of certain full-grown plants may be looked upon as a random sample from a normal population. If the heights of 14 such plants had a mean of 52.52 inches and a standard deviation of 3.37 inches, a 0.95 confidence interval for the "true" average height of this kind of plant is obtained by substituting these values together with $t_{.025,13} = 2.160$ into (10.2.2). We thus get

$$52.52 - 2.160\frac{3.37}{\sqrt{14}} < \mu < 52.52 + 2.160\frac{3.37}{\sqrt{14}}$$

or

$$50.58 < \mu < 54.47$$

and we can assert with a degree of confidence of 0.95 that the interval from 50.58 inches to 54.47 inches contains the true average height of the given kind of plant.

EXERCISES

1. A study made by staff officers of an armored division showed that the number of vehicles in operating condition on any one day may be looked upon as a value assumed by a random variable having a normal distribution with $\sigma = 220$. If in a random sample of 50 days there were on the average 1985 vehicles in operating condition, construct a 0.95 confidence interval for the true daily average number of vehicles which this armored division has in operating condition.

2. Suppose that it is known that the variance of the scores which high school seniors obtain in a certain clerical aptitude test is 150. If 25 high-school seniors, selected at random, had an average score of 68 on this test, construct a 0.99 confidence interval for the true average score high school seniors obtain on this test. Assume that the 25 scores may be looked upon as a random sample from a normal population.

3. If 16 measurements of the specific gravity of aluminum had a mean of 2.705 and a standard deviation of 0.029, construct a 0.95 confidence interval for the actual specific gravity of aluminum. Assume that these 16 measurements may be looked upon as a random sample from a normal population.

4. In an experiment conducted to determine the average lifetime of a certain kind of light bulb, a random sample of 20 of these bulbs lasted on the average 722 hours with a standard deviation of 54 hours. Assuming that these lifetimes may be looked upon as a random sample from a normal population, construct a 0.98 confidence interval for the true average lifetime of this kind of light bulb.

5. A random sample of 100 delinquent charge accounts of a certain large department store has a mean of \$58.14 and a standard deviation of \$15.30. Construct a 0.95 confidence interval for the actual average size of delinquent charge accounts at this store.

6. If $\bar{x}$ is used as a point estimate of μ, the *error* is given by their difference, that is, $\bar{x} - \mu$. Using (10.1.2), show that if we use the mean of a random sample of size n to estimate the mean of a normal population with the known variance σ^2, we can assert with a degree of confidence of $1 - \alpha$ that the *absolute* error is less than $z_{\alpha/2}\,\sigma/\sqrt{n}$. How large a sample is needed in a problem like this if $\sigma = 16$ and we want to be able to assert with a degree of confidence of 0.95 that the absolute error of our estimate is less than 2?

7. (*Confidence intervals for differences between means*) If $\bar{x}_1$ and $\bar{x}_2$ are the means of independent random samples of size n_1 and n_2 from two normal populations having the means μ_1 and μ_2 and the *known* variances σ_1^2 and σ_2^2, use Theorem 7.6 to construct a $1 - \alpha$ confidence interval for $\mu_1 - \mu_2$.

8. Suppose that the variances of the speeds with which men and women can perform a certain task are $\sigma_1^2 = 12$ seconds and $\sigma_2^2 = 15$ seconds. If 20 men and 25 women required on the average 29.4 seconds and 32.5 seconds to perform the given task, use the confidence interval of Exercise 7 to obtain a 0.95 confidence interval for the difference between the true average times it takes men and women to perform the task.

10.3 Confidence Intervals for Proportions

In many problems in which we are interested in estimating proportions, probabilities, or rates, say, the *proportion* of defectives in a large shipment of springs, the *probability* that a car stopped at a road block will have faulty lights, or the mortality *rate* of a given disease, we are, in fact, concerned with the problem of estimating the parameter θ of a binomial population. Making use of the fact that for large n the binomial distribution can be approximated with a normal distribution, that is, $(\mathbf{x} - n\theta)/\sqrt{n\theta(1 - \theta)}$ can be treated as if it were a random variable having the standard normal distribution, a $1 - \alpha$ confidence interval for θ may be obtained from

$$-z_{\alpha/2} < \frac{x - n\theta}{\sqrt{n\theta(1 - \theta)}} < z_{\alpha/2} \tag{10.3.1}$$

Solving this double inequality for θ (see Exercise 6 below), we obtain a $1 - \alpha$ confidence interval for θ whose upper and lower limits are given by

$$\frac{x + \frac{1}{2} z_{\alpha/2}^2 \pm z_{\alpha/2}\sqrt{\frac{x(n - x)}{n} + \frac{1}{4} z_{\alpha/2}^2}}{n + z_{\alpha/2}^2} \tag{10.3.2}$$

A somewhat simpler large sample approximation may be obtained by writing (10.3.1) as

$$\frac{x}{n} - z_{\alpha/2}\sqrt{\theta(1 - \theta)/n} < \theta < \frac{x}{n} + z_{\alpha/2}\sqrt{\theta(1 - \theta)/n} \tag{10.3.3}$$

and then substituting x/n for θ in the smallest and largest terms of this double inequality. We thus get the following approximate $1 - \alpha$

confidence interval for θ:

$$\frac{x}{n} - z_{\alpha/2}\sqrt{\frac{x}{n}\left(1 - \frac{x}{n}\right)\Big/ n} < \theta < \frac{x}{n} + z_{\alpha/2}\sqrt{\frac{x}{n}\left(1 - \frac{x}{n}\right)\Big/ n} \tag{10.3.4}$$

Thus, if a sample yielded 140 successes in 400 trials and the assumptions underlying the binomial distribution are met, substitution of these values together with $z_{.025} = 1.96$ into (10.3.2) gives the following 0.95 confidence interval for the parameter θ:

$$0.305 < \theta < 0.398$$

Substituting these same values into (10.3.4) gives $0.303 < \theta < 0.397$, which is practically identical with the interval obtained with (10.3.2).

In actual practice, confidence limits for θ are often obtained by means of a special table referred to in the Bibliography on page 236. This not only saves a good deal of arithmetic, but it makes it possible to obtain confidence intervals for θ when n is small.

EXERCISES

1. A random sample of 100 peaches (taken from a very large shipment) contains 14 with imperfections. Find a 0.95 confidence interval for the actual proportion of imperfect peaches in this shipment using (10.3.2).

2. A medical study showed that 57 of 300 persons failed to recover from a given disease. Find 0.95 confidence intervals for the mortality rate of this disease using both (10.3.2) and (10.3.4).

3. In a random sample of 1000 families owning television sets in Chicago, 270 were tuned to Network A during the broadcast of a certain show. Find a 0.99 confidence interval for the actual proportion of families with television sets in this area who at the given time were tuned to Network A. Use (10.3.4).

4. Repeat Exercise 1 using (10.3.4) and a degree of confidence of 0.99.

5. Repeat Exercise 3 using (10.3.2) and a degree of confidence of 0.95.

6. Show that (10.3.2) follows from (10.3.1).

7. If a sample proportion is used as a point estimate of the parameter θ of a binomial population, the *absolute error* is given by $|(x/n) - \theta|$.

Using (10.3.3), show that if a sample proportion is used to estimate the parameter θ of a binomial population, one can assert with a degree of confidence of *at least* $1 - \alpha$ that the absolute error is less than $z_{\alpha/2}/2\sqrt{n}$. [*Hint*: make use of the fact that $\theta(1 - \theta)$ is at most equal to $\frac{1}{4}$.]

8. Use the result of Exercise 7 to find the smallest sample size a public opinion poll can use and yet assert with a degree of confidence of at least 0.95 that its sample proportion is "off" by less than 0.04.

9. (*Confidence intervals for differences between proportions*) If independent random samples from two binomial populations with parameters θ_1 and θ_2 yielded, respectively, x_1 successes in n_1 trials and x_2 successes in n_2 trials, use (7.4.11) and (7.4.12) to construct approximate $1 - \alpha$ confidence intervals for $\theta_1 - \theta_2$. [*Hint:* treat $(\mathbf{x}_1/n_1) - (\mathbf{x}_2/n_2)$ as if it were a random variable having a normal distribution.]

10. Marketing studies conducted in Los Angeles and San Francisco showed that in Los Angeles 138 of 200 housewives preferred Beverage X to Beverage Y while in San Francisco 162 of 200 housewives preferred Beverage X to Beverage Y. Use the result obtained in Exercise 9 to construct a 0.95 confidence interval for $\theta_1 - \theta_2$, the difference between the true proportions of housewives in Los Angeles and San Francisco, who prefer Beverage X to Beverage Y.

10.4 Confidence Intervals for Variances

Given a random sample of size n from a normal population, a $1 - \alpha$ confidence interval for σ^2 may be obtained by making use of Theorem 8.6, according to which $(n - 1)\mathbf{s}^2/\sigma^2$ has a chi-square distribution with $n - 1$ degrees of freedom. We can, thus, assert with a probability of $1 - \alpha$ that this random variable assumes a value between $\chi^2_{1-\alpha/2,n-1}$ and $\chi^2_{\alpha/2,n-1}$ or with a degree of confidence of $1 - \alpha$ that for a given sample

$$\chi^2_{1-\alpha/2,n-1} < \frac{(n - 1)s^2}{\sigma^2} < \chi^2_{\alpha/2,n-1} \tag{10.4.1}$$

or

$$\frac{(n - 1)s^2}{\chi^2_{\alpha/2,n-1}} < \sigma^2 < \frac{(n - 1)s^2}{\chi^2_{1-\alpha/2,n-1}} \tag{10.4.2}$$

This $1 - \alpha$ confidence interval for σ^2 may be converted into a $1 - \alpha$ confidence interval for σ by taking square roots.

To illustrate the use of (10.4.2), suppose that a biologist, who is interested in the physical characteristics of a certain kind of insect, has measured the length of 12, getting a mean of 1.56 cm and a standard deviation of 0.38 cm. Treating these 12 lengths as a random sample from a normal population, he can obtain a 0.95 confidence interval for σ^2 by substituting $s = 0.38$, $\chi^2_{.025,11} = 21.920$, and $\chi^2_{.975,11} = 3.816$ into (10.4.2). He thus gets

$$\frac{11(0.38)^2}{21.920} < \sigma^2 < \frac{11(0.38)^2}{3.816}$$

or

$$0.0725 < \sigma^2 < 0.4162$$

Taking square roots, the corresponding 0.95 confidence interval for σ is $0.27 < \sigma < 0.64$.

EXERCISES

1. If 10 measurements of the density of a certain kind of glass had a variance of 0.0012, construct a 0.95 confidence interval for σ^2, which measures the true variability of the density of this kind of glass.

2. The weights of a random sample of 7 rats used in a certain experiment have a variance of 15 grams. Construct a 0.95 confidence interval for σ^2, the true variance of the weights of all the rats from which the sample was obtained.

3. Referring to the data of Exercise 2, find a 0.99 confidence interval for σ.

4. For large n, the distribution of **s** is sometimes approximated by a normal distribution having the mean σ and the variance $\sigma^2/2n$. Show that this leads to the following large sample $1 - \alpha$ confidence interval for σ:

$$\frac{s}{1 + (z_{\alpha/2}/\sqrt{2n})} < \sigma < \frac{s}{1 - (z_{\alpha/2}/\sqrt{2n})} \tag{10.4.3}$$

5. The intelligence scores of a random sample of 200 students have a variance of 132. Use (10.4.3) to construct an approximate 0.95 confidence interval for σ, the standard deviation of the intelligence scores of all the students from which the sample was obtained.

6. The lifetimes of 100 electronic tubes, selected at random from a very large shipment, have a standard deviation of 45 hours. Use (10.4.3) to construct an approximate 0.99 confidence interval for σ, the standard deviation of the lifetimes of all the electronic tubes in the given shipment.

BIBLIOGRAPHY

A general method for obtaining confidence intervals is given in

Mood, A. M., *Introduction to the Theory of Statistics*, New York: McGraw-Hill Book Co., Inc., 1950, Chapter 11,

and further criteria for evaluating the relative merits of confidence intervals may be found in

Lehmann, E. L., *Testing Statistical Hypotheses*, New York: John Wiley & Sons, Inc., 1959, Chapter 5

and in other advanced texts. Tables for constructing 0.95 and 0.99 confidence intervals for proportions (for the parameter θ of the binomial distribution) may be found in the *Biometrika Tables* referred to on Page 208.

Chapter 11

Tests of Hypotheses: Theory

11.1 Introduction

If an engineer has to decide on the basis of sample information whether the true average lifetime of certain tubes is at least 500 hours, if an agronomist has to decide on the basis of experiments whether one variety of corn has a higher yield than another, and if a drug manufacturer has to decide on the basis of samples whether 90 per cent of all patients given a new drug will recover from a certain disease, *these problems can all be translated into the language of statistical tests of hypotheses.* We might thus say that in the first case the engineer wants to test the hypothesis that $\theta \geq 500$, where θ is the parameter of an exponential distribution, in the second case the agronomist is concerned with testing the hypothesis $\mu_1 - \mu_2 = 0$, where μ_1 and μ_2 are the means of two normal populations with given variances, and in the third case the drug manufacturer wants to know whether $\theta = 0.90$, where θ is the parameter of a binomial distribution. In each of these examples it must be assumed, of course, that the chosen distribution correctly describes the experimental situation, namely, that it provides the correct *statistical model.*

As in the above examples, most statistical hypotheses concern the parameters of assumed or given distributions; sometimes they also concern the functional form of the distributions, themselves. Thus, in the first of our three examples the engineer may not only want to test whether the parameter θ of an exponential distribution is greater than or equal to 500, but also whether it is reasonable to assume that the population is exponential.

If a statistical hypothesis completely specifies the underlying distribution, that is, if it specifies its functional form as well as the values of all parameters, it is referred to as *simple*; if not, it is referred to as *composite*. Thus, in the first example on page 237 the hypothesis is composite since $\theta \geq 500$ does not specify a definite value for the parameter θ; in the second example the hypothesis is simple, looking at the difference $\mu_1 - \mu_2$ as one parameter; and in the third example the hypothesis is also simple for any given sample size n.

To construct a criterion for testing a given statistical hypothesis, it is always necessary to formulate an *alternative hypothesis*. For instance, in the example dealing with the lifetimes of the tubes we might formulate the alternative hypothesis that θ, the parameter of the exponential distribution, is less than 500. Similarly, in the second example we might formulate the alternative hypothesis that $\mu_1 - \mu_2 \neq 0$, and in the third example we might formulate the alternative hypothesis that θ, the parameter of the binomial distribution, is, say, only 0.75. The concept of simple and composite hypotheses applies, of course, also to alternative hypotheses and we can now say that in the first example we are testing the *composite hypothesis* $\theta \geq 500$, where θ is the parameter of an exponential distribution, against the *composite alternative* $\theta < 500$. Also, in the second example we are testing the *simple hypothesis* $\mu_1 - \mu_2 = 0$ against the *composite alternative* $\mu_1 - \mu_2 \neq 0$, and in the third example we are testing the *simple hypothesis* $\theta = 0.90$ against the *simple alternative* $\theta = 0.75$.

Symbolically, we shall use the symbol H_0 (standing for *null hypothesis*, see page 250) for whatever hypothesis we shall want to test and H_A for the alternative hypothesis. Problems in which there are several alternative hypotheses tend to be quite complicated and will not be considered.

11.2 Simple Hypotheses

In Section 11.2.1 we shall study some of the factors that are usually taken into account when testing a simple hypothesis against a simple alternative; in Section 11.2.2 we shall present a general theorem, the *Neyman–Pearson lemma,* which concerns the selection of the "best" criterion for testing a simple hypothesis against a simple alternative.

11.2.1 *Type I and type II errors*

Whenever a statistical hypothesis is accepted or rejected on the basis of a sample, there is always the risk of making a wrong decision, that is, accept H_A when H_0 is true or accept H_0 when H_A is true. It is customary to refer to the first of these errors as a *Type I error* and to the second as a *Type II error*; schematically, the various possibilities are

	H_0 *is true*	H_A *is true*
Accept H_0	correct decision	Type II error
Accept H_A	Type I error	correct decision

A Type I error is, thus, committed when we reject H_0 when it should be accepted and a Type II error is committed when we accept H_0 when it should be rejected. It is assumed here that rejecting H_0 is equivalent to accepting H_A, and vice versa.

An important aspect of the construction of statistical tests is to control, insofar as this is possible, the probabilities of committing these two types of errors. Denoting the probability of committing a Type I error with the Greek letter α and the probability of committing a Type II error with the Greek letter β, the following illustrates how a test criterion can be judged, how its merits can be evaluated with reference to the probabilities of committing the two types of errors: suppose that a public opinion poll wants to test a politician's claim that 60 per cent of the voters are for a given piece of legislation against the alternative hypothesis that only 45 per cent of the voters are for this legislation. It is decided, furthermore, to accept the politician's claim if 52 or more voters are for this legislation in a random sample of size 100; if not, his claim is to be rejected. Testing the null hypothesis

$$H_0\colon \theta = 0.60$$

against the alternative

$$H_A\colon \theta = 0.45$$

where θ is the parameter of a binomial population with $n = 100$, *a Type I error is committed if* $\theta = 0.60$ *and there are fewer than* 52 *successes in* 100 *trials*; similarly, *a Type II error is committed if* $\theta = 0.45$ *and there are* 52 *or more successes in* 100 *trials*. (It is assumed that the number of eligible voters is large enough to justify use of the binomial rather than the hypergeometric distribution.)

Referring to a table of binomial probabilities or using the normal approximation of Section 6.4.3, it can be shown that the probability of committing a Type I error with the given criterion is $\alpha = 0.042$ and that the probability of committing a Type II error is $\beta = 0.095$. If either (or both) of these probabilities is considered to be too high from a practical point of view, the criterion for accepting and rejecting the politician's claim could be modified by moving the *dividing line* of the criterion and (or) increasing the size of the sample.

11.2.2 *The Neyman-Pearson lemma*

To choose a criterion for testing a hypothesis H_0 against an alternative hypothesis H_A is to partition the sample space into two sets, a *region of acceptance* and a *region of rejection for* H_0, the latter being called the *critical region of the test*, or simply the *critical region*. To select a critical region is, thus, synonymous with selecting a criterion for testing a given hypothesis H_0 against a given alternative H_A. It is also customary to refer to the probability that a sample point will fall into the critical region when the simple hypothesis H_0 is true as the *size of the critical region*. Hence, the size of the critical region is α, the probability of committing a Type I error.

To illustrate the concepts introduced in the preceding paragraph, suppose that x_1 and x_2 constitute a random sample of size 2 from a normal population having $\sigma^2 = 1$, and that we want to test the null hypothesis

$$H_0\colon \mu = \mu_0$$

against the alternative hypothesis

$$H_A\colon \mu = \mu_A \qquad (\text{where } \mu_A > \mu_0)$$

Suppose, furthermore, that the null hypothesis is to be rejected if $\bar{x}$ exceeds $\mu_0 + 1.16$, namely, if $x_1 + x_2 > 2\mu_0 + 2.32$. As is indicated in Figure 11.1, this critical region consists of the portion of the plane which lies above the line $x_1 + x_2 = 2\mu_0 + 2.32$. It can easily be verified with the use of Theorem 8.1 that the *size* of this critical region is approximately 0.05.

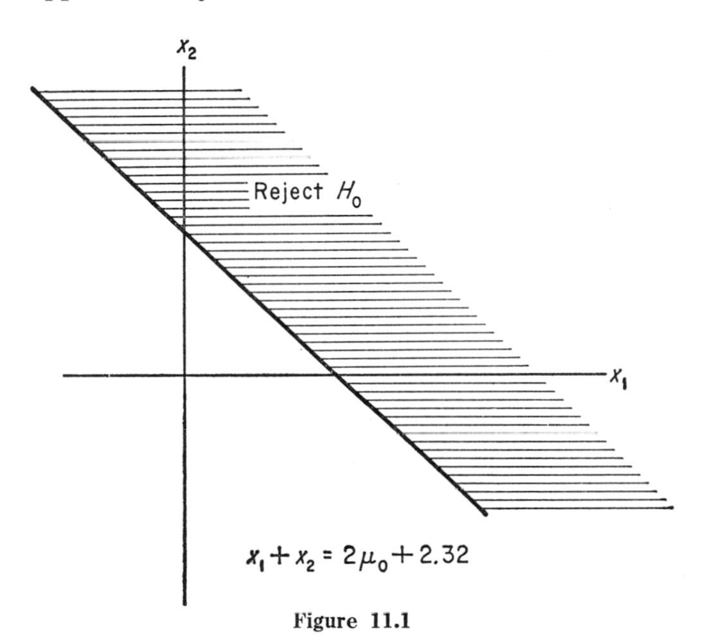

Figure 11.1

When H_0 and H_A are both simple, a critical region of size α is said to be *best* or *most powerful* if the probability of committing a Type II error is a minimum. Theorem 11.1, to be proved below, provides *sufficient conditions* for a most powerful critical region for testing the simple hypothesis $\theta = \theta_0$ against the simple alternative $\theta = \theta_A$, where θ is the parameter of a population, whose probability density or distribution is given by $f(x;\theta)$. In what follows, L_0 gives the likelihood function for a random sample of size n from this population when $\theta = \theta_0$, namely,

$$L_0 = \prod_{i=1}^{n} f(x_i;\theta_0)$$

and L_A gives the corresponding likelihood function when $\theta = \theta_A$, that is.

$$L_A = \prod_{i=1}^{n} f(x_i; \theta_A)$$

THEOREM 11.1:

If C is a critical region of size α and there exists a constant k such that

$$\frac{L_0}{L_A} \leq k \qquad \textit{inside } C$$

and

$$\frac{L_0}{L_A} \geq k \qquad \textit{outside } C$$

then C is a most powerful critical region for testing $\theta = \theta_0$ against $\theta = \theta_A$.

(Intuitively speaking, it stands to reason that L_0/L_A *should be small* for sample points inside C, which lead to Type I errors when $\theta = \theta_0$ and correct decisions when $\theta = \theta_A$; similarly, L_0/L_A *should be large* for sample points outside C, which lead to correct decisions when $\theta = \theta_0$ and Type II errors when $\theta = \theta_A$.)

Theorem 11.1 is usually called the *Neyman-Pearson lemma*, named after J. Neyman and E. S. Pearson, the two statisticians who first gave its proof. To prove the Neyman-Pearson lemma, suppose that C is a critical region satisfying the conditions of Theorem 11.1 and that D is any other critical region of size α. Thus,

$$\int_C L_0\,dx = \int_D L_0\,dx = \alpha$$

where dx stands for $dx_1\,dx_2 \ldots dx_n$ and the two multiple integrals are to be taken over the respective n-dimensional regions C and D. Since C is the union of the disjoint sets $C \cap D$ and $C \cap D'$ and D is the union of the disjoint sets $C \cap D$ and $C' \cap D$, see Figure 11.2, it follows that

$$\int_{C\cap D} L_0\,dx + \int_{C\cap D'} L_0\,dx = \int_{C\cap D} L_0\,dx + \int_{C'\cap D} L_0\,dx = \alpha$$

and, hence, that

$$\int_{C \cap D'} L_0 \, dx = \int_{C' \cap D} L_0 \, dx \tag{11.2.1}$$

Using the fact that $L_A \geq L_0/k$ inside C and $L_A \leq L_0/k$ outside C together with (11.2.1), we get

$$\int_{C \cap D'} L_A \, dx \geq \int_{C \cap D'} L_0/k \, dx = \int_{C' \cap D} L_0/k \, dx \geq \int_{C' \cap D} L_A \, dx$$

and

$$\int_{C \cap D'} L_A \, dx \geq \int_{C' \cap D} L_A \, dx \tag{11.2.2}$$

Finally, it follows from (11.2.2) that

$$\int_C L_A \, dx = \int_{C \cap D} L_A \, dx + \int_{C \cap D'} L_A \, dx \geq \int_{C \cap D} L_A \, dx + \int_{C' \cap D} L_A \, dx = \int_D L_A \, dx$$

or

$$\int_C L_A \, dx \geq \int_D L_A \, dx \tag{11.2.3}$$

and this completes the proof of Theorem 11.1. Inequality (11.2.3) states that for the critical region C the probability of rejecting H_0 when H_A is true, the probability of *not* committing a Type II error, is greater than or equal to the corresponding probability for any other critical region of size α. Note that for the discrete case the proof is the same with summations taking the place of integrals.

To illustrate how Theorem 11.1 is used in finding a most powerful critical region for testing a simple hypothesis against a simple

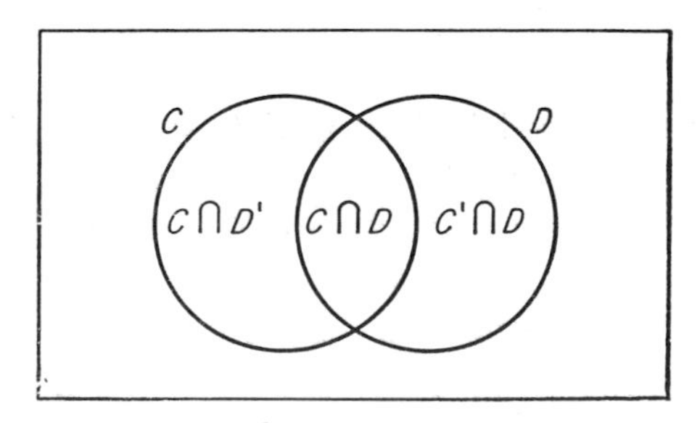

Figure 11.2

alternative, let us suppose that x_1, x_2, . . ., and x_n is a random sample from a normal population with $\sigma^2 = 1$ and that on the basis of this sample we want to test the null hypothesis $\mu = \mu_0$ against the alternative $\mu = \mu_A$ (where $\mu_A > \mu_0$; the case where $\mu_A < \mu_0$ can be handled analogously, see Exercise 6 below). The two likelihood functions are

$$L_0 = \frac{1}{(2\pi)^{n/2}} e^{-\frac{1}{2}\Sigma(x_i - \mu_0)^2}$$

and

$$L_A = \frac{1}{(2\pi)^{n/2}} e^{-\frac{1}{2}\Sigma(x_i - \mu_A)^2}$$

with the summations extending from $i = 1$ to $i = n$. After some simplifications, the ratio of these likelihood functions becomes

$$L_0/L_A = e^{\frac{n}{2}(\mu_A^2 - \mu_0^2) + (\mu_0 - \mu_A)\Sigma x_i}$$

and we must now find a constant k and a region C of the sample space such that

$$\begin{aligned} e^{\frac{n}{2}(\mu_A^2 - \mu_0^2) + (\mu_0 - \mu_A)\Sigma x_i} &\leq k \qquad \textit{inside } C \\ e^{\frac{n}{2}(\mu_A^2 - \mu_0^2) + (\mu_0 - \mu_A)\Sigma x_i} &\geq k \qquad \textit{outside } C \end{aligned} \tag{11.2.4}$$

Taking logarithms, subtracting $(n/2)(\mu_A^2 - \mu_0^2)$, and dividing by the negative quantity $n(\mu_0 - \mu_A)$, (11.2.4) becomes

$$\begin{aligned} \bar{x} &\geq K \qquad \textit{inside } C \\ \bar{x} &\leq K \qquad \textit{outside } C \end{aligned}$$

where K can be expressed in terms of k, n, μ_0, and μ_A. In actual practice, the constant K is determined so that the size of the critical region is α; in our example we find that $K = \mu_0 + z_\alpha(1/\sqrt{n})$, making use of the fact that for random samples of size n from the given normal population $\bar{\mathbf{x}}$ has a normal distribution with the mean μ_0 and the variance $1/n$. The most powerful critical region of size α for testing the null hypothesis $\mu = \mu_0$ against the alternative $\mu = \mu_A$

(with $\mu_A > \mu_0$) for the given population is, thus,

$$\bar{x} \geq \mu_0 + z_\alpha \frac{1}{\sqrt{n}} \tag{11.2.5}$$

Note that (11.2.5) does not depend on μ_A; this is an important property, to which we shall refer again in Section 11.3.1.

EXERCISES

1. Suppose that a public opinion poll is asked to test the hypothesis that Candidate X will win a certain election against the alternative that his only opponent, Candidate Y, will win the election. Explain under what conditions this poll would be committing a Type I error and under what conditions it would be committing a Type II error.

2. An urn contains 6 marbles, of which θ are white while the others are black. In order to test the null hypothesis that $\theta = 3$ against the alternative that $\theta = 5$, two marbles are drawn at random *without replacement* and the null hypothesis is rejected if both marbles are white; otherwise, the null hypothesis is accepted. Find the probabilities of committing Type I and Type II errors with this criterion.

3. A sample of size 1 from an exponential population, see (5.3.2), is to be used to test the hypothesis H_0 that $\theta = 1$ against the alternative hypothesis H_A that $\theta = 10$. If H_0 is accepted when the observed value is less than or equal to 2 and H_A is accepted when the observed value exceeds 2, find α and β, the probabilities of committing Type I and Type II errors with this criterion.

4. (*Error rates*) Suppose we want to test the null hypothesis that a large shipment of ball bearings contains 3 per cent defectives against the alternative that it contains 4 per cent defectives. It is known from past experience that 75 per cent of shipments of this kind contain 3 per cent defectives while the remaining 25 per cent contain 4 per cent defectives. If the criterion used to test the given hypothesis has $\alpha = 0.06$ and $\beta = 0.03$, what is the probability, the *error rate*, of committing an error with this criterion?

5. Verify that for the illustration on page 241 the size of the critical region is approximately 0.05.

6. Show that if $\mu_A < \mu_0$ in the example on page 244, the Neyman-Pearson lemma yields the critical region

$$\bar{x} \leq \mu_0 - z_\alpha \, (1/\sqrt{n}).$$

7. Given a random sample of size n from a population having the exponential distribution (5.3.2), use the Neyman-Pearson lemma to find the best critical region for testing the null hypothesis $\theta = \theta_0$ against the alternative $\theta = \theta_A$ (where $\theta_A > \theta_0$). Indicate how to evaluate the necessary constant to make the size of the critical region equal to α, making use of the illustration of Theorem 7.1 on page 171.

8. Use the Neyman-Pearson lemma to construct the most powerful critical region of size α to test the null hypothesis that θ, the parameter of a binomial population, equals θ_0 against the alternative that it equals θ_A, with $\theta_A < \theta_0$. (Assume that n is given).

9. If $n = 100$, $\theta_0 = 0.50$, $\theta_A = 0.40$, and α is as close as possible to 0.05 without exceeding 0.05, find the probability of committing a Type II error with the criterion constructed in Exercise 8. (*Hint*: use the normal approximation to the binomial distribution.)

10. Given a random sample of size n from a normal population having $\mu = 0$, use the Neyman-Pearson lemma to construct the best critical region for testing the null hypothesis $\sigma = \sigma_0$ against the alternative $\sigma = \sigma_A$ (where $\sigma_A > \sigma_0$). Indicate how the "dividing line" of the criterion might be obtained so that the size of the critical region is equal to α.

11.3 Composite Hypotheses

In actual practice, there are relatively few problems in which simple hypotheses are tested against simple alternatives; usually one or the other, or both, are composite. For instance, in the example on page 239 it may well be more realistic to test the null hypothesis that 60 per cent of the voters are for the given legislation against the alternative hypothesis that the percentage is less. Perhaps, it would be even more realistic to test the null hypothesis $\theta \geq 0.60$ against the alternative hypothesis $\theta < 0.60$.

When dealing with composite hypotheses, the problem of evaluating the merits of test criteria and, hence, the problem of choosing between critical regions, becomes more difficult. As will be illustrated in Section 11.3.1, we shall now have to consider the probabilities of making errors (wrong decisions) for all values of the parameter, or parameters, within the domains specified under H_0 and H_A.

Also, the Neyman-Pearson lemma does not apply to composite hypotheses. In Section 11.3.2 we shall introduce a general method for constructing tests of composite hypotheses which, specially for large samples, is usually very satisfactory. This method, which is called the *likelihood ratio method*, is based on an extension of the concepts introduced in Section 11.2.2.

11.3.1 *The power function of a test*

In the example on page 240 we were able to give unique values for α and β, the probabilities of committing Type I and Type II errors, because we were interested in testing the simple hypothesis $\theta = 0.60$ against the simple alternative $\theta = 0.45$. Had we been interested in testing the hypothesis

$$H_0: \theta \geq 0.60$$

against the alternative

$$H_A: \theta < 0.60$$

which, as we pointed out above, may well be a more realistic test of the politician's claim, the problem would have been more complicated. Using the same critical region as before, we would have had to calculate the probabilities of getting fewer than 52 successes in 100 trials for various values of θ greater than or equal to 0.60, and the probabilities of getting 52 or more successes in 100 trials for various values of θ less than 0.60.

In order to treat problems like this more uniformly, it is customary to calculate the probabilities of *rejecting* H_0 for various values of the parameter in question, getting, thus, in our example *the probabilities of committing Type I errors for* $\theta \geq 0.60$ *and the probabilities of not committing Type II errors for* $\theta < 0.60$. Using the normal approximation to the binomial distribution (see Section 6.4.3), we obtained the values shown in the following table and also in Figure 11.3:

θ	*Probability of rejecting* H_0
0.35	1^-
0.40	0.99
0.45	0.90
0.50	0.62
0.55	0.24
0.60	0.04
0.65	0^+

Here 0^+ stands for a probability less than 0.01 and 1^- for a probability greater than 0.99. For θ less than 0.35 the probability rapidly approaches 1 and for θ greater than 0.65 it rapidly approaches 0.

The function which is represented by the graph of Figure 11.3 is called the *power function* of the critical region. If the critical region had been "perfect," the graph of its power function would have been given by the dotted line of Figure 11.3; the probability of rejecting H_0 would have been 0 for $\theta \geq 0.60$ and 1 for $\theta < 0.60$.

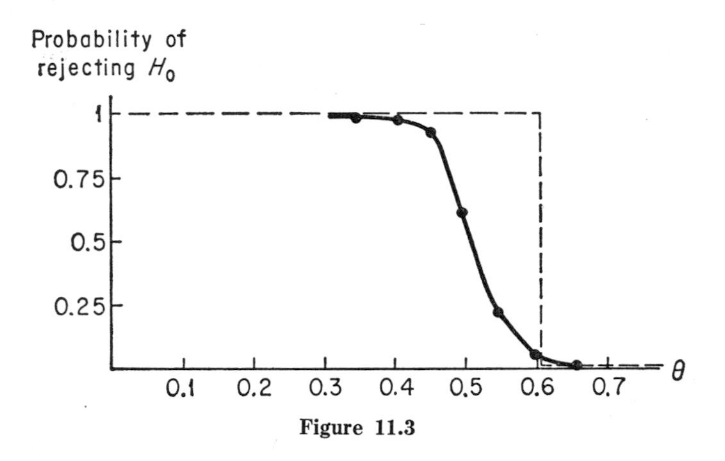

Figure 11.3

Power functions play a very important role in the evaluation of statistical tests, particularly in the comparison of critical regions which might all be used to test a given hypothesis against a given alternative. Had we calculated and plotted the probabilities of *accepting* H_0 instead of those of *rejecting* H_0, we would have obtained the graph of the *operating characteristic function*, or briefly the *OC-curve*, of the critical region. Thus, for each value of the parameter the value of the OC-function is 1 minus the corresponding value of the power function. Operating characteristic functions are used mainly in industrial applications.

Whenever possible, it is desirable to formulate (or reformulate) problems leading to tests of statistical hypotheses so that H_0 is a simple hypothesis. The advantage of this is that it simplifies the comparison of power functions; *if H_0 is a simple hypothesis we can specify the probability of committing a Type I error and the graphs of the power functions of different critical regions will coincide at the only point where the values of the power functions give the probability of making an error.* To illustrate, consider the graphs of Figure 11.4, giving the power functions of three critical regions designed to test the null hypothesis $\theta = \theta_0$ against the alternative $\theta \neq \theta_0$, where θ is the parameter of some distribution. For each θ except θ_0, the values of these power functions are probabilities of making *correct* decisions and it is desirable to have them as close to 1 as possible. Hence, it follows by inspection that the critical region whose power function is given by the *solid* curve of Figure 11.4 is preferable to the critical region whose power function is given by the curve which is *dashed*. The probability of *not* making a Type II error with the first of these critical regions is *always more*, and this critical region is said to be *uniformly more powerful* than the second; the latter is said to be *non-admissible.*

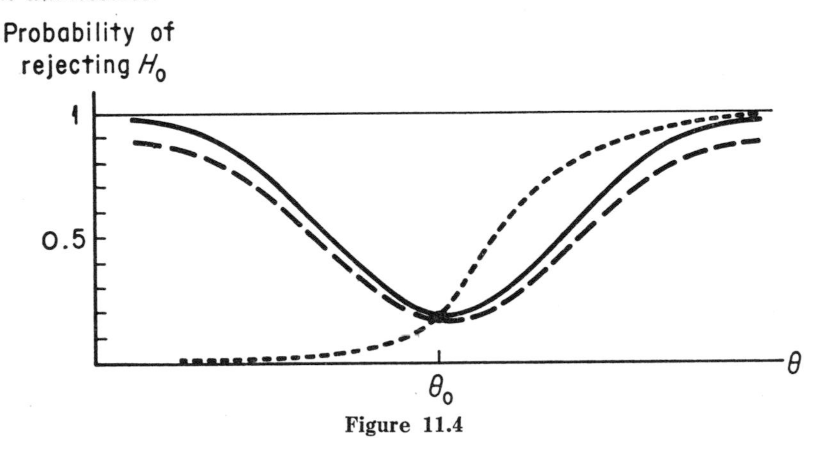

Figure 11.4

The same clear-cut distinction is not possible if we attempt to compare the critical regions whose power functions are given by the solid and dotted curves of Figure 11.4. The first is preferable for $\theta < \theta_0$ and the second is preferable for $\theta > \theta_0$. In a situation like this we need another criterion for comparing the two power functions, for example, that of Exercise 11 on page 257. Note that if the alternative hypothesis had been $\theta > \theta_0$, the critical region whose power function is given by the dotted curve would have been *uniformly more powerful* than the critical region whose power function is given by the solid curve.

In general, when testing a simple hypothesis against a composite alternative we specify α, the probability of committing a Type I error, and refer to one critical region of size α as *uniformly more powerful* than another if the probability of *not* committing a Type II error with the first is always greater than or equal to the probability of *not* committing a Type II error with the second, with the strict inequality holding for at least one value of the parameter in question. If, for a given problem, a critical region of size α is uniformly more powerful than any other critical region of size α, it is referred to as *uniformly most powerful*; unfortunately, uniformly most powerful critical regions seldom exist.

In order to formulate a problem so that H_0 is a simple hypothesis, it is often necessary to hypothesize the exact opposite of what we may want to prove. If we want to show that the students in one school have a higher average I.Q. than those of another, we have to formula the hypothesis that there is *no difference*, namely, that $\mu_1 = \mu_2$. Similarly, if we want to show that a new drug reduces the mortality rate of a disease, we have to formulate the hypothesis that it *does not*, and if we want to show that one kind of ore has a higher percentage content of uranium than another kind of ore, we have to formulate the hypothesis that the two percentages are *the same*. In view of the fact that we assumed that there is *no difference* between the average I.Q.'s, *no difference* regardless of whether we use the new drug, and *no difference* in the uranium contents of the two ores, hypotheses like these are referred to as *null hypotheses* and denoted as H_0. This explains how the term "null hypothesis" arose, although nowadays it is used for any hypothesis, whose false rejection is looked upon as a Type I error.

Until now we have always assumed that the acceptance of H_0 is equivalent to the rejection of H_A, and vice versa. This is not the case, for example, in *multi-stage* or *sequential* tests, where the alternatives are to accept H_0, to accept H_A, or to continue the experiment, that is, defer the ultimate decision concerning H_0 and H_A until the collection of further data. Another situation arises in so-called *tests of significance*, where the alternative to rejecting H_0 is *reserving judgment* instead of accepting H_A. Suppose, for instance, that we want to test the null hypothesis that a coin is perfectly balanced against the alternative that it is not perfectly balanced and that we decide to reject the null hypothesis if 100 tosses yield more than 60 or fewer than 40 heads. If the number of heads is, say, 53, we merely state that the difference between the 53 heads which we obtained and the 50 heads which we expected under the null hypothesis *may reasonably be attributed to chance*—or we say that *this difference is not large enough to permit us to reject the null hypothesis*. In either case, we do not commit ourselves one way or the other and we do not expose ourselves to the risk of committing a Type II error. Of course, it is questionable whether there are many practical situations where we can really afford the luxury of reserving judgment. In connection with tests of significance, it is customary to refer to α, the probability of committing a Type I error, as the *level of significance* at which the test is being conducted.

11.3.2 *Likelihood ratio tests*

Let us now present a general method for constructing critical regions, which generally have very satisfactory properties. It is called the *likelihood ratio method* and, conceptually, it is an extension of the method introduced in Section 11.2.2. We shall discuss this method here with reference to tests concerning one parameter θ and continuous populations; however, all arguments can easily be extended to the multi-parameter case and to discrete populations. An example where the likelihood ratio method fails, that is, where it leads to a very unsatisfactory (non-admissible) test, is given in Exercise 10 on page 257.

To illustrate the likelihood ratio technique, let us suppose that x_1, x_2, ..., and x_n constitute a random sample of size n from a population whose probability density is given by $f(x; \theta)$ and that Ω is the set of values the parameter θ can assume. The null hypothesis we shall want to test is

$$H_0: \theta \text{ is an element of } \omega$$

where ω is a subset of Ω, and the alternative hypothesis is

$$H_A: \theta \text{ is an element of } \Omega \cap \omega'$$

In other words, the set of values the parameter θ can assume is partitioned into the disjoint sets ω and $\Omega \cap \omega'$; the null hypothesis states that θ belongs to the first and the alternative hypothesis states that it belongs to the second. In most practical problems Ω is either the set of all real numbers, the set of all positive real numbers, some interval of real numbers (say, the interval from 0 to 1), or a discrete set of real numbers.

When H_0 and H_A are both simple, ω and $\Omega \cap \omega'$ each have one element and we can proceed as in Section 11.2.2, working with the likelihood functions L_0 and L_A. In the more general case, where at least one of the hypotheses is composite, we shall compare instead the likelihood functions max L_0 and max L, where max L_0 is the greatest value the likelihood function can assume with θ belonging to ω and max L is the greatest value the likelihood function can assume with θ belonging to Ω. In other words, if $\hat{\theta}$ is the maximum likelihood estimate of θ subject to the restriction that θ must belong to ω and $\hat{\hat{\theta}}$ is the maximum likelihood estimate of θ with θ being allowed to assume any value in Ω, then

$$\max L_0 = \prod_{i=1}^{n} f(x_i; \hat{\theta}) \tag{11.3.1}$$

and

$$\max L = \prod_{i=1}^{n} f(x_i; \hat{\hat{\theta}}) \tag{11.3.2}$$

Using (11.3.1) and (11.3.2), let us now define their ratio as the *likelihood ratio statistic* λ, that is,

$$\lambda = \frac{\max L_0}{\max L} \tag{11.3.3}$$

Since max L_0 and, hence, λ is apt to be *small* when the null hypothesis is false, it would seem reasonable to reject H_0 when λ is less than or equal to some constant k. Indeed, the critical region

$$\lambda \leq k \tag{11.3.4}$$

gives the so-called *likelihood ratio test.* If H_0 is simple, k is usually chosen so that the size of the critical region equals some specified value α; if H_0 is composite, k is usually chosen so that the probability of committing a Type I error is less than or equal to α. In other words, if H_0 is simple and $f(\lambda)$ is the probability density of λ under the assumption that H_0 is true, then k must be such that

$$\int_0^k f(\lambda)\, d\lambda = \alpha \tag{11.3.5}$$

In the discrete case, the integral in (11.3.5) is replaced with a sum and k is usually taken to be the largest value for which the sum is less than or equal to α. Note that λ cannot exceed 1 since max L_0 cannot exceed max L and, of course, λ is always positive.

To illustrate the likelihood ratio technique, suppose we have a random sample of size n from a normal population having the *known* variance σ^2 and that we want to test the simple null hypothesis

$$H_0: \mu = \mu_0$$

against the composite alternative

$$H_A: \mu \neq \mu_0$$

where μ is, as always, the mean of the population.

Using the notation introduced earlier in this section, Ω is the set of all real numbers and ω consists of the single value μ_0. Hence, $\hat{\mu} = \mu_0$, there is no other choice, and, as can easily be verified by the method of Section 9.4.2, $\hat{\hat{\mu}} = \bar{x}$. Substituting $N(x_i; \mu_0, \sigma^2)$ and $N(x_i; \bar{x}, \sigma^2)$ into (11.3.1) and (11.3.2), we obtain

$$\max L_0 = \frac{1}{\sigma^n (2\pi)^{n/2}} e^{-\frac{1}{2\sigma^2}\Sigma(x_i - \mu_0)^2}$$

and

$$\max L = \frac{1}{\sigma^n (2\pi)^{n/2}} e^{-\frac{1}{2\sigma^2}\Sigma(x_i - \bar{x})^2}$$

with the summations extending from $i = 1$ to $i = n$. Consequently, the likelihood ratio statistic becomes

$$\lambda = \frac{e^{-\frac{1}{2\sigma^2}\Sigma(x_i - \mu_0)^2}}{e^{-\frac{1}{2\sigma^2}\Sigma(x_i - \bar{x})^2}} \tag{11.3.6}$$

and after suitable simplifications this can be written as

$$\lambda = e^{-\frac{n}{2\sigma^2}(\bar{x} - \mu_0)^2} \tag{11.3.7}$$

The critical region of the resulting likelihood ratio test is, thus,

$$e^{-\frac{n}{2\sigma^2}(\bar{x} - \mu_0)^2} \leq k$$

and after taking logarithms and dividing by $-(n/2\sigma^2)$ it becomes

$$(\bar{x} - \mu_0)^2 \geq -\frac{2\sigma^2}{n}(\ln k)$$

or

$$|\bar{x} - \mu_0| \geq K \tag{11.3.8}$$

where K will have to be determined so that the size of this critical region is equal to α. Note that $-(2\sigma^2/n)(\ln k)$ is positive since $0 < k < 1$, as was pointed out on page 252.

Making use of the fact that if H_0 is true $\bar{\mathbf{x}}$ has (in this example) a normal distribution with the mean μ_0 and the variance σ^2/n, it follows that the critical region of the likelihood ratio test is

$$|\bar{x} - \mu_0| \geq z_{\alpha/2}\, \sigma/\sqrt{n}$$

that is, the null hypothesis is rejected if $\bar{x}$ is greater than or equal to $\mu_0 + z_{\alpha/2}\, \sigma/\sqrt{n}$ or if it is less than or equal to $\mu_0 - z_{\alpha/2}\, \sigma/\sqrt{n}$, where $z_{\alpha/2}$ is as defined on page 227.

In the above example it was easy to find the constant which made the size of the critical region equal to α, referring to the distribution of $\bar{\mathbf{x}}$ rather than the distribution of $\boldsymbol{\lambda}$. Since the distribution of $\boldsymbol{\lambda}$ is usually rather complicated, making it difficult to find k with the use of (11.3.5), it is often convenient to use an approximation based on the following theorem: (A proof of this theorem which, incidentally, applies only to the one-parameter case, is referred to in the Bibliography on page 258.)

THEOREM 11.2:
For large n, the distribution of $-2 \ln \boldsymbol{\lambda}$ approaches, under very general conditions, the chi-square distribution with 1 degree of freedom.

Using this approximation, the null hypothesis is rejected if

$$-2 \ln \lambda \geq \chi^2_{\alpha,1} \tag{11.3.9}$$

where $\chi^2_{\alpha,1}$ is as defined on page 196. If the population distribution involves more than one unknown parameter and the null hypothesis subjects these parameters to r restrictions, the number of degrees of freedom in the chi-square approximation of the distribution of $-2 \ln \boldsymbol{\lambda}$ is equal to r. Thus, when testing the null hypothesis that the unknown mean and variance of a normal population are, respectively, $\mu = \mu_0$ and $\sigma^2 = \sigma_0^2$ against the alternative $\mu \neq \mu_0$ and $\sigma^2 \neq \sigma_0^2$, the number of degrees of freedom in the chi-square approximation to the distribution of $-2 \ln \boldsymbol{\lambda}$ is 2; the two restrictions are $\mu = \mu_0$ and $\sigma^2 = \sigma_0^2$.

Investigating the distribution of $-2 \ln \lambda$ for the example which we began on page 253, we find from (11.3.7) that

$$-2 \ln \lambda = \frac{n}{\sigma^2}(\bar{x} - \mu_0)^2 = \left(\frac{\bar{x} - \mu_0}{\sigma/\sqrt{n}}\right)^2$$

Since $\bar{\mathbf{x}}$ has a normal distribution with the mean μ_0 and the variance σ^2/n, it follows that $(\bar{\mathbf{x}} - \mu_0)/(\sigma/\sqrt{n})$ has the standard normal distribution and, according to Theorem 8.2, $-2 \ln \lambda$ has a chi-square distribution with 1 degree of freedom. We, thus, find that in this *special* case the distribution of $-2 \ln \lambda$ is, in fact, the chi-square distribution with 1 degree of freedom.

EXERCISES

1. An urn contains 6 marbles, of which θ are white while the others are black. In order to test the null hypothesis that $\theta = 3$ against the alternative that $\theta \neq 3$, two marbles are drawn at random *without replacement* and the null hypothesis is rejected if both marbles are of the same color. Otherwise the null hypothesis is accepted.
   (a) Find the probability of committing a Type I error with this criterion.
   (b) Find the probabilities of committing Type II errors with this criterion for $\theta = 0, 1, 2, 4, 5$, and 6, and plot the graph of the power function.

2. Use the normal approximation to the binomial distribution to verify the probabilities of rejecting H_0 given in the table on page 247.

3. Suppose that in Exercise 1 sampling is *with replacement.* Compare the critical region according to which the null hypothesis is rejected if both marbles are of the same color with the critical region according to which the null hypothesis is rejected if the two marbles are of different colors. Is one of these critical regions non-admissible?

4. Verify that on page 253 (11.3.6) leads to (11.3.7).

5. If $x_1, x_2, \ldots$, and x_n is a random sample of size n from a population having the Poisson distribution

$$f(x) = \frac{\mu^x e^{-\mu}}{x!} \qquad \text{for} \quad x = 0, 1, 2, \ldots$$

find an expression for the likelihood ratio statistic λ for testing the null hypothesis $\mu = \mu_0$ against the alternative $\mu \neq \mu_0$. What are Ω and ω in this case? (*Hint*: see Exercise 1 on page 225.)

6. Given a random sample of size n from a normal population having $\mu = 0$, find an expression for the likelihood ratio statistic λ for testing the null hypothesis $\sigma = \sigma_0$ against the alternative $\sigma \neq \sigma_0$. What are Ω and ω in this case? (*Hint*: see Exercise 2 on page 225.)

7. A random sample of size n from a normal population with unknown mean and variance is to be used to test the null hypothesis $\mu = \mu_0$ against the alternative hypothesis $\mu \neq \mu_0$. Using the maximum likelihood estimates of μ and σ^2 obtained in Section 9.4.2, show that the likelihood ratio statistic can be written in the form

$$\lambda = \left[1 + \frac{t^2}{n-1}\right]^{-n/2}$$

where $t = (\bar{x} - \mu_0)/(s/\sqrt{n})$. Note that the likelihood ratio test can, thus, be based on the Student-t distribution.

8. Independent random samples of size $n_1, n_2, \ldots,$ and n_k from k normal populations with unknown means and variances are to be used to test the null hypothesis

$$H_0\colon \sigma_1^2 = \sigma_2^2 = \ldots = \sigma_k^2 = \sigma^2$$

against the alternative that these variances are not all equal.

(a) Show that under the null hypothesis the maximum likelihood estimates of the means μ_i and σ^2 are

$$\hat{\mu}_i = \bar{x}_i \quad \text{and} \quad \hat{\sigma}^2 = \sum_{i=1}^{k} \frac{(n_i - 1)s_i^2}{n}$$

while without restrictions the maximum likelihood estimates of the μ_i and σ_i^2 are

$$\hat{\hat{\mu}}_i = \bar{x}_i \quad \text{and} \quad \hat{\hat{\sigma}}_i^2 = \frac{(n_i - 1)s_i^2}{n_i}$$

(This last result follows immediately from the illustration of Section 9.4.2.) Here n equals the sum of the n_i.

(b) Using the results obtained in (a), show that the likelihood ratio statistic can be written as

$$\lambda = \frac{\prod_{i=1}^{k} \left[\frac{(n_i - 1)s_i^2}{n_i}\right]^{n_i/2}}{\left[\sum_{i=1}^{k} \frac{(n_i - 1)s_i^2}{n}\right]^{n/2}}$$

(c) The following are the sample sizes and variances of 4 independent random samples from 4 normal populations:

$$n_1 = 8 \quad n_2 = 10 \quad n_3 = 6 \quad n_4 = 8$$

$$s_1^2 = 16 \quad s_2^2 = 25 \quad s_3^2 = 12 \quad s_4^2 = 24$$

Using the result obtained in (b), calculate $-2 \ln \lambda$ and use this value to test the hypothesis that the four normal populations have equal variances with $\alpha = 0.05$. (*Hint*: reject the null hypothesis if the value obtained for $-2 \ln \lambda$ exceeds $\chi^2_{.05,3}$; the number of degrees of freedom is 3 since $\sigma_1^2 = \sigma_2^2 = \sigma_3^2 = \sigma_4^2$ imposes 3 restrictions on the parameters, see remark on page 254.)

9. Show that for $k = 2$ the likelihood ratio statistic of Exercise **8** can be expressed in terms of the ratio of the two sample variances and that the likelihood ratio test can, therefore, be based on the F distribution.

10. (*An example where the likelihood ratio method fails*) Given one observation of a random variable $\mathbf{x}$ whose range is $\{1, 2, 3, 4, 5, 6, 7\}$, suppose we want to test the null hypothesis that its probability distribution is given by

$$H_0\colon f(1) = \tfrac{1}{12}, f(2) = \tfrac{1}{12}, f(3) = \tfrac{1}{12}, f(4) = \tfrac{1}{4},$$
$$f(5) = \tfrac{1}{6}, f(6) = \tfrac{1}{6}, \text{ and } f(7) = \tfrac{1}{6}$$

against the alternative hypothesis that its probability distribution is given by

$$H_A\colon f(1) = a/3, f(2) = b/3, f(3) = c/3, f(4) = 2/3,$$
$$f(5) = 0,\ f(6) = 0,\ f(7) = 0, \text{ where } a, b, \text{ and } c \text{ are non-negative and } a + b + c = 1$$

(a) Show that the likelihood ratio method leads to a critical region of size 0.25 for which the null hypothesis is rejected if $x = 1$, $x = 2$, or $x = 3$. Also show that the probability of committing a Type II error with this criterion is $\frac{2}{3}$.

(b) Show that the critical region according to which the null hypothesis is rejected if $x = 4$ is also of size 0.25 and that this critical region is *more powerful* than that of the likelihood ratio criterion.

11. (*Unbiased critical regions*) When testing a simple hypothesis against a composite alternative, a critical region is said to be *unbiased* if the corresponding power function assumes its minimum value at the value of the parameter assumed under the simple null hypothesis. (In other words, a critical region is unbiased if the probability of rejecting the null hypothesis is least when the null hypothesis is true.) Given a random variable having the probability density

$$f(x) = 1 + \theta^2(\tfrac{1}{2} - x) \qquad \text{for} \quad 0 < x < 1$$

and $f(x) = 0$ elsewhere, where $-1 \leq \theta \leq 1$, suppose we want to test the null hypothesis $\theta = 0$ against the alternative $\theta \neq 0$ on the basis of a single observation. Show that the critical region $x \leq \alpha$ is of size α, that is is *unbiased,* and that it is *uniformly most powerful.*

BIBLIOGRAPHY

Discussions of various properties of likelihood ratio tests, particularly large-sample properties and Theorem 11.2, may be found in several articles by A. Wald, which are reproduced in

Selected Papers in Statistics and Probability by Abraham Wald, Stanford, Calif.; Stanford University Press, 1957.

Chapter 12

Tests of Hypotheses: Applications

12.1 Introduction

In Chapter 11 we discussed some of the theory which underlies tests of statistical hypotheses; in this chapter we shall present some of the tests which are most widely used in applied statistics. Most of these tests, at least those based on known population distributions, may be derived with the likelihood ratio technique.

To clarify a problem which often seems to confuse the beginner, let us discuss briefly what is meant by *one-sided* and *two-sided* alternatives and the appropriate use of *one-tail* and *two-tail* (or *one-sided* and *two-sided*) critical regions. Referring to a random sample from a normal population with the known variance σ^2, suppose that we want to test the null hypothesis $\mu = \mu_0$ against the one-sided alternative $\mu > \mu_0$; it is called *one-sided* because it asserts that μ lies on one side, in this case to the right, of μ_0. By the same token $\mu < \mu_0$ is also a one-sided alternative, but $\mu \neq \mu_0$ is not. The latter is called a *two-sided* alternative since $\mu \neq \mu_0$ includes values of the parameter lying on both sides of μ_0.

Referring to the one-sided alternative $\mu > \mu_0$, it stands to reason that the null hypothesis should be rejected *only* if $\bar{x}$ (the statistic on which, according to the likelihood ratio technique, the test is to be based) is *large*. Clearly, if $\bar{x}$ is small, say, smaller than μ_0, this tends to support H_0 rather than H_A. In fact, the critical region is

$$\bar{x} \geq \mu_0 + z_\alpha \frac{\sigma}{\sqrt{n}}$$

and the corresponding *one-tail* test (or *one-sided* test) is shown in Figure 12.1. It goes by this name because the null hypothesis is

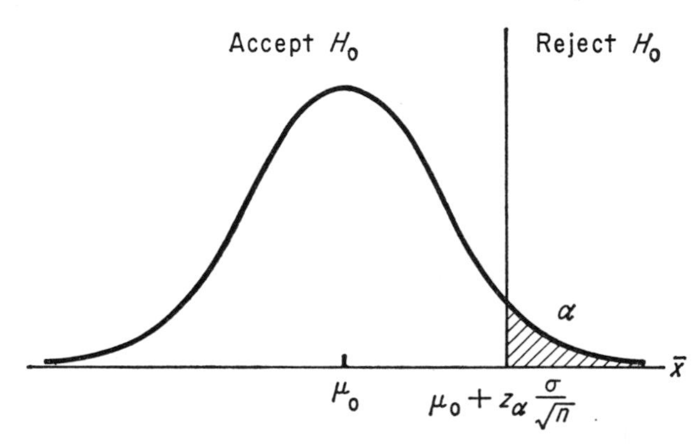

Figure 12.1

rejected only for values of $\bar{x}$ falling into one tail, in this case the right-hand tail, of its sampling distribution. Had the one-sided alternative been $\mu < \mu_0$, the critical region would have been

$$\bar{x} \leq \mu_0 - z_\alpha \frac{\sigma}{\sqrt{n}}$$

which corresponds to the one-tail test shown in Figure 12.2. On the

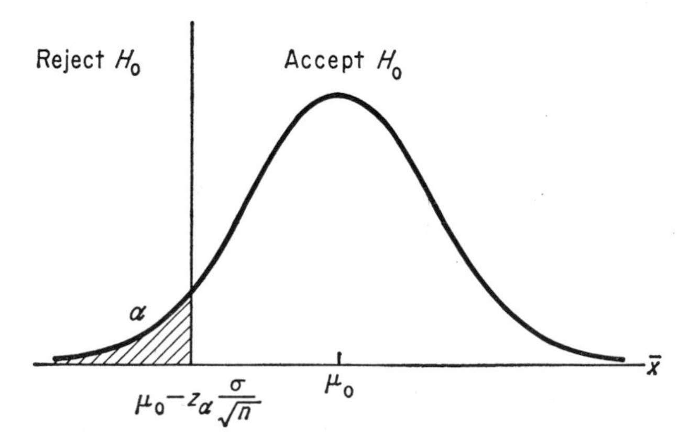

Figure 12.2

other hand, had the alternative hypothesis been $\mu \neq \mu_0$, which is two-sided, the appropriate critical region would have been

$$|\bar{x} - \mu_0| \geq z_{\alpha/2} \frac{\sigma}{\sqrt{n}}$$

as we showed in Section 11.3.2. This *two-tail* criterion is illustrated in Figure 12.3; the null hypothesis is rejected for values of $\bar{\mathbf{x}}$ falling into either tail of its sampling distribution.

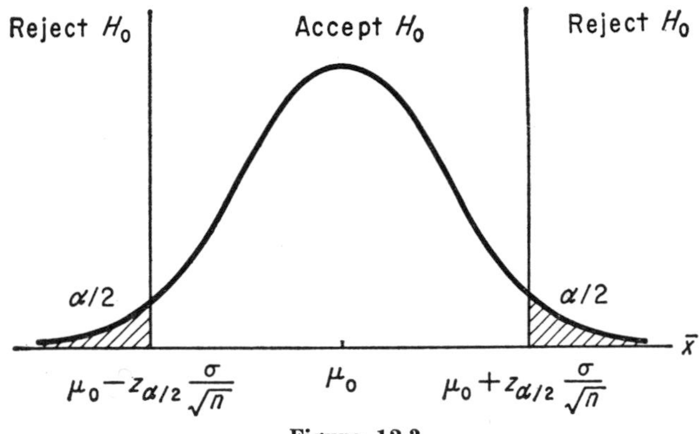

Figure 12.3

Although there are exceptions to this rule (see, for example, Exercise 5 on page 265), *one-sided alternatives* usually lead to *one-tail tests* while *two-sided alternatives* usually lead to *two-tail tests*. Which tail of a distribution is to be used as the critical region of a one-tail test is a question which can be decided only on the basis of the nature of H_A.

12.2 Tests Concerning Means

In Sections 12.2.1 and 12.2.2 we shall discuss some of the most important one-sample tests concerning the mean of a population and two-sample tests concerning the means of two populations; tests concerning the means of more than two populations will be taken up later in Chapter 14. All of the tests discussed in Sections 12.2.1 and 12.2.2 are based on normal distribution theory, assuming either that the samples come from normal populations or that they are large enough to justify normal approximations. Some *nonparametric* alternatives to these tests are given in Section 12.5; as will be explained later, these nonparametric tests apply under very general assumptions concerning the populations from which the samples are obtained.

12.2.1 *One-sample tests concerning means*

The first test which we shall consider is the one used as an example in Section 11.3.2; given a random sample of size n from a normal population having the known variance σ^2, the "best" critical regions of size α for testing the null hypothesis

$$H_0\colon \mu = \mu_0$$

against the alternatives $\mu > \mu_0$, $\mu < \mu_0$, or $\mu \neq \mu_0$ are, respectively, $z \geq z_\alpha$, $z \leq -z_\alpha$, and $|z| \geq z_{\alpha/2}$, where

$$z = \frac{(\bar{x} - \mu_0)\sqrt{n}}{\sigma} \tag{12.2.1}$$

and z_α is as defined on page 227. The most frequently used values are $z_{.05} = 1.64$, $z_{.025} = 1.96$, $z_{.01} = 2.33$, and $z_{.005} = 2.58$. Simple algebra will show that the above criteria are identical with those referred to in the introduction to this chapter.

It should be noted that the critical regions $z \geq z_\alpha$ and $z \leq -z_\alpha$, with z given by (12.2.1), can also be used to test the null hypothesis $\mu = \mu_0$ against the simple alternative $\mu = \mu_A$ for $\mu_A > \mu_0$ and $\mu_A < \mu_0$, respectively. (We demonstrated this in Section 11.2.2 for the special case where $\sigma^2 = 1$.) In that case it is possible to specify α and β, the probabilities of committing Type I and Type II errors, and determine the minimum sample size needed to attain this degree of precision (see Exercise 6 on page 265).

The critical regions $z \geq z_\alpha$ and $z \leq -z_\alpha$ can also be used to test the null hypothesis $\mu \leq \mu_0$ against the alternative $\mu > \mu_0$ or the null hypothesis $\mu \geq \mu_0$ against the alternative $\mu < \mu_0$. In that case α is not the probability of committing a Type I error; we can only say that this probability is *less than or equal to* α.

To give an example where we use the above test, suppose that it is known that the standard deviation of the amount of coffee a machine puts into 1 lb cans is 0.02 lb. In order to test the hypothesis that on a given day the machine is under control, namely, that the true average amount of coffee per can is 1 lb, a random sample of 25 cans is inspected, yielding an average weight of $\bar{x} = 1.014$ lb.

The null hypothesis we shall want to test is $\mu = 1$ and, since the manufacturer stands to lose money when $\mu > 1$ and the customers lose when $\mu < 1$, the appropriate alternative is $\mu \neq 1$. Choosing $\alpha = 0.01$, we get

$$\frac{(\bar{x} - \mu_0)\sqrt{n}}{\sigma} = \frac{(1.014 - 1)\sqrt{25}}{0.02} = 3.5$$

which exceeds $z_{.005} = 2.58$. Hence, the null hypothesis must be rejected and the machine will have to be adjusted. (To perform this test it was necessary, of course, to look upon the measurements as a random sample from a normal population.)

When dealing with a *large sample* from a population which is not necessarily normal, but which has the finite variance σ^2, we can use the central limit theorem, approximate σ with s, and use the above tests with

$$z = \frac{(\bar{x} - \mu_0)\sqrt{n}}{s} \tag{12.2.2}$$

To illustrate such an approximate *large-sample test* (n must be greater than or equal to 30), suppose we want to test the null hypothesis that the average distance required to stop a car going 20 miles per hour is 25 feet against the alternative that this distance is greater than 25 feet. Suppose, furthermore, that 100 drivers thus tested averaged $\bar{x} = 27.3$ feet with a standard deviation of $s = 4.1$ feet and that α is to be 0.01. Substituting these values into (12.2.2), we get

$$z = \frac{(27.3 - 25)\sqrt{100}}{4.1} = 5.6$$

which exceeds $z_{.01} = 2.33$. Hence, the sample value falls into the critical region, the null hypothesis must be rejected, and we conclude that on the average it takes more than 25 feet to stop a car going 20 miles per hour. (To perform this approximate test we did not have to assume that the sample came from a normal population—only that it came from a population for which the central limit theorem applies.)

When n is small and σ is unknown, the tests which we have discussed so far cannot be used. However, we saw in Exercise 7 on page 256 that *for random samples from normal populations* the likelihood ratio technique yields a test based on the statistic

$$t = \frac{(\bar{x} - \mu_0)\sqrt{n}}{s} \tag{12.2.3}$$

and the t distribution. We, thus, find that appropriate critical regions of size α for testing the null hypothesis

$$H_0\colon \mu = \mu_0$$

against the alternatives $\mu > \mu_0$, $\mu < \mu_0$, or $\mu \neq \mu_0$ are, respectively, $t \geq t_{\alpha,n-1}$, $t \leq -t_{\alpha,n-1}$, and $|t| \geq t_{\alpha/2,n-1}$, where t is given by (12.2.3) and $t_{\alpha,n-1}$ is as defined on page 202. It should be noted that the comments made on page 262 in connection with the alternative hypotheses $\mu = \mu_A$ with $\mu_A > \mu_0$ and $\mu_A < \mu_0$ and the null hypotheses $\mu \leq \mu_0$ and $\mu \geq \mu_0$ apply also in this case.

To illustrate these *small-sample tests*, as they are usually called, suppose that a manufacturer claims that the area covered on the average by a gallon of his paint is at least 600 square feet. Suppose, furthermore, that a random sample of 12 such cans of paint covered on the average $\bar{x} = 589$ square feet with a standard deviation of $s = 26$ square feet and that α is to equal 0.05. To test the null hypothesis $\mu \geq 600$ against the alternative $\mu < 600$ with the probability of committing a Type I error less than or equal to 0.05, the appropriate critical region is $t \leq -t_{.05,11}$, assuming that the measurements may be looked upon as a random sample from a normal population. Substituting $\bar{x} = 589$, $\mu_0 = 600$, $n = 12$, and $s = 26$ into (12.2.3), we get

$$t = \frac{(589 - 600)\sqrt{12}}{26} = -1.46$$

which is *greater* than $-t_{.05,11} = -1.796$. Hence, the null hypothesis cannot be rejected; if we accept the manufacturer's claim, which under the circumstances may be the most appropriate action, we are, of course, exposed to the unknown risk of committing a Type II error.

EXERCISES

1. A random sample of size 36 is taken from a normal population with the known variance $\sigma^2 = 25$. If the mean of this sample is $\bar{x} = 42.6$, test the null hypothesis $\mu = 45$ against the alternative hypothesis $\mu < 45$ with $\alpha = 0.05$.

2. A survey showed that a random sample of 100 private passenger cars were driven on the average 11,800 miles a year with a standard deviation of 2250 miles. Use this information to test the hypothesis that private passenger cars are driven on the average 12,000 miles a year against the alternative that the correct average is not 12,000 miles a year. Use $\alpha = 0.05$.

3. A random sample of 8 steel beams has an average compressive strength of 54,312 psi with a standard deviation of 486 psi. Test the hypothesis that the true average compressive strength of the steel beams from which this sample was obtained is 55,000 against the alternative hypothesis that it is less. Use $\alpha = 0.01$.

4. A study of 20 families in a certain large city showed that their average income during 1960 was $7245 with a standard deviation of $864. Test the hypothesis that the true average income of families in this city during 1960 was $6500 against the alternative that it was more. Use $\alpha = 0.05$.

5. Given a random sample of size n from a normal population with the known variance σ^2, show that the null hypothesis $\mu = \mu_0$ can be tested against the alternative hypothesis $\mu \neq \mu_0$ with a *one-tail* criterion based on the chi-square distribution.

6. Given a random sample from a normal population with the known variance σ^2, suppose that we want to test the hypothesis $\mu = \mu_0$ against the alternative hypothesis $\mu = \mu_A$ (with $\mu_A > \mu_0$) and that we want to have the probabilities of committing Type I and Type II errors equal preassigned values α and β. Show that the size of the sample must be

$$n = \frac{\sigma^2(z_\alpha + z_\beta)^2}{(\mu_A - \mu_0)^2}$$

Use this formula to find n when $\sigma = 10$, $\mu_0 = 27$, $\mu_A = 30$, $\alpha = 0.05$, and $\beta = 0.01$.

7. (*Control charts for means*) In industrial quality control it is often necessary to test the same hypothesis over and over again at regular intervals of time. Suppose, for example, that a process for making compression springs is under control if the free lengths of the springs have a mean of $\mu = 1.5$; it is known that the standard deviation of the free lengths of these springs is $\sigma = 0.02$. In order to test whether the process is under control, random samples of size n are taken, say, every hour, and it is decided in each case on the basis of $\bar{x}$ whether to accept or reject the null hypothesis $\mu_0 = 1.5$. To simplify this task, quality control engineers use *control charts* like that of Figure 12.4,

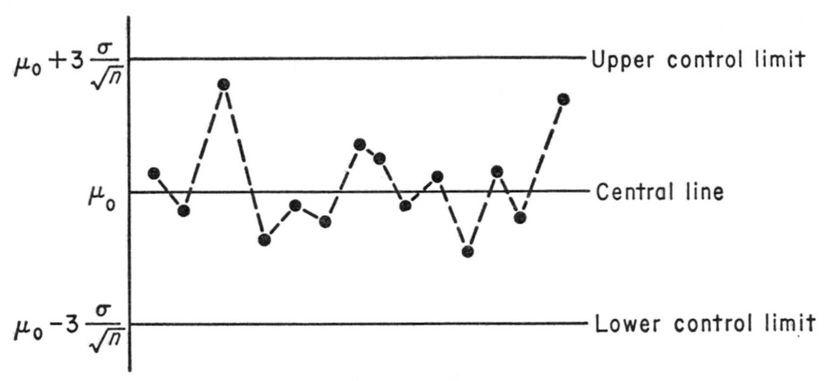

Figure 12.4

where the vertical scale is the scale of measurement of $\bar{x}$, the *central line* is at $\mu_0 = 1.5$ and the *upper and lower control limits* are at $\mu_0 + 3(\sigma/\sqrt{n})$ and $\mu_0 - 3(\sigma/\sqrt{n})$. Each sample mean is plotted on this chart and the process is considered to be in control so long as the $\bar{x}$'s fall between the control limits. Assuming that the data constitute random samples from a normal population, α is less than 0.003. Using $\mu_0 = 1.5$ and $\sigma = 0.02$, construct a control chart for the mean of samples of size 5. Also plot on this chart the following data, constituting the means of random samples of size 5 taken at hourly intervals during the operation of the manufacturing process:

1.510, 1.495, 1.521, 1.505, 1.524, 1.520, 1.488, 1.465, 1.529, 1.444,

1.531, 1.502, 1.490, 1.531, 1.475, 1.478, 1.522, 1.491, 1.491, 1.482.

Was the process ever out of control?

12.2.2 *Differences between means*

There are many problems in applied research where we are interested in testing hypotheses concerning differences between the means of two populations. For instance, we may want to decide on the basis of appropriate samples whether there is actually a difference between the true average speeds with which men and women can perform a certain task, or we may want to decide on the basis of suitable experiments whether the true average lifetime of one kind of flashlight battery actually exceeds that of another kind by 10 hours.

Let us suppose first that we are dealing with *independent* random samples of size n_1 and n_2 from two normal populations having the means μ_1 and μ_2 and the *known* variances σ_1^2 and σ_2^2, and that we want to test the null hypothesis

$$H_0: \mu_1 - \mu_2 = \delta$$

against one of the alternatives $\mu_1 - \mu_2 > \delta$, $\mu_1 - \mu_2 < \delta$, or $\mu_1 - \mu_2 \neq \delta$. Applying the likelihood ratio technique, we arrive at a test based on $\bar{x}_1 - \bar{x}_2$, the difference between the two sample means, and using Theorem 7.6 on page 179 we can write the respective critical regions as $z \geq z_\alpha$, $z \leq -z_\alpha$, and $|z| \geq z_{\alpha/2}$, where

$$z = \frac{\bar{x}_1 - \bar{x}_2 - \delta}{\sqrt{(\sigma_1^2/n_1) + (\sigma_2^2/n_2)}} \tag{12.2.4}$$

To illustrate this kind of test, suppose that the nicotine contents of two kinds of cigarettes have variabilities of $\sigma_1 = 1.2$ and $\sigma_2 = 1.4$ milligrams. Suppose, furthermore, that in an experiment designed to test the claim that the true average nicotine content of the first kind of cigarette is less than that of the second, 50 cigarettes of the first kind had an average nicotine content of $\bar{x}_1 = 23.8$ milligrams while 40 cigarettes of the second kind had an average nicotine content of $\bar{x}_2 = 24.1$ milligrams. Testing the null hypothesis $\mu_1 - \mu_2 = 0$ against the alternative $\mu_1 - \mu_2 < 0$ with $\alpha = 0.05$, the appropriate critical region is $z \leq -z_{.05}$ with z given by (12.2.4). We thus get

$$z = \frac{23.8 - 24.1}{\sqrt{(1.2^2/50) + (1.4^2/40)}} = -1.08$$

which is *not* less than $-z_{.05} = -1.64$. Hence, the null hypothesis must be accepted, or, looking upon the test as a *test of significance*, we might merely state that the observed difference between the sample means may reasonably be attributed to chance, without committing ourselves one way or the other.

When dealing with *large samples* from populations which are not necessarily normal, but which are such that the central limit theorem applies, we can approximate σ_1 and σ_2 with s_1 and s_2, and use the above test with

$$z = \frac{\bar{x}_1 - \bar{x}_2 - \delta}{\sqrt{(s_1^2/n_1) + (s_2^2/n_2)}} \tag{12.2.5}$$

When n_1 and n_2 are small and σ_1 and σ_2 are unknown, the tests which we have discussed so far cannot be used. However, *for random samples from two normal populations having* $\sigma_1 = \sigma_2$ the likelihood ratio technique yields a test based on the statistic

$$t = \frac{\bar{x}_1 - \bar{x}_2 - \delta}{\sqrt{\frac{(n_1 - 1)s_1^2 + (n_2 - 1)s_2^2}{n_1 + n_2 - 2}} \sqrt{\frac{1}{n_1} + \frac{1}{n_2}}} \tag{12.2.6}$$

and the t distribution. In order to prove that under the null hypothesis (12.2.6) gives a value assumed by a random variable having the t distribution with $n_1 + n_2 - 2$ degrees of freedom, let us point out first that according to Theorems 7.6, 8.4, and 8.6.

$$\frac{\bar{\mathbf{x}}_1 - \bar{\mathbf{x}}_2 - \delta}{\sigma\sqrt{(1/n_1) + (1/n_2)}} \tag{12.2.7}$$

has the standard normal distribution while

$$\frac{(n_1 - 1)\mathbf{s}_1^2 + (n_2 - 1)\mathbf{s}_2^2}{\sigma^2} \tag{12.2.8}$$

has a chi-square distribution with $n_1 + n_2 - 2$ degrees of freedom. Here σ is the common standard deviation of the two populations, that is, $\sigma = \sigma_1 = \sigma_2$. Assuming that the two random variables given by (12.2.7) and (12.2.8) are independent, a fact which we shall not be able to prove, the definition of the t distribution, see page 201, leads to the desired result that (12.2.6) gives a value assumed by a random variable having the t distribution with $n_1 + n_2 - 2$ degrees of freedom. We, thus, find that appropriate critical regions of size α for testing the null hypothesis

$$H_0\colon \mu_1 - \mu_2 = \delta$$

against the alternatives $\mu_1 - \mu_2 > \delta$, $\mu_1 - \mu_2 < \delta$, or $\mu_1 - \mu_2 \neq \delta$ are, respectively, $t \geq t_{\alpha, n_1+n_2-2}$, $t \leq -t_{\alpha, n_1+n_2-2}$, and $|t| \geq t_{\alpha/2, n_1+n_2-2}$, where t is given by (12.2.6).

To illustrate this *two-sample t test*, suppose that 8 test plots planted with one variety of corn yielded on the average 94.3 bushels per acre with a standard deviation of 5.7 bushels per acre while 7 test plots planted with a second variety of corn yielded on the average 85.7 bushels per acre with a standard deviation of 6.2 bushels per acre. To test the null hypothesis $\mu_1 - \mu_2 = 0$ against the two-sided alternative $\mu_1 - \mu_2 \neq 0$ with $\alpha = 0.05$, we substitute the given values into (12.2.6), getting

$$t = \frac{94.3 - 85.7 - 0}{\sqrt{\frac{7(5.7)^2 + 6(6.2)^2}{13}}\sqrt{\frac{1}{8} + \frac{1}{7}}} = 2.8$$

Since this exceeds $t_{.025,13} = 2.160$, the null hypothesis must be rejected; we conclude that there is a difference between the true average yields of the two varieties of corn.

If the assumption $\sigma_1 = \sigma_2$ is unreasonable, there are several alternative methods that can be used. A relatively simple one consists of pairing the values obtained in the two samples in a random fashion and then looking upon their differences as a random sample of size n_1 or n_2, whichever is smaller, from a normal population whose mean equals δ under the null hypothesis. We, thus, test the null hypothesis $\mu = \delta$ against an appropriate alternative with the method of Section 12.2.1. An alternate method of handling this kind of problem is given by the *Behrens-Fisher test* referred to in the Bibliography on page 294.

If we wanted to study the effectiveness of a new diet on the basis of weights "before and after," or if we wanted to study whatever differences there may be between the I.Q.'s of husbands and wives, the methods which we have introduced in this section cannot be used. In each of these examples the two samples are *not* independent; in fact, the data are *paired*. The following is a possible way of handling this kind of problem: referring to the values obtained in the first sample as x_{1i} for $i = 1, 2, \ldots, n$, and the values obtained in the second sample as x_{2i} for $i = 1, 2, \ldots, n$, we can test the null hypothesis

$$H_0\colon \mu_1 - \mu_2 = \delta$$

against an appropriate alternative on the basis of the differences

$$d_i = x_{1i} - x_{2i} \qquad \text{for} \quad i = 1, 2, \ldots, n$$

Looking upon these differences as a random sample of size n from a population having the mean $\mu = \delta$ if the null hypothesis is true, we can then use one of the tests of Section 12.2.1. If n is large we can use the one described on page 263; if n is small we can use the t test described on page 264, provided that the differences may be looked upon as a random sample from a normal population.

EXERCISES

1. Referring to the numerical example on page 267, the one dealing with the nicotine content of the two kinds of cigarettes, what is the greatest value of $\bar{x}_1 - \bar{x}_2$ for which we would have rejected the null hypothesis $\mu_1 - \mu_2 = 0$ with $\alpha = 0.05$? Also find the probabilities of committing Type II errors with the criterion of this example if (a) $\mu_1 - \mu_2 = -0.2$, (b) $\mu_1 - \mu_2 = -0.5$, and (c) $\mu_1 - \mu_2 = -1.0$.

2. Random samples of the heights of adult males living in two different countries produced the following results (in inches):

$$n_1 = 180 \qquad \bar{x}_1 = 68.7 \qquad s_1 = 2.1$$

$$n_2 = 150 \qquad \bar{x}_2 = 67.1 \qquad s_2 = 2.9$$

Test at a level of significance of 0.01 whether the difference between the two sample means is significant.

3. In order to compare the mileage yield of two kinds of gasoline, several tests were run and the following results were obtained: (Each figure represents the number of miles obtained with a gallon of the respective gasoline)

Gasoline A	*Gasoline B*
21	17
19	20
18	19
20	21
21	17
21	20

Calculate t according to (12.2.6) and use it to test the null hypothesis that there is no difference in the true average mileage yield of the two kinds of gasoline against a two-sided alternative. Use $\alpha = 0.05$.

4. An economist claims that the average weekly food expenditures of families in one city exceeds that of families in another city by at least \$2.50. Test this claim at α at most 0.05, if a random sample of 12 families in the first city showed an average weekly food expenditure of \$38.25 with a standard deviation of \$10.30, and a random sample of 15 families in the second city showed an average weekly food expenditure of \$32.50 with a standard deviation of \$8.65.

5. The following are the weights "before and after" of 8 adult females experimenting with a new diet:

	Before	*After*
Mrs. Abel	127	122
Mrs. Brown	130	120
Mrs. Collins	114	116
Mrs. Green	139	132
Mrs. Taylor	150	144
Mrs. White	147	138
Mrs. Doe	167	155
Miss Black	153	152

Test the null hypothesis that the diet is not effective against an appropriate one-sided alternative with $\alpha = 0.01$.

6. Given independent random samples of size n from two normal populations having the known variances σ_1^2 and σ_2^2, suppose we want to test the null hypothesis $\mu_1 - \mu_2 = \delta$ against the alternative hypothesis $\mu_1 - \mu_2 = \delta'$ with the probabilities of committing Type I and Type II errors assuming preassigned values α and β. Show that the sample size must be

$$n = \frac{(\sigma_1^2 + \sigma_2^2)(z_\alpha + z_\beta)^2}{(\delta - \delta')^2}$$

Use this formula to find n when $\sigma_1 = 10$, $\sigma_2 = 12$, $\delta = 100$, $\delta' = 105$, $\alpha = 0.05$, and $\beta = 0.05$.

12.3 Tests Concerning Variances

There are several reasons why it is important to test hypotheses concerning variances of populations. So far as *direct* applications are concerned, a manufacturer (who has to meet rigid specifications) may have to know something about the variability of his product, a teacher may have to know what variability he can expect in the performance of his students, and a department store buyer may want to know what variability there is due to chance in the demand for a certain product. So far as *indirect* applications are concerned, tests concerning variances are often a prerequisite for tests concerning other parameters of populations. For instance, we saw in Section 12.2.2 that the two-sample t test is based on the assumption that the variances of the two populations are equal; in practice, this means that we may have to test the reasonableness of this assumption before we can actually perform the t test concerning the means.

The tests which we shall study in this section include a criterion for testing the null hypothesis that the variance of a normal population equals a given constant, an approximate criterion for testing the null hypothesis that k normal populations have equal variances, and an exact test of the null hypothesis that the variances of two normal populations are equal.

The test which we shall describe first is essentially that of Exercise 10 on page 246, although it is based on the likelihood ratio procedure instead of the Neyman-Pearson Lemma to accommodate composite alternatives and it does not make the simplifying assumption that $\mu = 0$. Given a random sample of size n from a normal population, we shall want to test the null hypothesis

$$H_0\colon \sigma^2 = \sigma_0^2$$

against one of the alternatives $\sigma^2 > \sigma_0^2$, $\sigma^2 < \sigma_0^2$, or $\sigma^2 \neq \sigma_0^2$. Applying the likelihood ratio technique, we arrive at a test based on the sample variance s^2, and using Theorem 8.6 on page 195, we can write the critical regions for testing the null hypothesis against the two one-sided alternatives as $\chi^2 \geq \chi^2_{\alpha,n-1}$ and $\chi^2 \leq \chi^2_{1-\alpha,n-1}$, respectively, where

$$\chi^2 = \frac{(n-1)s^2}{\sigma_0^2} \tag{12.3.1}$$

and $\chi^2_{\alpha,n-1}$ is as defined on page 196. When using the two-sided alternative, the null hypothesis is rejected if either

$$\chi^2 \geq \chi^2_{\alpha/2,n-1} \qquad \text{or} \qquad \chi^2 \leq \chi^2_{1-\alpha/2,n-1}.$$

The size of all these critical regions is α.

To illustrate this test, suppose that an optical firm orders glass, whose index of refraction is allowed a variability of $\sigma = 0.01$, and that it is desired to test the null hypothesis $\sigma = 0.01$ against the alternative $\sigma > 0.01$ on the basis of a random sample of size 20. If measurements of the index refraction of 20 pieces of this glass yielded a sample variance of $s^2 = 0.00023$, substitution into (12.3.1) gives

$$\chi^2 = \frac{19(0.00023)}{(0.01)^2} = 43.7$$

Since this value exceeds $\chi^2_{.01,19} = 36.191$ the null hypothesis must be rejected for $\alpha = 0.01$. It follows that the glass will have to be rejected.

In Exercise 8 on page 256 the reader was asked to develop the likelihood ratio criterion for testing the null hypothesis that k samples come from normal populations having the common variance σ^2. Since the resulting expression for the likelihood ratio statistic was relatively complicated, it was suggested that the test be based on Theorem 11.2, namely, on the large-sample distribution of $-2 \ln \lambda$. In Exercise 9 on page 257 the reader was asked to show that for $k = 2$ the likelihood ratio can be expressed in terms of the ratio s_1^2/s_2^2, so that the resulting test can be based on the F distribution, see discussion on page 201. Given independent random samples of size n_1 and n_2 from two normal populations having the variances σ_1^2 and σ_2^2, appropriate critical regions of size α for testing the null hypothesis

$$H_0\colon \sigma_1^2 = \sigma_2^2$$

against the one-sided alternatives $\sigma_1^2 > \sigma_2^2$ or $\sigma_1^2 < \sigma_2^2$ are, respectively,

$$s_1^2/s_2^2 \geq F_{\alpha, n_1-1, n_2-1} \qquad \text{and} \qquad s_2^2/s_1^2 \geq F_{\alpha, n_2-1, n_1-1}$$

The appropriate critical region for testing the null hypothesis against the two-sided alternative $\sigma_1^2 \neq \sigma_2^2$ is

$$s_1^2/s_2^2 \geq F_{\alpha/2, n_1-1, n_2-1} \quad \text{if} \quad s_1^2 \geq s_2^2$$

and

$$s_2^2/s_1^2 \geq F_{\alpha/2, n_2-1, n_1-1} \quad \text{if} \quad s_1^2 < s_2^2$$

These criteria may look somewhat complicated because they are all based on the righthand tail of the F distribution and the result obtained in Exercise 1 on page 203, namely, the fact that if a random variable $\mathbf{x}$ has the F distribution with ν_1 and ν_2 degrees of freedom, then $1/\mathbf{x}$ has the F distribution with ν_2 and ν_1 degrees of freedom.

To illustrate this F test for the equality of two population variances, suppose we are interested in using the two-sample t test to compare the average tensil strength of two kinds of structural steel and that we must, therefore, determine first whether it is reasonable to assume that $\sigma_1^2 = \sigma_2^2$. Suppose, furthermore, that we want to test this null hypothesis against the two-sided alternative $\sigma_1^2 \neq \sigma_2^2$ with $\alpha = 0.02$ and that an experiment yielded the following results: (units of tensile strength are 1000 psi)

$$n_1 = 13 \qquad s_1^2 = 19.2 \qquad n_2 = 16 \qquad s_2^2 = 3.5$$

Since s_1^2 is greater than s_2^2, the statistic on which the decision will have to be based is $s_1^2/s_2^2 = 19.2/3.5 = 5.49$. This value exceeds $F_{.01,12,15} = 3.67$, the null hypothesis will have to be rejected, and the two-sample t test cannot be used.

EXERCISES

1. The lifetimes of certain batteries are supposed to have a variance of 5000 hours. Test the null hypothesis $\sigma^2 = 5000$ against the two-sided alternative $\sigma^2 \neq 5000$ with $\alpha = 0.02$, if 25 of these batteries had a sample variance of $s^2 = 7200$ hours. Assume that it is reasonable to treat these data as a random sample from a normal population.

2. Test the hypothesis that for the diameters of certain bolts $\sigma = 0.02$ against the alternative hypothesis that $\sigma < 0.02$, if the diameters of a random sample of 15 of these bolts had a variance of $s^2 = 0.00016$. Use $\alpha = 0.05$ and assume that the data may be looked upon as a random sample from a normal population.

3. Test whether it was reasonable to make the assumption $\sigma_1^2 = \sigma_2^2$ in the example on page 268, the one which dealt with the average yield of two varieties of corn. Use $\alpha = 0.10$.

4. Test whether it was reasonable to make the assumption $\sigma_1^2 = \sigma_2^2$ in Exercise 3 on page 270. Use $\alpha = 0.02$.

5. The following are scores obtained in a personality test by samples of married and unmarried women:

Unmarried:	85	65	74	79	60	77	75	68	69
Married:	72	76	66	73	73	63	70	70	71

Assuming that these data may be looked upon as independent random samples from two normal populations, test the null hypothesis $\sigma_1^2 = \sigma_2^2$ against the alternative hypothesis $\sigma_1^2 \neq \sigma_2^2$ with $\alpha = 0.02$.

12.4 Tests Based on Count Data

If the outcome of an experiment is the number of defectives in a sample of light bulbs, the number of imperfections in 100 yards of a certain cloth, the number of persons in a sample of size 400 whose sense of humor is rated very low, the number of cures among n persons having a given disease, . . ., we refer to these data as *count data,* contrasting them, thus, to measurements given on a continuous scale. The appropriate models for analyzing count data are the binomial distribution, the Poisson distribution, the multinomial distribution, and the many other discrete distributions which we studied in Chapter 3. In this section we shall present some of the most common tests based on count data, primarily those concerning the parameters of binomial and multinomial distributions.

12.4.1 *Tests concerning proportions*

The parameter θ of a binomial distribution gives the probability of success on an individual trial and, hence, the proportion of successes one can expect to get in the long run. To test on the basis of samples whether the true proportion of cures from a certain disease is 0.80 or whether the true proportion of defectives in a very large shipment of ball bearings is 0.02 is, thus, equivalent to testing the hypothesis that the parameters of binomial distributions are, respectively, $\theta = 0.80$ and $\theta = 0.02$. (In the case of the ball bearings we are assuming that the binomial approximation to the hypergeometric distribution is justified.)

In Exercise 8 on page 246 the reader was asked to show that the best criterion for testing the null hypothesis $\theta = \theta_0$ against the alternative $\theta = \theta_A$, where θ is the parameter of a binomial population, is based on x, the actual number of successes obtained in n trials. When dealing with composite alternatives, the likelihood ratio technique, similarly, yields tests based on the observed number of successes. In fact, the critical region of the likelihood ratio criterion for testing the null hypothesis

$$H_0\colon \theta = \theta_0$$

against the alternative $\theta > \theta_0$ is

$$x \geq k_\alpha$$

where k_α is the *smallest* integer for which

$$\sum_{y=k_\alpha}^{n} b(y; n, \theta_0) \leq \alpha \qquad (12.4.1)$$

and $b(y; n, \theta_0)$ is the probability of getting y successes in n binomial trials with $\theta = \theta_0$. The probability of committing a Type I error with this criterion (as well as the ones which follow) is, thus, as close as possible to α without exceeding α.

Similarly, the critical region of the likelihood ratio criterion for testing the null hypothesis $\theta = \theta_0$ against the alternative $\theta < \theta_0$ is

$$x \leq k'_\alpha$$

where k'_α is the *largest* integer for which

$$\sum_{y=0}^{k'_\alpha} b(y; n, \theta_0) \leq \alpha \tag{12.4.2}$$

and, finally, the critical region for testing the null hypothesis $\theta = \theta_0$ against the two-sided alternative $\theta \neq \theta_0$ is

$$x \geq k_{\alpha/2} \qquad \text{or} \qquad x \leq k'_{\alpha/2}$$

To illustrate this test concerning the parameter of a binomial population, suppose we want to test the null hypothesis $\theta = 0.50$ against the two-sided alternative $\theta \neq 0.50$ with $\alpha = 0.05$. If the test is to be based on 20 trials, we find from Table I that $k_{.025} = 15$, $k'_{.025} = 5$, and that, therefore, the null hypothesis must be rejected if the observed number of successes in 20 trials is greater than or equal to 15 or less than or equal to 5. It will be left to the reader to verify that the corresponding probability of committing a Type I error is 0.0414.

In order to perform the tests which we have described it is desirable, almost necessary, to refer to tables of binomial probabilities. For $n \leq 20$ we can use Table I at the end of this book and for $n \leq 100$ we can use the tables referred to in the Bibliography on page 89. For larger values of n it is customary to approximate the binomial distribution with a normal distribution and treat

$$z = \frac{x - n\theta}{\sqrt{n\theta(1 - \theta)}} \tag{12.4.3}$$

as a value assumed by a random variable having the standard normal distribution. For large n we can, thus, test the null hypothesis $\theta = \theta_0$ against the alternatives $\theta > \theta_0$. $\theta < \theta_0$, or $\theta \neq \theta_0$ using, respectively, the critical regions $z \geq z_\alpha$, $z \leq -z_\alpha$, and $|z| \geq z_{\alpha/2}$, with z given by (12.4.3) and $\theta = \theta_0$.

12.4.2 *Differences among k proportions*

In applied research there are many problems in which inferences must be based on differences among two or more sample proportions. For instance, if 83 per cent of the seeds in one sample germinate and only 79 per cent of the seeds in another, we may want to arrive at some conclusion concerning the corresponding true proportions for the two kinds of seed. Similarly, we may want to use sample proportions obtained in a survey to test whether the true proportions of sons taking up the occupations of their fathers is the same for lawyers, bankers, teachers, and engineers.

To indicate a general method for handling problems of this kind, suppose that independent random samples from k binomial populations with parameters θ_1, θ_2, ..., and θ_k have yielded, respectively, x_1, x_2, ..., and x_k successes in n_1, n_2, ..., and n_k trials. If the sizes of these samples are sufficiently large, we can approximate the distributions of the random variables.

$$\frac{\mathbf{x}_i - n_i\theta_i}{\sqrt{n_i\theta_i(1 - \theta_i)}} \quad \text{for} \quad i = 1, 2, \ldots, k \tag{12.4.4}$$

with independent standard normal distributions, and according to Theorem 8.3 we can then approximate the distribution of

$$\sum_{i=1}^{k} \frac{(\mathbf{x}_i - n_i\theta_i)^2}{n_i\theta_i(1 - \theta_i)} \tag{12.4.5}$$

with a chi-square distribution having k degrees of freedom. Using the value obtained for this random variable with $\theta_1 = \theta_2 = \ldots = \theta_k = \theta$, we can thus reject the null hypothesis that the θ_i are all equal to θ *if this value is greater than or equal to* $\chi^2_{\alpha,k}$.

When θ is unknown, which is very often the case, it is customary to substitute for it the *pooled estimate*

$$\hat{\theta} = \frac{x_1 + x_2 + \ldots + x_k}{n_1 + n_2 + \ldots + n_k} \tag{12.4.6}$$

and test the null hypothesis $\theta_1 = \theta_2 = \cdots = \theta_k = \theta$ against the alternative that the θ_i are *not all equal* with the critical region

$$\chi^2 \geq \chi^2_{\alpha,k-1} \tag{12.4.7}$$

where χ^2, the statistic on which the criterion is based, is given by the formula

$$\chi^2 = \sum_{i=1}^{k} \frac{(x_i - n_i\hat{\theta})^2}{n_i\hat{\theta}(1 - \hat{\theta})} \tag{12.4.8}$$

The loss of one degree of freedom in (12.4.7) is due to the fact that an estimate is substituted for the unknown parameter θ; a formal discussion of this is referred to in the Bibliography on page 294.

Before we actually give an example to illustrate this test, let us first present an alternate form of the χ^2 statistic (12.4.8), which lends itself more readily to other applications. Arranging the data as in the following table

	Sample 1	*Sample* 2		*Sample* k
Successes	x_1	x_2	...	x_k
Failures	$n_1 - x_1$	$n_2 - x_2$	...	$n_k - x_k$

let us refer to its entries as the *observed cell frequencies* f_{ij}, with the first subscript indicating the row and the second subscript indicating the column of this *2 by k table*. Under the null hypothesis $\theta_1 = \theta_2 = \ldots = \theta_k = \theta$ the *expected cell frequencies* for the first row are $n_j\theta$, those for the second row are $n_j(1 - \theta)$. Estimating θ as before by means of (12.4.6), we shall estimate the expected cell frequencies as

$$e_{1j} = n_j\hat{\theta} \qquad \text{and} \qquad e_{2j} = n_j(1 - \hat{\theta}) \tag{12.4.9}$$

for $j = 1, 2, \ldots,$ and k. Using the observed cell frequencies f_{ij} and the (estimated) expected cell frequencies e_{ij} as given by (12.4.9), it can be shown that the χ^2 statistic (12.4.8) can also be written in the form

$$\chi^2 = \sum_{i=1}^{2} \sum_{j=1}^{k} \frac{(f_{ij} - e_{ij})^2}{e_{ij}} \tag{12.4.10}$$

It will be left to the reader to show in Exercise 5 on page 280 that formulas (12.4.8) and (12.4.10) are, indeed, equivalent.

To illustrate this χ^2 test, suppose we want to determine, on the basis of the data in the following table, whether the true proportion of defectives produced by a machine remains constant from day to day:

	1st day	*2nd day*	*3rd day*
Number of defectives	12	15	6
Number of nondefectives	88	105	74

The pooled estimate of θ, the assumedly constant proportion of defectives produced by the machine, is

$$\hat{\theta} = \frac{12 + 15 + 6}{100 + 120 + 80} = 0.11$$

and the expected cell frequencies, calculated according to (12.4.9), are 11.0, 13.2, 8.8 for the first row and 89.0, 106.8, 71.2 for the second. Substituting these expected cell frequencies together with the observed cell frequencies into (12.4.10), we get

$$\chi^2 = \frac{(12 - 11.0)^2}{11.0} + \frac{(15 - 13.2)^2}{13.2} + \frac{(6 - 8.8)^2}{8.8} + \frac{(88 - 89.0)^2}{89.0} + \frac{(105 - 106.8)^2}{106.8} + \frac{(74 - 71.2)^2}{71.2}$$

$$= 1.379$$

Since this value is less than $\chi^2_{.05,2} = 5.991$, the null hypothesis cannot be rejected. It seems reasonable to conclude that the production process is under control.

EXERCISES

1. (a) The null hypothesis that the parameter of a binomial distribution is $\theta = 0.40$ is to be tested against the alternative hypothesis $\theta > 0.40$ on the basis of $n = 18$ trials. Use Table I to find $k_{.05}$, the probability of committing a Type I error with this criterion, and the probabilities of committing Type II errors when $\theta = 0.50$ and $\theta = 0.60$.

(b) The null hypothesis that the parameter of a binomial distribution is $\theta = 0.75$ is to be tested against the alternative hypothesis $\theta < 0.75$ on the basis of $n = 15$ trials. Use Table I to find $k'_{.01}$, the probability of committing a Type I error with this criterion, and the probabilities of committing Type II errors when $\theta = 0.65$ and $\theta = 0.60$.

(c) The null hypothesis that the parameter of a binomial distribution is $\theta = 0.60$ is to be tested against the alternative hypothesis $\theta \neq 0.60$ on the basis of $n = 20$ trials. Use Table I to find $k_{.025}$ and $k'_{.025}$, the probability of committing a Type I error with this criterion, and the probabilities of committing Type II errors when $\theta = 0.55$ and $\theta = 0.65$.

2. A market research organization is asked to test the hypothesis that at least 65 per cent of all housewives prefer a certain kind of soap to a competing product. Show that the null hypothesis $\theta = 0.65$

(or $\theta \geq 0.65$) cannot be rejected against the alternative hypothesis $\theta < 0.65$ for $\alpha = 0.05$, if 311 of 500 housewives interviewed expressed a preference for the given soap.

3. A sample survey showed that 627 of 800 persons interviewed preferred to live in medium-sized towns. Using a two-sided alternative and $\alpha = 0.05$, test the hypothesis that the true percentage of persons preferring to live in medium-sized towns is $\theta = 0.75$.

4. (a) Modify the criterion on page 276 so that it can be used to test the null hypothesis $\lambda = \lambda_0$ against the alternative hypothesis $\lambda \neq \lambda_0$ on the basis of one observation from a population having a Poisson distribution with the parameter λ. Use Table II to find values corresponding to $k_{.025}$ and $k'_{.025}$ to test the null hypothesis $\lambda = 20$ against the alternative hypothesis $\lambda \neq 20$.

(b) Modify the criterion on page 276 so that it can be used to test the null hypothesis $\lambda = 5$ against the alternative hypothesis $\lambda < 5$ on the basis of a random sample of size 4 from a population having a Poisson distribution with the parameter λ. Test this hypothesis with $\alpha = 0.05$, if such a random sample consisted of the values 3, 7, 2, and 4. (*Hint*: see discussion on page 172.)

5. Show that the two formulas for the χ^2 statistic given by (12.4.8) and (12.4.10) are equivalent.

6. In a random sample of 100 registered voters *with low incomes* 62 are for a certain piece of legislation while 38 are against it; in a random sample of 100 voters *with average incomes* 48 are for the legislation while 52 are against it; and in a random sample of 100 voters *with high incomes* 41 are for the legislation while 59 are against it. Test the null hypothesis that the proportion of voters favoring the legislation is the same for all three populations with $\alpha = 0.05$.

7. A research organization, interested in testing whether the proportions of sons taking up the occupations of their fathers are equal for a selected set of occupations, obtained the following results:

	Doctors	*Bankers*	*Teachers*	*Lawyers*
Same occupation	34	27	28	19
Different occupation	166	123	152	81

Test the null hypothesis that the true proportion of sons taking up the occupations of their fathers is the same for the given occupations. Calculate χ^2 with (12.4.10) and use $\alpha = 0.05$.

8. Show that for $k = 2$ the χ^2 statistic (12.4.8) can be written

$$\chi^2 = \frac{(n_1 + n_2)(n_2x_1 - n_1x_2)^2}{n_1n_2(x_1 + x_2)[(n_1 + n_2) - (x_1 + x_2)]}$$

9. In a poll taken at the preview of a new movie 38 of 100 men said that they liked it, and 52 of 100 women also reacted favorably. Use the form of the χ^2 statistic given in Exercise 8 to test the null hypothesis that there is no difference between the reactions of the corresponding populations. Use $\alpha = 0.05$.

10. A test item in an objective test is *good* if it discriminates between good students and poor students. Is a certain test item *good* if it is answered correctly by 178 of 250 good students and by 89 of 200 poor students? Use the χ^2 statistic of Exercise 8 and $\alpha = 0.01$.

11. (a) Show that for $k = 2$ and *large samples* the null hypothesis $\theta_1 = \theta_2 = \theta$, where θ_1 and θ_2 are the parameters of two binomial populations, can also be tested on the basis of the statistic

$$z = \frac{(x_1/n_1) - (x_2/n_2)}{\sqrt{\hat{\theta}(1 - \hat{\theta})\left(\frac{1}{n_1} + \frac{1}{n_2}\right)}}$$

which is a value assumed by a random variable having *approximately* the standard normal distribution. Here

$$\hat{\theta} = (x_1 + x_2)/(n_1 + n_2)$$

[*Hint*: refer to (7.4.11) and (7.4.12).]

(b) Show that the *square* of the z statistic of part (a) equals the χ^2 statistic (12.4.8) with $k = 2$ and that the two tests are, therefore, *equivalent*. (*Hint*: use the form of the χ^2 statistic given in Exercise 8.)

12. (*Control charts for attributes*) In order to control the proportion of defectives or other characteristics (attributes) of mass produced items, quality control engineers take random samples of size n at regular intervals of time and plot their results on a *control chart* like that of Figure 12.5. If the production process is considered to be under control when the true proportion of defectives (or the true proportion of items having some other characteristic) is θ_0, the *central line* of the control chart is at θ_0 and the *3-sigma upper and lower control limits* are at

$$\theta_0 + 3\sqrt{\frac{\theta_0(1 - \theta_0)}{n}} \quad \text{and} \quad \theta_0 - 3\sqrt{\frac{\theta_0(1 - \theta_0)}{n}}$$

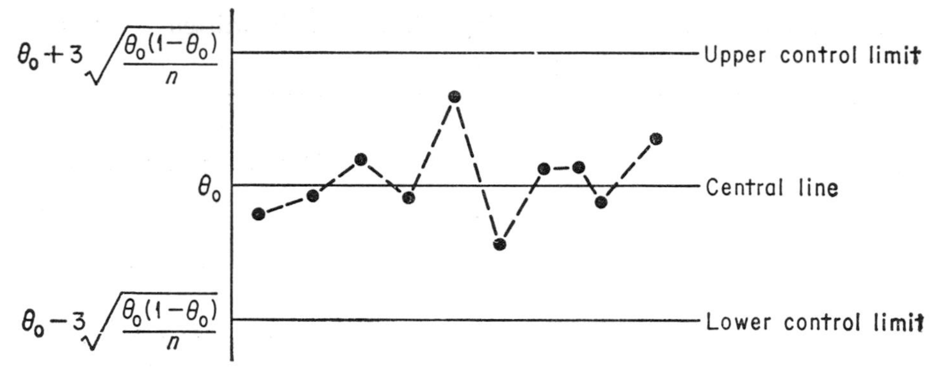

Figure 12.5

As was explained in Exercise 7 on page 265, a process is assumed to be under control so long as the sample proportions, plotted on the control chart, remain between the upper and lower control limits.

Construct a control chart for the proportion of defectives obtained in repeated random samples of size 200 from a process which is considered to be under control when $\theta_0 = 0.05$. Given that 20 consecutive samples of size 200 contained 12, 10, 8, 13, 16, 9, 15, 19, 6, 10, 5, 9, 14, 7, 12, 10, 17, 15, 10, and 18 defectives, plot the corresponding sample proportions on the control chart and comment on the performance of the process.

12.4.3 *Contingency tables*

The χ^2 statistic (12.4.10) plays an important role in many problems dealing with the analysis of count data. In this section we shall use it to analyze *contingency tables* like the following 3 by 3 table obtained in a study of the relationship between the adequacy of a family's milk consumption and the education of its homemaker:

	ADEQUACY OF MILK CONSUMPTION		
	Inadequate	*Barely adequate*	*Very adequate*
Did not finish high school	75	54	12
Finished high school	64	106	28
At least one year of college	28	82	51

The general notation used in the analysis of an *r by k table* is as shown below, where f_{ij} is the observed cell frequency for the cell belonging to the ith row and jth column, the row totals are

$$\sum_{j=1}^{k} f_{ij} = f_{i.}$$

the column totals are

$$\sum_{i=1}^{r} f_{ij} = f_{.j}$$

and the grand total, the sum of all the $r \cdot k$ cell frequencies, is f:

	A_1	A_2		A_k	
B_1	f_{11}	f_{12}	...	f_{1k}	$f_{1.}$
B_2	f_{21}	f_{22}	...	f_{2k}	$f_{2.}$
...	...	...	...	...	...
B_r	f_{r1}	f_{r2}	...	f_{rk}	$f_{r.}$
	$f_{.1}$	$f_{.2}$	...	$f_{.k}$	f

Here one variable has the k categories $A_1, A_2, \ldots, A_k$ and the other variable has the r categories $B_1, B_2, \ldots, B_r$.

The null hypothesis we shall want to test is that the two variables are *independent*. More specifically, if θ_{ij} is the probability that an item will fall into the cell belonging to the ith row and jth column, $\theta_{i.}$ is the probability that an item will fall into the ith row, and $\theta_{.j}$ is the probability that an item will fall into the jth column, the null hypothesis of independence is

$$H_0\colon \theta_{ij} = (\theta_{i.})(\theta_{.j}) \qquad \text{for } i = 1, 2, \ldots, r$$
$$\text{and } j = 1, 2, \ldots, k$$

To test this null hypothesis against the alternative hypothesis that $\theta_{ij} \neq (\theta_{i.})(\theta_{.j})$ for at least one pair of values of i and j, we estimate the probabilities $\theta_{i.}$ and $\theta_{.j}$ as $\hat{\theta}_{i.} = f_{i.}/f$ and $\hat{\theta}_{.j} = f_{.j}/f$, and the expected cell frequencies as

$$e_{ij} = (\hat{\theta}_{i.})(\hat{\theta}_{.j})f = \frac{(f_{i.})(f_{.j})}{f} \tag{12.4.11}$$

Then we base our decision on the statistic

$$\chi^2 = \sum_{i=1}^{r} \sum_{j=1}^{k} \frac{(f_{ij} - e_{ij})^2}{e_{ij}} \tag{12.4.12}$$

and reject the null hypothesis if the value thus obtained is greater than or equal to $\chi^2_{\alpha,(r-1)(k-1)}$. Since the statistic given by (12.4.12) is a value assumed by a random variable whose distribution is only *approximately* chi-square with $(r - 1)(k - 1)$ degrees of freedom, it is customary to use this test only when none of the e_{ij} is less than 5. Consequently, it is sometimes necessary to combine cells as we shall have to in the example on page 285.

To justify the formula given above for the number of degrees of freedom, let us make the following observation: whenever a χ^2 statistic like the one given by (12.4.12) is used *with the expected cell frequencies estimated on the basis of samples,* the number of degrees of freedom is $s - t - 1$, where s is the number of terms in the double sum and t is the number of independent parameters replaced by estimates. In the analysis of an r by k contingency table $s = r \cdot k$ and $t = r + k - 2$, since the r parameters $\theta_{i.}$ and the k parameters $\theta_{.j}$ are subject to the two restrictions that their respective sums are equal to 1. Hence, $s - t - 1 = rk - (r + k - 2) - 1 = (r - 1)(k - 1)$.

Returning now to the numerical example, we find that the expected cell frequencies for the first row are 47.1, 68.2, 25.7, those of the second row are 66.1, 95.8, 36.1, those of the third row are 53.8, 78.0, 29.2, and that

$$\begin{aligned} \chi^2 = & \frac{(75 - 47.1)^2}{47.1} + \frac{(54 - 68.2)^2}{68.2} + \frac{(12 - 25.7)^2}{25.7} \\ & + \frac{(64 - 66.1)^2}{66.1} + \frac{(106 - 95.8)^2}{95.8} + \frac{(28 - 36.1)^2}{36.1} \\ & + \frac{(28 - 53.8)^2}{53.8} + \frac{(82 - 78.0)^2}{78.0} + \frac{(51 - 29.2)^2}{29.2} \\ = & \ 58.63 \end{aligned}$$

Since this value exceeds $\chi^2_{.05,4} = 9.4888$, the null hypothesis must be rejected; we conclude that there is a dependence between a family's milk drinking habits and the education of its homemaker.

12.4.4 *Tests of goodness of fit*

The term "goodness of fit" applies to tests in which we want to determine whether a set of data may be looked upon as values assumed by a random variable having a given distribution. To illustrate, suppose that in the manufacture of yard goods a quality control engineer inspects samples at regular intervals of time, noting the number of imperfections per 10 yards of a given cloth. Having taken 400 such samples in which he obtained 0, 1, 2, 3, ... imperfections with the frequencies shown below, he wants to decide whether these data may be looked upon as values assumed by a random variable having a *Poisson* distribution.

Number of imperfections	*Observed frequencies* f_i	*Poisson probabilities with* $\lambda = 1.5$	*Expected frequencies* e_i
0	89	.2231	89.2
1	143	.3347	133.9
2	94	.2510	100.4
3	42	.1255	50.2
4	20	.0471	18.8
5	8 } 12	.0141	5.6 } 7.3
6	3	.0035	1.4
7	1	.0008	0.3
8	0	.0001	0.0

Using the mean to estimate the parameter of the Poisson distribution, we get $\hat{\lambda} = \bar{x} = 602/400 = 1.505$ or, approximately, 1.5. Then, copying the Poisson probabilities for $\lambda = 1.5$ from Table II and multiplying by 400, the total frequency, we get the *expected frequencies* shown in the righthand column of the above table.

An appropriate test of the null hypothesis that the given data come from a population having a Poisson distribution (against the alternative that the population has some other distribution) is to reject the null hypothesis if

$$\chi^2 \geq \chi^2_{\alpha, m-2}$$

where

$$\chi^2 = \sum_{i=1}^{m} \frac{(f_i - e_i)^2}{e_i} \tag{12.4.13}$$

As was explained on page 284, the number of degrees of freedom is $s - t - 1$, which equals $m - 1 - 1 = m - 2$, since there are m terms in (12.4.13) and 1 parameter is estimated on the basis of the data.

In order to apply this test to the given data, we shall have to combine (pool) the last four classes; this will make each expected frequency greater than or equal to 5. We thus get

$$\chi^2 = + \frac{(89 - 89.2)^2}{89.2} + \frac{(143 - 133.9)^2}{133.9} + \frac{(94 - 100.4)^2}{100.4}$$

$$+ \frac{(42 - 50.2)^2}{50.2} + \frac{(20 - 18.8)^2}{18.8} + \frac{(12 - 7.3)^2}{7.3}$$

$$= 5.48$$

which is less than $\chi^2_{.05,4} = 9.488$. Hence the null hypothesis cannot be rejected, and the fairly close agreement between the observed and expected frequencies makes it reasonable to accept the null hypothesis that the data come from a Poisson population. In other words, the Poisson distribution provides a "good fit."

The method outlined in this example applies equally well to testing the fit of other kinds of distributions. In each case the number of degrees of freedom must be determined by means of the formula $s - t - 1$, as was explained on page 284. Exercise 7 below illustrates how the method is used to test the fit of a normal distribution to grouped data.

EXERCISES

1. Show that the expected cell frequencies given by (12.4.11) satisfy the equations

$$\sum_{i=1}^{r} e_{ij} = f_{.j} \qquad \text{and} \qquad \sum_{j=1}^{k} e_{ij} = f_{i.}$$

and, hence, that only $(r - 1)(k - 1)$ of the expected cell frequencies have to be calculated with the use of (12.4.11). [The others may then be obtained by subtraction from the totals of appropriate rows and columns.]

2. Samples of four kinds of ceramic materials, subjected to extreme temperature changes, produced the results shown in the following table:

	Material A	*Material B*	*Material C*	*Material D*
Broke completely	22	27	34	31
Showed slight defects	48	56	41	52
Remained perfect	30	17	25	17

Test whether the actual probabilities that an item will fall into the three categories is the same for all four materials. Use $\alpha = 0.05$.

3. Decide on the basis of the sample data given in the following table whether students' interest in statistics is *independent* of their ability in mathematics; use $\alpha = 0.01$.

		ABILITY IN MATHEMATICS		
		Low	*Average*	*High*
INTEREST IN STATISTICS	*Low*	43	24	15
	Average	31	46	37
	High	12	20	49

4. In order to check whether a die is balanced, it was rolled 120 times and the following results were obtained: 1 occurred 17 times, 2 occurred 19 times, 3 occurred 25 times, 4 occurred 23 times, 5 occurred 14 times, and 6 occurred 22 times. Using the fact that under the null hypothesis that the die is balanced the expected frequencies are all 20, calculate χ^2 and test the null hypothesis at $\alpha = 0.05$.

5. The following table contains a distribution obtained in 320 tosses of 6 coins and the corresponding expected frequencies calculated with the formula for the binomial distribution for $\theta = 0.50$ and $n = 6$:

Number of heads	*Observed frequencies*	*Expected frequencies*
0	3	5
1	21	30
2	85	75
3	110	100
4	62	75
5	32	30
6	7	5

Test the null hypothesis that the coins are all balanced with $\alpha = 0.05$.

6. A quality control engineer takes a daily sample of 20 electronic components, checking them for slight imperfections. Working, thus, for 100 days, there were 23 days on which he obtained 0 defectives, 51 days on which he obtained 1 defective, 23 days on which he obtained 2 defectives, and 3 days on which he obtained 3 defectives. Using $\alpha = 0.05$, test the null hypothesis that these data may be looked upon as samples from a binomial population. Round the estimate of θ so that the binomial probabilities may be found with the use of Table I.

7. (*Fitting normal distribution to grouped data*) The following is a distribution of the speeds with which 200 west-bound cars passed a checkpoint on U.S. 66 in Arizona:

Speed (in miles per hour)	*Number of cars*
39 or less	6
40–44	13
45–49	40
50–54	65
55–59	52
60 and over	24

The mean of these speeds, calculated before they were grouped, is $\bar{x} = 52.5$ mph and their standard deviation is $s = 6.6$ mph.

(a) Find the probabilities that a random variable having a normal distribution with $\mu = 52.5$ and $\sigma = 6.6$ assumes a value less than 39.5. that it assumes a value between 39.5 and 44.5, a value between 44.5 and 49.5, a value between 49.5 and 54.5, a value between 54.5 and 59.5, and a value greater than 59.5.

(b) Multiply the probabilities obtained in (a) by 200, getting thus the *expected normal curve frequencies* corresponding to the six classes of the given distribution.

(c) Test the null hypothesis that the given data may be looked upon as a random sample from a normal population by performing an appropriate χ^2 test. Use $\alpha = 0.05$.

12.5 Nonparametric Tests

To handle problems in which the various assumptions underlying standard tests cannot be met, statisticians have developed many alternate techniques which have become known as *nonparametric tests*. This name is meant to imply that we are *not* testing hypotheses concerning the parameters of populations *of a given kind*. Many of these tests can also be classified under the heading of "short-cut statistics"; they are usually easy to perform and require fewer computations than the corresponding "standard" tests. As should be expected, though, by making fewer assumptions we expose ourselves to greater risks. In other words, for fixed α, a nonparametric test is apt to expose us to greater probabilities of committing Type II errors.

12.5.1 *The sign test*

When testing hypotheses concerning the mean of a population, all of the tests of Section 12.2.1 (except the large-sample test mentioned on page 263) assume that the sample comes from a normal population. As it happens quite often that this assumption cannot be met, there is an obvious need for an appropriate nonparametric test. The one which we shall describe in this section is called the *sign test*; to test the null hypothesis $\mu = \mu_0$ against the alternative hypothesis $\mu \neq \mu_0$ (or $\mu > \mu_0$ or $\mu < \mu_0$) it only requires that the population be such that the probability of getting a value less than μ_0 equals the probability of getting a value greater than μ_0. (For continuous populations this is equivalent to the assumption that μ_0 coincides with the population median.) In the sign test, each sample value exceeding μ_0 is replaced by a *plus sign*, each sample value less than μ_0 is replaced by a *minus sign*, while sample values actually equalling μ_0 are discarded. Under the given assumption we can, thus, test the original null hypothesis by testing the hypothesis that the plus and minus signs constitute a sample from a binomial population with θ, the probability of getting a plus sign, equal to 0.50.

To illustrate, suppose that we want to test the hypothesis that the average time it takes an adult to react to a given visual stimulus (say, changing lights) is $\mu_0 = 0.15$ seconds against the alternative hypothesis $\mu \neq 0.15$ seconds, with $\alpha = 0.05$. Suppose, furthermore, that an experiment in which 20 persons were, thus, timed yielded the following results (in seconds):

0.16	0.12	0.19	0.16	0.17	0.18	0.15	0.20	0.16	0.18
+	−	+	+	+	+		+	+	+
0.13	0.17	0.18	0.21	0.18	0.17	0.19	0.11	0.16	0.16
−	+	+	+	+	+	+	−	+	+

Since 16 of these measurements exceed 0.15, 3 are less than 0.15, and 1 equals 0.15, we shall have to see whether 16 plus signs and 3 minus signs, *16 successes in 19 trials*, supports the hypothesis $\theta = 0.50$, where θ is the parameter of a binomial distribution with $n = 19$. Using Table I, we find that for the criterion on page 276 the constants $k_{.025}$ and $k'_{.025}$ are equal to 15 and 4, respectively, and that, therefore, the null hypothesis must be rejected. We conclude that the average reaction time to the given stimulus is *not* 0.15 seconds.

The sign test has many other applications. For instance, it can be used as a nonparametric alternative for the *paired-sample test* described on page 269. To test the null hypothesis $\mu_1 - \mu_2 = \delta$ against an appropriate one-sided or two-sided alternative, we replace the quantities $x_{1i} - x_{2i} - \delta$ by their *signs* and then proceed as above.

12.5.2 *Tests based on rank sums*

Statisticians have developed several nonparametric methods for testing the null hypothesis that two samples come from identical populations against the alternative that these populations have unequal means. In this section we shall describe one of these tests, which is based on rank sums; it is called the *U test* and also the Mann-Whitney test and the Wilcoxon test, after the statisticians by whom it was introduced.

To illustrate this test, suppose that we want to compare two kinds of gasoline and that the following are the mileages obtained in test runs (each performed with 1 gallon of the respective gasoline):

Gasoline A: 17.0 17.8 15.2 16.8 18.4 16.2 18.3 18.1 17.3

Gasoline B: 18.6 18.8 17.1 19.5 17.6 19.0 15.7 19.8 17.5 18.0

Arranging these values *jointly* (as if they were one sample) in an increasing order of magnitude and assigning them in this order the ranks 1, 2, 3, . . ., and 19, we find that the values of the first sample occupy ranks 1, 3, 4, 5, 7, 10, 12, 13, and 14, while those of the second sample occupy ranks 2, 6, 8, 9, 11, 15, 16, 17, 18, and 19. (If there are *ties* in rank, we assign to each of the tied observations the mean of the ranks which they jointly occupy.)

If there is a sizeable difference between the means of the two populations, most of the lower ranks will be occupied by the values of one sample while the higher ranks will be occupied mostly by those of the other sample. Making use of this fact, the *U test* tests the null hypothesis on the basis of the sums of the ranks occupied by the two samples; more specifically, it is based on the statistic

$$U = n_1n_2 + \frac{n_1(n_1 + 1)}{2} - R_1 \tag{12.5.1}$$

where n_1 and n_2 are the sizes of the respective samples and R_1 is the sum of the ranks occupied by the first. (As it is immaterial which sample is referred to as the first, U can be based on whichever rank sum is most easily obtained.)

Under the null hypothesis that the two samples come from identical populations, that they constitute, in fact, one random sample of size $n_1 + n_2$, $\mathbf{R}_1$ is the sum of n_1 positive integers selected at random from among the first $n_1 + n_2$. Thus, making use of Theorem 7.8 with $n = n_1$ and $N = n_1 + n_2$, we find that

$$E(\mathbf{R}_1) = \frac{n_1(n_1 + n_2 + 1)}{2} \quad \text{and} \quad \text{var}(\mathbf{R}_1) = \frac{n_1n_2(n_1 + n_2 + 1)}{12}$$

and that

$$E(\mathbf{U}) = \frac{n_1n_2}{2} \tag{12.5.2}$$

and

$$\text{var}(\mathbf{U}) = \frac{n_1n_2(n_1 + n_2 + 1)}{12} \tag{12.5.3}$$

according to (12.5.1) and Theorem 6.1.

As it can be shown that when n_1 and n_2 are both greater than 8 the distribution of $\mathbf{U}$ can be approximated closely with a normal distribution, we can test the null hypothesis that the two samples come from identical populations against the alternatives $\mu_1 > \mu_2$, $\mu_1 < \mu_2$, or $\mu_1 \neq \mu_2$ on the basis of the statistic

$$z = \frac{U - E(\mathbf{U})}{\sqrt{\text{var}(\mathbf{U})}} \tag{12.5.4}$$

The appropriate critical regions of size α are $z \leq -z_\alpha$, $z \geq z_\alpha$, and $|z| \geq z_{\alpha/2}$, respectively. Tables for conducting exact tests for small values of n_1 and n_2 are referred to in the Bibliography on page 294.

Returning now to the numerical example, we find that $U = 66$, $E(\mathbf{U}) = 45$, $\text{var}(\mathbf{U}) = 150$, and, hence, that

$$z = \frac{66 - 45}{\sqrt{150}} = 1.71$$

Using the two-sided alternative $\mu_1 \neq \mu_2$ and $\alpha = 0.05$, we conclude that the null hypothesis cannot be rejected since $|z| = 1.71$ does not exceed $z_{.025} = 1.96$. If the decision that there is no difference in the performance of the gasolines seems too drastic, we could *reserve judgment*, saying that whatever difference there is between the values obtained in the two samples may reasonably be attributed to chance.

An interesting feature of the U test is that, with a slight modification, it can also be used to test the null hypothesis that the two samples come from identical populations against the alternative hypothesis that these populations have unequal *dispersions*, that is, unequal measures of variation. As before, the values obtained in the two samples are arranged jointly in an increasing order of magnitude, but now they are ranked *from both ends towards the middle*, assigning rank 1 to the smallest, ranks 2 and 3 to the largest and second largest, ranks 4 and 5 to the second and third smallest, ranks 6 and 7 to the third and fourth largest, and so forth. Subsequently, U is calculated according to (12.5.1) and the test is the same as before.

EXERCISES

1. The following are 106 time lapses (in minutes) between eruptions of Old Faithful Geyser in Yellowstone National Park: 68, 62, 68, 72, 50, 76, 59, 69, 62, 70, 67, 44, 71, 63, 62, 65, 69, 62, 70, 40, 62, 74, 59, 68,

66, 68, 66, 55, 60, 65, 63, 57, 66, 68, 67, 58, 74, 74, 66, 63, 62, 61, 66, 67, 67, 74, 76, 63, 70, 65, 71, 67, 61, 67, 71, 64, 52, 76, 63, 71, 76, 60, 74, 41, 72, 44, 73, 60, 69, 55, 81, 55, 68, 51, 67, 62, 66, 66, 60, 72, 68, 59, 69, 55, 58, 60, 69, 58, 66, 63, 68, 62, 55, 67, 67, 64, 45, 65, 60, 64, 67, 71, 72, 72, 71, 67. Use the *sign test* to test the null hypothesis that the true average time between eruptions of Old Faithful is $\mu = 60$ minutes against the alternative hypothesis that this average is more than 60 minutes. Use $\alpha = 0.05$.

2. The following are the lengths of 20 sea trouts caught by a commercial trawler in Delaware Bay: (in centimeters) 19.5, 19.8, 18.9, 20.4, 20.2, 21.5, 19.9, 20.9, 18.1, 20.5, 18.3, 19.5, 18.3, 19.0, 18.2, 23.9, 17.0, 19.7, 21.7, 19.5. Use the *sign test* to test the null hypothesis that these lengths constitute a random sample from a population having $\mu = 20.8$. Use a two-sided alternative and $\alpha = 0.05$.

3. Use the *sign test* to reach a decision concerning the effectiveness of the diet referred to in Exercise 5 on page 271.

4. A test rating a person's sense of humor on a scale from 0 to 130 was given to 15 married couples. Use the *sign test*, a two-sided alternative, and $\alpha = 0.05$, to decide on the basis of the following data whether there is a difference in the average sense of humor of husbands and wives:

Husbands	*Wives*	*Husbands*	*Wives*
56	49	68	83
90	88	74	89
38	51	83	77
47	50	87	62
85	83	60	65
49	41	31	44
55	52	89	92
58	69		

5. The following are scores obtained in a personality test in random samples of married and unmarried women:

Unmarried:	85	65	74	79	60	77	75	68	69
Married:	72	76	66	73	73	63	70	70	71

Use the *U test* with $\alpha = 0.05$ to test the null hypothesis that these two samples come from identical populations against the alternative that the two populations have unequal means.

6. An agricultural experiment was performed to compare the average yield of two varieties of corn. Use the *U test* with $\alpha = 0.05$ on the following data (in bushels per acre) obtained for 9 test plots of Variety A and 10 test plots of Variety B:

Variety A: 92.2 90.3 85.2 85.7 89.1 87.4 91.5 83.6 91.6

Variety B: 82.9 96.1 94.0 87.7 102.0 87.8 100.2 86.0 88.5 89.8

7. It is desired to compare the variability of two kinds of tires on the basis of the following mileages obtained for 10 tires of each kind: (figures in 1000 miles)

Brand A: 20.6 19.1 19.6 21.3 20.4 19.4 20.0 20.2 20.0 20.5

Brand B: 20.9 21.5 19.8 18.0 19.0 22.0 24.1 18.8 21.0 19.2

Use the *U test* with $\alpha = 0.05$ to test the null hypothesis that these two samples come from identical populations against the alternative that the two populations have unequal variances.

BIBLIOGRAPHY

A discussion of the Behrens-Fisher test may be found in

Kenney, J. F., and E. S. Keeping, *Mathematics of Statistics, Part Two.* New York: D. Van Nostrand Company, Inc., 1951, Chapter 9.

The problem of determining the appropriate number of degrees of freedom for various uses of the χ^2 statistic is treated in

Cramer, H., *Mathematical Methods of Statistics,* Princeton, N. J.: Princeton University Press, 1946, Chapter 30.

Tables required to perform the U test when dealing with very small samples are given in

Siegel, S., *Nonparametric Statistics for the Behavioral Sciences,* New York: McGraw-Hill Book Co., Inc., 1956.

Chapter 13

Regression and Correlation

13.1 The Problem of Regression

A major objective of many statistical investigations is to establish relationships which make it possible to predict one or more variables in terms of others. Thus, studies are made to predict students' success in college on the basis of their I.Q.'s, used car prices on the basis of their age and make, accident frequency on the basis of road width, beef consumption on the basis of the retail prices of certain foods and national income, ...

Although it is, of course, desirable to be able to predict one quantity *exactly* in terms of another, there are many situations, particularly in the social sciences, where we can at best predict averages or expected values. Thus, we may not be able to say exactly how much money Mr. A. B. Jones will make 10 years after graduating from college, but we can predict the *average* income of college graduates on the basis of the number of years they have been out of college. Similarly, we may only be able to predict the *average* yield of a certain variety of corn on the basis of information concerning rainfall in July or the *average* performance of students taking a course in statistics on the basis of the grades which they received in elementary mathematics.

Formally, if a pair of random variables $\mathbf{x}$ and $\mathbf{y}$ have the joint probability density $f(x, y)$ and $\mathbf{x}$ is *known* to assume the value x, the basic problem of *bivariate regression* is that of determining the conditional expectation $E(\mathbf{y} \mid x)$, namely, the mean of the conditional density $f(y \mid x)$.* In problems involving more than two random variables, that is, in *multivariate regression*, we are, similarly, interested in quantities such as $E(\mathbf{z} \mid x, y)$, the expected value of $\mathbf{z}$ for given values of $\mathbf{x}$ and $\mathbf{y}$, and $E(\mathbf{x}_5 \mid x_1, x_2, x_3, x_4)$, the expected value of $\mathbf{x}_5$ for given values of the random variables $\mathbf{x}_1$, $\mathbf{x}_2$, $\mathbf{x}_3$, and $\mathbf{x}_4$.

Given a joint probability density $f(x, y)$, the problem of determining $E(\mathbf{y} \mid x)$ is simply that of evaluating the integral

$$E(\mathbf{y} \mid x) = \int y \cdot f(y \mid x)\, dy = \int \frac{y \cdot f(x, y)}{f_1(x)}\, dy \qquad (13.1.1)$$

where $f_1(x)$ is the marginal density of $\mathbf{x}$. (Analogous expressions for the discrete case may be obtained by replacing the integrals with sums.)

If we are *not* given the joint density $f(x, y)$, or at least not all of its parameters, the problem of determining $E(\mathbf{y} \mid x)$ becomes considerably more involved; essentially, it becomes a problem of estimation and we shall treat it separately in Sections 13.4.2 and 13.5.

13.2 Regression Curves

To illustrate the determination of $E(\mathbf{y} \mid x)$, the conditional expectation of $\mathbf{y}$ for a given value of $\mathbf{x}$, consider a pair of random variables having the joint density

$$f(x, y) = \begin{cases} \frac{2}{3}(x + 2y) & \text{for } 0 < x < 1 \text{ and } 0 < y < 1 \\ 0 & \text{elsewhere} \end{cases}$$

Integrating on y we obtain the marginal density

$$f_1(x) = \int_0^1 \tfrac{2}{3}(x + 2y)\, dy = \tfrac{2}{3}(x + 1)$$

the conditional density

$$f(y \mid x) = \frac{f(x, y)}{f_1(x)} = \frac{x + 2y}{x + 1}$$

and, hence,

$$E(\mathbf{y} \mid x) = \int_0^1 \frac{y(x + 2y)}{x + 1}\, dy = \frac{3x + 4}{6(x + 1)}$$

* The term *regression*, as it is used here, is due to Francis Galton; he employed it first in connection with a study of the heights of fathers and sons, observing a regression (a turning back) from the heights of sons to the heights of their fathers.

The graph of this relationship between x and $E(\mathbf{y} \mid x)$, the *regression curve of* $\mathbf{y}$ *on* $\mathbf{x}$, is shown in Figure 13.1. It will be left to the reader to verify in Exercise 3 on page 299 that the *regression curve of* $\mathbf{x}$ *on* $\mathbf{y}$, indicated by means of the dotted curve of Figure 13.1, is given by

$$E(\mathbf{x} \mid y) = \frac{2(1 + 3y)}{3(1 + 4y)}$$

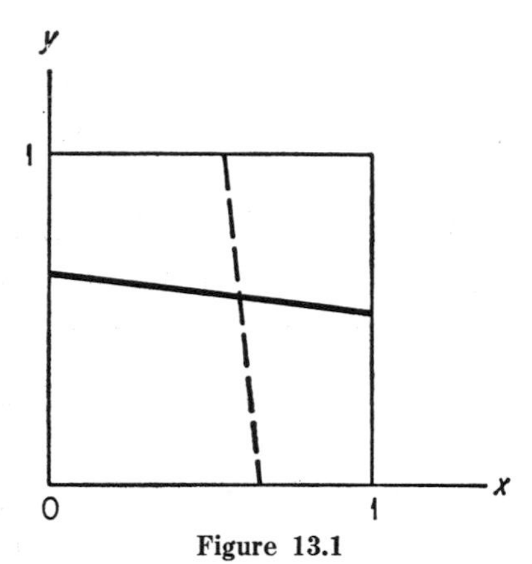

Figure 13.1

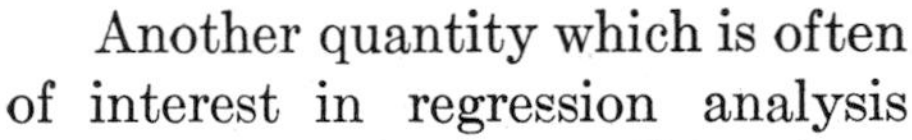

Another quantity which is often of interest in regression analysis (see page 314) is the conditional variance of $\mathbf{y}$ for a given value of $\mathbf{x}$, namely,

$$\operatorname{var}(\mathbf{y} \mid x) = E(\mathbf{y}^2 \mid x) - E(\mathbf{y} \mid x)^2 \tag{13.2.1}$$

Leaving it to the reader to evaluate the necessary integrals, let us merely state the result that for our example

$$\operatorname{var}(\mathbf{y} \mid x) = \frac{3x^2 + 6x + 2}{36(x + 1)^2}$$

To give an illustration dealing with the discrete case, let us find $E(\mathbf{y} \mid x)$ for a pair of random variables having the *multinomial distribution*

$$f(x, y) = \frac{n!}{x!y!(n - x - y)!} \theta_1^x \theta_2^y (1 - \theta_1 - \theta_2)^{n-x-y}$$

for $x = 0, 1, 2, \ldots, n$, $y = 0, 1, 2, \ldots, n$, and $x + y \leq n$. As we saw in Exercise 11 on page 89, the marginal distribution of $\mathbf{x}$ is the binomial distribution $b(x; n, \theta_1)$; hence, the conditional distribution of $\mathbf{y}$ given x is

$$f(y \mid x) = \frac{\binom{n - x}{y} \theta_2^y (1 - \theta_1 - \theta_2)^{n-x-y}}{(1 - \theta_1)^{n-x}}$$

for $y = 0, 1, 2, \ldots, n - x$. Using the same technique as in Section

4.3.1, it can then be seen that

$$E(\mathbf{y} \mid x) = \frac{(n - x)\theta_2}{1 - \theta_1}$$

Thus, if $\mathbf{x}$ stands for the number of times an *even number* comes up in 30 rolls of a balanced die, while $\mathbf{y}$ stands for the number of times the result is a *five*, we have

$$E(\mathbf{y} \mid x) = \frac{(30 - x)\frac{1}{6}}{1 - \frac{1}{2}} = \tfrac{1}{3}(30 - x)$$

For $x = 18$ the expected number of fives is $\frac{1}{3} \cdot 12 = 4$ and for $x = 10$ it is $\frac{1}{3} \cdot 20 = 6\frac{2}{3}$; this stands to reason since each roll which does *not* come up 2, 4, or 6 must come up 1, 3, or 5, that is, one of *three* possibilities.

To give an example illustrating the *multivariate* case, let us refer to the example of Section 5.5, where three random variables had the joint density

$$f(x, y, z) = \begin{cases} (x + y)e^{-z} & \text{for } 0 < x < 1, 0 < y < 1, z > 0 \\ 0 & \text{elsewhere} \end{cases}$$

As was shown on page 138, the joint marginal density of $\mathbf{x}$ and $\mathbf{z}$ is given by

$$f(x, z) = (x + \tfrac{1}{2})e^{-z}$$

and, hence,

$$E(\mathbf{y} \mid x, z) = \int_0^1 \frac{y(x + y)}{(x + \frac{1}{2})}\, dy = \frac{x + \frac{2}{3}}{2x + 1}$$

Note that this conditional expectation depends on x but not on z; this should have been expected since there is pairwise independence between $\mathbf{y}$ and $\mathbf{z}$.

EXERCISES

1. Given the joint density

$$f(x, y) = \begin{cases} 2 & \text{for } 0 < x < y \text{ and } 0 < y < 1 \\ 0 & \text{elsewhere} \end{cases}$$

show that $E(\mathbf{y} \mid x) = \frac{1}{2}(1 + x)$, $E(\mathbf{x} \mid y) = y/2$, and $\text{var}(\mathbf{y} \mid x) = \frac{1}{12}(x - 1)^2$.

2. Given the joint density

$$f(x, y) = \begin{cases} \dfrac{2x}{(1 + x + xy)^3} & \text{for } x > 0 \text{ and } y > 0 \\ 0 & \text{elsewhere} \end{cases}$$

show that $E(\mathbf{y} \mid x) = 1 + (1/x)$ and that $\text{var}(\mathbf{y} \mid x)$ does not exist.

3. Verify the values given for $E(\mathbf{x} \mid y)$ and $\text{var}(\mathbf{y} \mid x)$ on page 297.

4. Referring to Exercise 1 on page 88, show that $E(\mathbf{y} \mid 1) = 16/9$, $E(\mathbf{y} \mid 2) = 2$, and $E(\mathbf{y} \mid 3) = 2$.

13.3 Linear Regression

An important feature of the illustration on page 297 (which dealt with the multinomial distribution) and Exercise 1 above is that the regression equations are *linear*, namely, that

$$E(\mathbf{y} \mid x) = \alpha + \beta x \tag{13.3.1}$$

where α and β are constants. There are several reasons why linear regression equations are of special interest: (1) they lend themselves readily to further mathematical treatment, (2) they often provide good approximations to otherwise complicated regression equations, and (3) in the case of the *bivariate normal distribution*, to be discussed in Section 13.4, the regression equations are, in fact, linear.

To simplify work connected with linear regression equations, let us express the constants α and β in (13.3.1), called the *regression coefficients*, in terms of some of the lower moments of the joint density of $\mathbf{x}$ and $\mathbf{y}$. In what follows we shall write the mean and the variance of $\mathbf{x}$ as μ_1 and σ_1^2, the mean and the variance of $\mathbf{y}$ as μ_2 and σ_2^2, and the covariance of $\mathbf{x}$ and $\mathbf{y}$ as σ_{12}. Substituting $\alpha + \beta x$ for $E(\mathbf{y} \mid x)$ in (13.1.1), multiplying both sides of the equation by $f_1(x)$, and integrating on x, we obtain

$$\iint y \cdot f(x, y)\, dy\, dx = \alpha \int f_1(x)\, dx + \beta \int x \cdot f_1(x)\, dx$$

or

$$\mu_2 = \alpha + \beta\mu_1 \tag{13.3.2}$$

Had we multiplied both sides of the equation by x before integrating with respect to x, we would have obtained

$$\iint xy \cdot f(x, y)\, dy\, dx = \alpha \int x \cdot f_1(x)\, dx + \beta \int x^2 \cdot f_1(x)\, dx$$

or

$$E(\mathbf{xy}) = \alpha\mu_1 + \beta E(\mathbf{x}^2) \tag{13.3.3}$$

Solving (13.3.2) and (13.3.3) simultaneously for α and β, making use of the fact that $\sigma_{12} = E(\mathbf{xy}) - \mu_1\mu_2$ and $\sigma_1^2 = E(\mathbf{x}^2) - \mu_1^2$, we find that

$$\alpha = \mu_2 - \frac{\sigma_{12}}{\sigma_1^2}\mu_1 \qquad \text{and} \qquad \beta = \frac{\sigma_{12}}{\sigma_1^2}$$

Hence, (13.3.1) can be written

$$E(\mathbf{y} \mid x) = \mu_2 + \frac{\sigma_{12}}{\sigma_1^2}(x - \mu_1) \tag{13.3.4}$$

and, *when it is linear*, $E(\mathbf{x} \mid y)$ can, similarly, be written as

$$E(\mathbf{x} \mid y) = \mu_1 + \frac{\sigma_{12}}{\sigma_2^2}(y - \mu_2) \tag{13.3.5}$$

A quantity which is closely related to the covariance is the *correlation coefficient, rho*, which is defined as

$$\rho = \frac{\sigma_{12}}{\sigma_1\sigma_2} \tag{13.3.6}$$

Using it in (13.3.4) and (13.3.5), we can write these linear regression equations as

$$E(\mathbf{y} \mid x) = \mu_2 + \rho\frac{\sigma_2}{\sigma_1}(x - \mu_1)$$

and (13.3.7)

$$E(\mathbf{x} \mid y) = \mu_1 + \rho\frac{\sigma_1}{\sigma_2}(y - \mu_2)$$

It follows that if a regression equation is linear and $\rho = 0$, then $E(\mathbf{y} \mid x)$ does not depend on x (or $E(\mathbf{x} \mid y)$ does not depend on y).

In general, when $\sigma_{12} = 0$ and, hence, $\rho = 0$, the two random variables are said to be *uncorrelated*, and, in view of the result obtained in Exercise 3 on page 113, we find that *if two random variables are independent they are also uncorrelated.* The fact that *if two random variables are uncorrelated they are not necessarily independent* is illustrated in Exercise 3 below.

The correlation coefficient and its estimates, which play important roles in many problems of statistical analysis, will be discussed in more detail in Section 13.4.1. Let us merely point out at this time that $-1 \leq \rho \leq +1$, as the reader will be asked to show in Exercise 4 below, and that the sign of ρ determines whether the lines given by (13.3.7) have upward or downward slopes.

EXERCISES

1. (a) Show that for the joint density of Exercise 1 on page 298

$$E(\mathbf{x}^r\mathbf{y}^s) = \frac{2}{(r+1)(r+s+2)}$$

(b) Use the result obtained in (a) to show that $\mu_1 = \frac{1}{3}$, $\mu_2 = \frac{2}{3}$, $\sigma_1^2 = \frac{1}{18}$, $\sigma_2^2 = \frac{1}{18}$, $\sigma_{12} = \frac{1}{36}$, and $\rho = \frac{1}{2}$.

(c) Substituting the results obtained in (b) into (13.3.4) and (13.3.5) or (13.3.7), verify that $E(\mathbf{y} \mid x) = \frac{1}{2}(1 + x)$ and $E(\mathbf{x} \mid y) = y/2$.

2. Given a pair of random variables having the joint density

$$f(x, y) = \begin{cases} 24xy & \text{for } x > 0, y > 0 \text{ and } x + y \leq 1 \\ 0 & \text{elsewhere} \end{cases}$$

(a) Show that $E(\mathbf{y} \mid x) = \frac{2}{3}(1 - x)$ using (13.1.1).

(b) Verify the result obtained in (a) by calculating the necessary moments and substituting into (13.3.4).

(c) Show that $\text{var}(\mathbf{y} \mid x) = \frac{1}{18}(x - 1)^2$.

3. (*Uncorrelated but dependent random variables*) Given a pair of random variables having the joint density

$$f(x, y) = \begin{cases} 1 & \text{for } -y < x < y \text{ and } 0 < y < 1 \\ 0 & \text{elsewhere} \end{cases}$$

(a) Show that the two marginal densities are

$$f_2(y) = \begin{cases} 2y & \text{for } 0 < y < 1 \\ 0 & \text{elsewhere} \end{cases}$$

$$f_1(x) = \begin{cases} 1 - x & \text{for } 0 < x < 1 \\ 1 + x & \text{for } -1 < x \leq 0 \\ 0 & \text{elsewhere} \end{cases}$$

and, hence, that **x** and **y** are *not independent.*

(b) Show that the two random variables are *uncorrelated.*

4. (*Proof that* $-1 \leq \rho \leq +1$) Given a pair of random variables having the variances σ_1^2 and σ_2^2 and the correlation coefficient ρ, use Theorem 7.2 to express

$$\text{var}\left(\frac{\mathbf{x}}{\sigma_1} + \frac{\mathbf{y}}{\sigma_2}\right) \quad \text{and} \quad \text{var}\left(\frac{\mathbf{x}}{\sigma_1} - \frac{\mathbf{y}}{\sigma_2}\right)$$

in terms of σ_1, σ_2 and ρ. Then use the expressions obtained for these variances to show that $-1 \leq \rho \leq +1$, making use of the fact that a variance cannot be negative.

5. (*Multivariate linear regression*) Given the random variables $\mathbf{x}_1$, $\mathbf{x}_2$, and $\mathbf{x}_3$ having the joint density $f(x_1, x_2, x_3)$, show that if $E(\mathbf{x}_3 \mid x_1, x_2)$ is of the form

$$E(\mathbf{x}_3 \mid x_1, x_2) = \alpha + \beta_1(x_1 - \mu_1) + \beta_2(x_2 - \mu_2)$$

then

$$\alpha = \mu_3$$

$$\beta_1 = \frac{\sigma_{13}\sigma_2^2 - \sigma_{12}\sigma_{23}}{\sigma_1^2\sigma_2^2 - \sigma_{12}^2}$$

$$\beta_2 = \frac{\sigma_{23}\sigma_1^2 - \sigma_{12}\sigma_{13}}{\sigma_1^2\sigma_2^2 - \sigma_{12}^2}$$

where $\mu_i = E(\mathbf{x}_i)$, $\sigma_i^2 = \text{var}(\mathbf{x}_i)$, and $\sigma_{ij} = \text{cov}(\mathbf{x}_i, \mathbf{x}_j)$. (*Hint*: proceed as on page 299, integrating both sides of the equation with respect to x_1 and x_2 to get one equation, multiplying both sides by $x_1 - \mu_1$ and then integrating to get a second equation, and multiplying both sides by $x_2 - \mu_2$ and then integrating to get a third equation.)

6. Show that if $E(\mathbf{y} \mid x)$ is linear in x and $\operatorname{var}(\mathbf{y} \mid x)$ is constant, then $\operatorname{var}(\mathbf{y} \mid x) = \sigma_2^2(1 - \rho^2)$.

7. (*Least squares approximation to regression curve*) If it is reasonable to approximate a regression curve of $\mathbf{y}$ on $\mathbf{x}$ with a straight line of the form $y = a + bx$, the constants a and b are usually chosen so that

$$\int_{-\infty}^{\infty} \int_{-\infty}^{\infty} [E(\mathbf{y} \mid x) - (a + bx)]^2 f(x, y)\, dx\, dy$$

is a *minimum*. Show that the resulting expressions for a and b are identical with those given for α and β on page 300. (Note that $E(\mathbf{y} \mid x)$ depends on x alone.)

8. Use the method suggested in Exercise 7 to approximate the regression curve of $\mathbf{y}$ on $\mathbf{x}$ obtained on page 296 for the first example of Section 13.2. Plot graphs of the regression curve as well as the linear approximation in order to judge the "goodness" of this approximation.

13.4 The Bivariate Normal Distribution

If a random variable $\mathbf{x}$ has a normal distribution, its density is of the form

$$f(x) = k \cdot e^{-(ax^2+bx+c)} \qquad \text{for} \qquad -\infty < x < \infty$$

where a, b, c, and k are constants, $k > 0$, and the second degree polynomial $ax^2 + bx + c$ is positive or zero for all values of x. Ordinarily, the constants a, b, c, and k are expressed in terms of moments; for instance, $a = 1/2\sigma^2$ and $k = 1/(\sqrt{2\pi}\sigma)$, as can be verified by comparison with (6.3.7) on page 148.

A logical way to extend the normal distribution to the bivariate case would be to consider the following joint density defined for $-\infty < x < \infty$ and $-\infty < y < \infty$:

$$f(x, y) = k \cdot e^{-(ax^2+by^2+cxy+dx+ey+f)}$$

Here a, b, c, d, e, f, and k are constants, $k > 0$, and the second degree polynomial $ax^2 + by^2 + cxy + dx + ey + f$ is positive or zero for all values of x and y.

Although we could proceed as in Section 6.3.3, expressing the various constants in terms of appropriate moments, let us instead state the result and then verify later that the symbols μ_1, μ_2, σ_1^2, σ_2^2, and ρ appearing in (13.4.1) are, indeed, the two means, the two variances, and the correlation coefficient of the two random variables. Thus, let us define the *bivariate normal density* as

$$f(x, y) = \frac{e^{-\frac{1}{2(1-\rho^2)}\left[\left(\frac{x-\mu_1}{\sigma_1}\right)^2 - 2\rho\left(\frac{x-\mu_1}{\sigma_1}\right)\left(\frac{y-\mu_2}{\sigma_2}\right) + \left(\frac{y-\mu_2}{\sigma_2}\right)^2\right]}}{2\pi\sigma_1\sigma_2\sqrt{1-\rho^2}} \qquad (13.4.1)$$

for $-\infty < x < \infty$ and $-\infty < y < \infty$. Also, $\sigma_1 > 0$, $\sigma_2 > 0$, and $-1 < \rho < +1$.

In order to show that the symbols μ_1 and σ_1 in (13.4.1) actually represent the mean and the standard deviation of the marginal distribution of **x**, let us find $f_1(x)$ by integrating out y. We thus get

$$f_1(x) = \frac{e^{-\frac{1}{2(1-\rho^2)}\left(\frac{x-\mu_1}{\sigma_1}\right)^2}}{2\pi\sigma_1\sigma_2\sqrt{1-\rho^2}} \int_{-\infty}^{\infty} e^{-\frac{1}{2(1-\rho^2)}\left[\left(\frac{y-\mu_2}{\sigma_2}\right)^2 - 2\rho\left(\frac{x-\mu_1}{\sigma_1}\right)\left(\frac{y-\mu_2}{\sigma_2}\right)\right]} dy$$

and to simplify the notation let us make the *substitution* $u = (x - \mu_1)/\sigma_1$. Also *changing the variable of integration* by letting $v = (y - \mu_2)/\sigma_2$, we obtain

$$f_1(x) = \frac{e^{-\frac{1}{2(1-\rho^2)}u^2}}{2\pi\sigma_1\sqrt{1-\rho^2}} \int_{-\infty}^{\infty} e^{-\frac{1}{2(1-\rho^2)}[v^2 - 2\rho uv]} dv$$

and after completing the square letting $v^2 - 2\rho uv = (v - \rho u)^2 - \rho^2 u^2$ and collecting terms we get

$$f_1(x) = \frac{e^{-(1/2)u^2}}{\sqrt{2\pi}\sigma_1} \left\{\frac{1}{\sqrt{2\pi}\sqrt{1-\rho^2}} \int_{-\infty}^{\infty} e^{-\frac{1}{2}\left(\frac{v-\rho\mu}{\sqrt{1-\rho^2}}\right)^2} dv\right\}$$

Finally, identifying the quantity in parentheses as the integral of a normal density from $-\infty$ to ∞ and, hence, equalling 1, we obtain

$$f_1(x) = \frac{e^{-(1/2)u^2}}{\sqrt{2\pi}\sigma_1} = \frac{1}{\sqrt{2\pi}\sigma_1} e^{-\frac{1}{2}\left(\frac{x-\mu_1}{\sigma_1}\right)^2} \qquad (13.4.2)$$

for $-\infty < x < \infty$. It follows by inspection that the marginal density of **x** is normal with the mean μ_1 and the standard deviation σ_1, which justifies using these symbols as we did in (13.4.1). By symmetry, it also follows that the marginal density of **y** is normal with the mean μ_2 and the standard deviation σ_2.

To verify that the symbol ρ in (13.4.1), indeed, represents the correlation coefficient as defined by (13.3.6), let us first find the conditional density

$$f(y \mid x) = \frac{f(x, y)}{f_1(x)}$$

Substituting $u_1 = (x - \mu_1)/\sigma_1$ and $u_2 = (y - \mu_2)/\sigma_2$, we get

$$f(y \mid x) = \frac{\dfrac{1}{2\pi\sigma_1\sigma_2\sqrt{1 - \rho^2}} e^{-\frac{1}{2(1-\rho^2)}[u_1^2 - 2\rho u_1 u_2 + u_2^2]}}{\dfrac{1}{\sqrt{2\pi}\sigma_1} e^{-(1/2)u_1^2}}$$

$$= \frac{1}{\sqrt{2\pi}\sigma_2\sqrt{1 - \rho^2}} e^{-\frac{1}{2(1-\rho^2)}[u_2^2 - 2\rho u_1 u_2 + \rho^2 u_1^2]}$$

$$= \frac{1}{\sqrt{2\pi}\sigma_2\sqrt{1 - \rho^2}} e^{-\frac{1}{2}\left[\frac{u_2 - \rho u_1}{\sqrt{1-\rho^2}}\right]^2}$$

Expressing this result in terms of the original variables x and y, we finally obtain

$$f(y \mid x) = \frac{1}{\sqrt{2\pi}\sigma_2\sqrt{1 - \rho^2}} e^{-\frac{1}{2}\left[\frac{y - \{\mu_2 + \rho(\sigma_2/\sigma_1)(x - \mu_1)\}}{\sigma_2\sqrt{1-\rho^2}}\right]^2} \tag{13.4.3}$$

for $-\infty < y < \infty$, and it can be seen by inspection that this is a normal distribution with the mean

$$E(\mathbf{y} \mid x) = \mu_2 + \rho(\sigma_2/\sigma_1)(x - \mu_1) \tag{13.4.4}$$

and the variance

$$\operatorname{var}(\mathbf{y} \mid x) = \sigma_2^2(1 - \rho^2) \tag{13.4.5}$$

We have, thus, shown that the regression equation of **y** on **x** is linear and, comparing (13.4.4) with (13.3.7), we find that the constant ρ in (13.4.1) is, indeed, the correlation coefficient. By symmetry, the regression equation of **x** on **y** is also linear, with

$$E(\mathbf{x} \mid y) = \mu_1 + \rho(\sigma_1/\sigma_2)(y - \mu_2) \tag{13.4.6}$$

and $\operatorname{var}(\mathbf{x} \mid y) = \sigma_1^2(1 - \rho^2)$.

The bivariate normal distribution has many interesting properties, some statistical and some of a purely mathematical nature. Among the statistical properties we find, for example, that two random variables having the bivariate normal distribution are independent if and only if they are uncorrelated (see Exercise 1 on page 307). Also, if two random variables have the bivariate normal distribution the marginal distributions are normal, but the converse is not necessarily true. To illustrate this, suppose that $f(x, y)$ is a bivariate normal density with zero means and with $\rho = 0$ and that $f^*(x, y)$ is defined as follows:

$$f^*(x, y) = \begin{cases} 0 & \text{inside squares 1 and 3 of Figure 13.2} \\ 2f(x, y) & \text{inside squares 2 and 4 of Figure 13.2} \\ f(x, y) & \text{elsewhere} \end{cases}$$

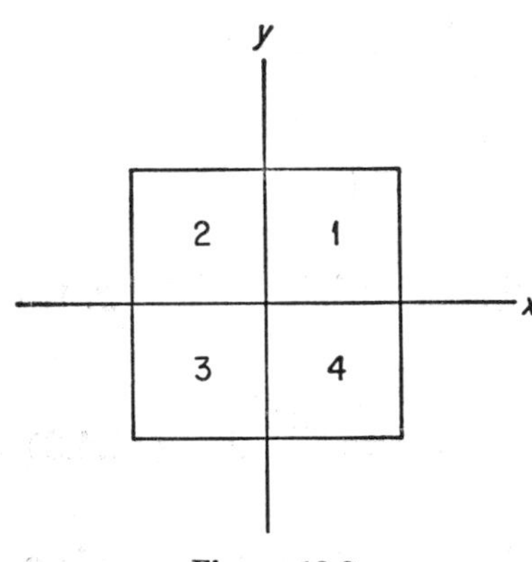

Figure 13.2

It is fairly easy to see that even though $f^*(x, y)$ is *not* a bivariate normal density, the corresponding marginal densities of $\mathbf{x}$ and $\mathbf{y}$ are normal.

It is also of interest to note that instead of using the argument on page 303 we could have *defined* the bivariate normal distribution by specifying that the marginal density of $\mathbf{x}$ be normal, that the conditional density of $\mathbf{y}$ given x be normal for each x, that the regression equation of $\mathbf{y}$ on $\mathbf{x}$ be linear, and that $\text{var}(\mathbf{y} \mid x)$ be constant.

Many interesting mathematical properties are obtained by studying the *bivariate normal surface* whose equation is $z = f(x, y)$, with $f(x, y)$ given by (13.4.1). This surface, shown in Figure 13.3, is also referred to sometimes as a *normal regression surface*. It will be

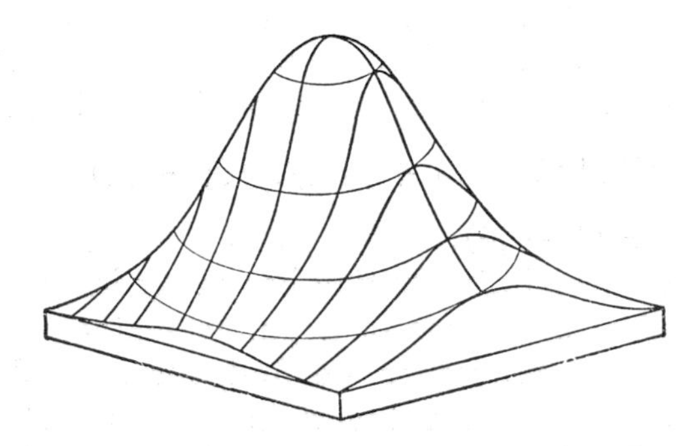
Figure 13.3

left to the reader to verify that this surface has a maximum at $x = \mu_1$ and $y = \mu_2$, and that any plane parallel to the z-axis intersects the surface in a curve having the shape of a normal distribution. Also, planes parallel to the xy-plane intersect the surface in ellipses, which are called *contours of constant probability density*. The axes of these ellipses do not coincide with the regression lines except in the special case where $\rho = 0$. When $\rho = 0$ and $\sigma_1 = \sigma_2$, the contours of constant probability density are circles, and it is customary to refer to the corresponding probability density as a *circular normal distribution*.

The study of the elliptical contours of constant probability density is of special interest when $\rho \to 1$. In that case the major axes of the ellipses as well as the two regression lines approach the line

$$y = \mu_2 + (\sigma_2/\sigma_1)(x - \mu_1)$$

the major axes get longer while the minor axes get shorter, and in the limiting case $\rho = 1$ the ellipses *degenerate* to the line

$$y = \mu_2 + (\sigma_2/\sigma_1)(x - \mu_1)$$

From a probabilistic point of view this means that when $\rho \to 1$ the probability of obtaining points outside any narrow strip containing the line

$$y = \mu_2 + (\sigma_2/\sigma_1)(x - \mu_1)$$

approaches 0. In fact, in the limiting case where $\rho = 1$, the entire probability is concentrated along this line and the bivariate distribution degenerates to the univariate case. All these arguments apply also to the case where $\rho \to -1$, and this is why $\rho = -1$ and $\rho = +1$ are excluded in the definition of the bivariate normal distribution.

EXERCISES

1. Show that if two random variables have the bivariate normal distribution they are independent if and only if they are uncorrelated.

2. If the exponent of e in (13.4.1) is

$$\frac{-1}{216}[16(x - 2)^2 - 12(x - 2)(y + 3) + 9(y + 3)^2]$$

find μ_1, μ_2, σ_1, σ_2, and ρ.

3. Given a pair of random variables $\mathbf{x}$ and $\mathbf{y}$ having the bivariate normal distribution,

   (a) find the joint density of $\mathbf{x}$ and $\mathbf{v}_2$, where

$$v_2 = \frac{y - \{\mu_2 + \rho(\sigma_2/\sigma_1)(x - \mu_1)\}}{\sigma_2\sqrt{1 - \rho^2}}$$

   [*Hint*: write $f(x, y)$ as the product of $f_1(x)$ and $f(y \mid x)$ as given by (13.4.2) and (13.4.3).]

   (b) using the result obtained in (a) show that if $v_1 = (x - \mu_1)/\sigma_1$, the joint density of $\mathbf{v}_1$ and $\mathbf{v}_2$ is bivariate normal with zero means, unit variances, and zero covariance.

4. Given a pair of random variables $\mathbf{x}$ and $\mathbf{y}$ having the bivariate normal density, show that the probability of obtaining a point (x, y) inside the ellipse

$$\frac{1}{2(1 - \rho^2)}\left[\left(\frac{x - \mu_1}{\sigma_1}\right)^2 - 2\rho\left(\frac{x - \mu_1}{\sigma_1}\right)\left(\frac{y - \mu_2}{\sigma_2}\right) + \left(\frac{y - \mu_2}{\sigma_2}\right)^2\right] = k^2$$

   is $1 - e^{-k^2}$. (*Hint*: use the result obtained in Exercise 3 and then change to polar coordinates.)

5. The center of a target at which a missile is aimed is taken as the origin of a coordinate system, with reference to which the point at which the missile hits has the coordinates $\mathbf{x}$ and $\mathbf{y}$. Given that $\mathbf{x}$ and $\mathbf{y}$ have a bivariate normal density with $\mu_1 = 0$, $\mu_2 = 0$, $\sigma_1 = 1000$ feet, $\sigma_2 = 1000$ feet, and $\rho = 0$, find the probability that the missile will hit the target if

   (a) it is a square with sides of 1200 feet,

   (b) it is a circle with a radius of 800 feet.

13.4.1 *Some sampling theory: correlation analysis*

When analyzing a set of paired data (x_1, y_1), (x_2, y_2), . . ., and (x_n, y_n), it is important to make the following distinction: *if the x_i and y_i are values assumed by corresponding random variables $\mathbf{x}_i$ and $\mathbf{y}_i$ for $i = 1, 2, \ldots,$ and n, the analysis of the data is called correlation analysis; if the x_i are constants and the y_i are values assumed by random variables $\mathbf{y}_i$ having the conditional densities $f(y_i \mid x_i)$ for $i = 1, 2, \ldots,$ and n, the analysis of the data is called regression analysis.* Thus, if we want to analyze data on the heights and weights of a sample of individuals, and height and weight are both looked upon as random variables, this is a problem of *correlation analysis*. On the other hand, if we want to analyze data on the ages and prices of used cars, treating ages as known constants and prices as random variables, this is a problem of *regression analysis.* In this section we shall study some problems of correlation analysis, leaving regression analysis to Section 13.4.2.

To introduce the subject of *normal correlation analysis,* let us define a random sample of size n from a bivariate normal population as a set of paired data (x_1, y_1), (x_2, y_2), ..., and (x_n, y_n), whose likelihood function is

$$L = \prod_{i=1}^{n} f(x_i, y_i) \tag{13.4.7}$$

where $f(x_i, y_i)$ is given by (13.4.1) and the parameters μ_1, μ_2, σ_1, σ_2, and ρ are the same for each value of i. Given such a sample, normal correlation analysis concerns the estimation of the five parameters μ_1, μ_2, σ_1, σ_2, and ρ, and tests of hypotheses, particularly, tests concerning the correlation coefficient ρ.

Using the method of maximum likelihood to estimate the five parameters of a bivariate normal population, we shall have to differentiate the likelihood function (13.4.7), or its logarithm, partially with respect to μ_1, μ_2, σ_1, σ_2, and ρ, equate these partial derivatives to 0, and solve the resulting system of equations for the five parameters. Leaving it to the reader to fill in the detail, let us merely state the result that equating $\dfrac{\partial \ln L}{\partial \mu_1}$ and $\dfrac{\partial \ln L}{\partial \mu_2}$ to 0 gives the equations

$$-\frac{\sum_{i=1}^{n}(x_i - \mu_1)}{\sigma_1^2} + \frac{\rho \sum_{i=1}^{n}(y_i - \mu_2)}{\sigma_1 \sigma_2} = 0 \tag{13.4.8}$$

$$-\frac{\rho \sum_{i=1}^{n}(x_i - \mu_1)}{\sigma_1 \sigma_2} + \frac{\sum_{i=1}^{n}(y_i - \mu_2)}{\sigma_2^2} = 0 \tag{13.4.9}$$

Solving these two equations simultaneously for μ_1 and μ_2, we find that the maximum likelihood estimates of these two parameters are $\hat{\mu}_1 = \bar{x}$ and $\hat{\mu}_2 = \bar{y}$, namely, the two sample means. Subsequently, equating $\dfrac{\partial \ln L}{\partial \sigma_1}$, $\dfrac{\partial \ln L}{\partial \sigma_2}$, and $\dfrac{\partial \ln L}{\partial \rho}$ to 0 and substituting

x and y for μ_1 and μ_2, we obtain three simultaneous equations whose solution is

$$\hat{\sigma}_1 = \sqrt{\frac{\sum_{i=1}^{n} (x_i - \bar{x})^2}{n}} \qquad \hat{\sigma}_2 = \sqrt{\frac{\sum_{i=1}^{n} (y_i - \bar{y})^2}{n}} \tag{13.4.10}$$

$$\hat{\rho} = \frac{\sum_{i=1}^{n} (x_i - \bar{x})(y_i - \bar{y})}{\sqrt{\sum_{i=1}^{n} (x_i - \bar{x})^2} \sqrt{\sum_{i=1}^{n} (y_i - \bar{y})^2}} \tag{13.4.11}$$

(A detailed derivation of these maximum likelihood estimates is referred to in the Bibliography on page 327.) It should be noted that the maximum likelihood estimates for σ_1 and σ_2 are identical with the one obtained on page 225 for the standard deviation of the univariate normal distribution; they differ from the respective sample variances by the multiplicative factor $\sqrt{(n-1)/n}$.

The estimate $\hat{\rho}$, called the *sample correlation coefficient,* is usually denoted by the letter r and its calculation is facilitated by use of the formula

$$r = \frac{n \cdot \sum_{i=1}^{n} x_i y_i - \left(\sum_{i=1}^{n} x_i\right)\left(\sum_{i=1}^{n} y_i\right)}{\sqrt{n \cdot \sum_{i=1}^{n} x_i^2 - \left(\sum_{i=1}^{n} x_i\right)^2} \sqrt{n \cdot \sum_{i=1}^{n} y_i^2 - \left(\sum_{i=1}^{n} y_i\right)^2}} \tag{13.4.12}$$

It will be left to the reader to verify in Exercise 1 on page 312 that (13.4.11) and (13.4.12) are, indeed, equivalent.

As we have said earlier, there are many applications in which the estimation of ρ and tests concerning ρ are of special interest. This is due to the fact that ρ is a measure of the strength of the *linear relationship* between **x** and **y**. When $\rho = 0$, the two random variables are uncorrelated, and in the case of the bivariate normal distribution they are also independent; when $\rho \to 1$, the probability of obtaining a pair of values yielding a point lying outside any narrow strip containing the line $y = \mu_2 + (\sigma_2/\sigma_1)(x - \mu_1)$ approaches 0. If the points (x_i, y_i) actually fall on a straight line, then r equals $+1$ or -1, depending on whether this line has a positive or negative slope.

Since the sampling distribution of **r** for random samples from bivariate normal populations is rather complicated, it is customary to base tests concerning ρ on the statistic $\frac{1}{2}\ln\frac{1+r}{1-r}$. It can be shown that for random samples from bivariate normal populations the distribution of $\frac{1}{2}\ln\frac{1+\mathbf{r}}{1-\mathbf{r}}$ is approximately normal with the mean $\frac{1}{2}\ln\frac{1+\rho}{1-\rho}$ and the variance $1/(n-3)$. In other words,

$$z = \frac{\frac{1}{2}\ln\frac{1+r}{1-r} - \frac{1}{2}\ln\frac{1+\rho}{1-\rho}}{1/\sqrt{n-3}} = \frac{\sqrt{n-3}}{2}\ln\frac{(1+r)(1-\rho)}{(1-r)(1+\rho)} \tag{13.4.13}$$

can be looked upon as a value assumed by a random variable having approximately the standard normal distribution. Using this approximation, we can test hypotheses concerning ρ as is illustrated below, or calculate confidence intervals for ρ as is illustrated in Exercise 3 on page 312.

To give an example of a test concerning ρ, suppose that we want to test whether there is a relationship between the heights and weights of male college freshmen and that the following heights, x, and weights, y, may be looked upon as a random sample from a bivariate normal population:

x (inches)	y (pounds)	x (inches)	y (pounds)
72	191	66	147
70	172	68	159
63	125	72	188
74	210	70	164
69	154	73	175
72	186	71	163

Since $n = 12$,

$$\sum_{i=1}^{n} x_i = 840, \quad \sum_{i=1}^{n} y_i = 2034, \quad \sum_{i=1}^{n} x_i^2 = 58{,}908,$$

$$\sum_{i=1}^{n} y_i^2 = 350{,}426, \quad \text{and} \quad \sum_{i=1}^{n} x_i y_i = 143{,}103$$

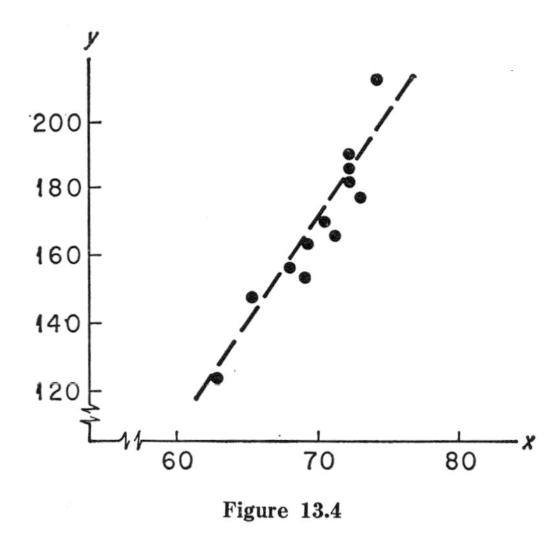

Figure 13.4

substitution into (13.4.12) yields $r = 0.92$, which seems to indicate a *positive linear association* between the heights and weights. This relationship is also displayed by the *scattergram* of Figure 13.4.

To justify any statement to the effect that there *is* a relationship between the heights and weights of the students constituting the given population, we shall now have to test the null hypothesis $\rho = 0$ against the alternative hypothesis $\rho \neq 0$. Substituting $r = 0.92$, $n = 12$, and $\rho = 0$ into (13.4.13), we get $z = \frac{3}{2} \ln (1.92/0.08) = 4.77$, and since this exceeds $z_{.005} = 2.58$, the null hypothesis must be rejected (for $\alpha = 0.01$). In other words, there is a significant correlation (linear relationship) between the heights and weights of the individuals from which the sample was obtained.

EXERCISES

1. Show that (13.4.11) and (13.4.12), the two formulas given for the sample correlation coefficient, are equivalent.

2. Verify equations (13.4.8) and (13.4.9) on page 309.

3. (a) Solving the double inequality $-z_{\alpha/2} \leq z \leq z_{\alpha/2}$, with z given by (13.4.13), so that the middle term is ρ, construct a $1 - \alpha$ confidence interval for ρ.

(b) Using the result obtained in (a), find a 0.95 confidence interval for ρ for the example in the text, where $n = 12$ and $r = 0.92$.

4. The following are the weekly wages, x, of workers in a certain industry and their weekly expenditures, y, for entertainment, movies, sports, etc.: (all figures are given in dollars)

x	y	x	y	x	y
57.30	2.47	93.50	7.12	71.15	5.62
68.75	4.76	85.60	3.81	105.25	8.75
78.40	6.67	75.00	3.69	87.25	4.75
90.00	8.92	87.27	7.40	79.25	7.48
60.87	0.75	83.75	7.82	110.90	9.65
72.10	6.55	79.82	5.63	94.50	6.75

Calculate r and, assuming that the conditions underlying normal correlation analysis can be met, test the null hypothesis $\rho = 0$ against the alternative $\rho \neq 0$ with $\alpha = 0.05$.

5. The following are final examination grades in psychology, x, and economics, y, obtained by 36 students:

x	y	x	y	x	y	x	y
53	70	24	38	62	55	90	78
18	35	94	91	73	69	85	83
25	51	71	53	81	60	52	58
31	72	80	86	45	46	78	57
71	71	84	72	58	59	9	14
16	42	97	93	65	61	42	58
35	57	56	72	65	63	78	76
49	53	82	90	22	38	90	82
77	82	35	19	52	43	93	79

Calculate r and, assuming that the data may be treated as a random sample from a bivariate normal population, test the null hypothesis $\rho = 0$ against the alternative hypothesis $\rho \neq 0$ with $\alpha = 0.05$. Also use the confidence interval obtained in part (a) of Exercise 3 to calculate a 0.95 confidence interval for ρ.

6. (*Rank correlation*) If the ranks 1, 2, ..., and n are assigned to the x's arranged according to size, there are no ties, and the y's are ranked in a similar fashion, show that

$$r = 1 - \frac{6 \sum_{i=1}^{n} d_i^2}{n(n^2 - 1)}$$

where d_i is the difference between the ranks assigned to x_i and y_i. When the x's and y's are, thus, replaced by their ranks, the resulting correlation coefficient is called the *coefficient of rank correlation.* (In actual practice, the formula above is also used when there are ties; in that case tied observations are assigned the mean of the ranks which they jointly occupy.)

7. Calculate the coefficient of rank correlation for the data of Exercise 5.

13.4.2 *Some sampling theory: regression analysis*

In *normal regression analysis* we consider paired data (x_1, y_1), (x_2, y_2), $\ldots$, and (x_n, y_n), where $x_1, x_2, \ldots$, and x_n are constants, while $y_1, y_2, \ldots$, and y_n are values assumed by independent random variables having the conditional densities

$$f(y_i \mid x_i) = \frac{1}{\sqrt{2\pi}\sigma} e^{-\frac{1}{2}\left(\frac{y_i-(\alpha+\beta x_i)}{\sigma}\right)^2} \tag{13.4.14}$$

for $-\infty < y_i < \infty$; the parameters α, β, and σ are the same for each value of i. Given such a random sample of paired data, normal regression analysis concerns the estimation of the regression coefficients α and β, tests of hypotheses concerning the parameters in (13.4.14), and predictions based on the estimated regression equation $y = \hat{\alpha} + \hat{\beta} x$, where $\hat{\alpha}$ and $\hat{\beta}$ are estimates of α and β.

Using the method of maximum likelihood to estimate the parameters α, β, and σ in (13.4.14), we shall have to differentiate the likelihood function (or its logarithm) partially with respect to α, β, and σ, equate these partial derivatives to zero, and solve the resulting system of equations. Differentiating

$$\ln L = -n \cdot \ln \sigma - \frac{n}{2} \cdot \ln 2\pi - \frac{1}{2\sigma^2} \sum_{i=1}^{n} [y_i - (\alpha + \beta x_i)]^2$$

partially with respect to α, β, and σ, and equating these partial derivatives to zero, we get

$$\frac{\partial \ln L}{\partial \alpha} = \frac{1}{\sigma^2} \sum_{i=1}^{n} [y_i - (\alpha + \beta x_i)] = 0 \tag{13.4.15}$$

$$\frac{\partial \ln L}{\partial \beta} = \frac{1}{\sigma^2} \sum_{i=1}^{n} x_i[y_i - (\alpha + \beta x_i)] = 0 \tag{13.4.16}$$

$$\frac{\partial \ln L}{\partial \sigma} = -\frac{n}{\sigma} + \frac{1}{\sigma^3} \sum_{i=1}^{n} [y_i - (\alpha + \beta x_i)]^2 = 0 \tag{13.4.17}$$

As the reader will be asked to verify in Exercise 1 on page 318, solving the first two of these equations simultaneously yields the maximum likelihood estimates

$$\hat{\alpha} = \frac{\left(\sum_{i=1}^{n} x_i^2\right)\left(\sum_{i=1}^{n} y_i\right) - \left(\sum_{i=1}^{n} x_i\right)\left(\sum_{i=1}^{n} x_i y_i\right)}{n\left(\sum_{i=1}^{n} x_i^2\right) - \left(\sum_{i=1}^{n} x_i\right)^2} \tag{13.4.18}$$

$$\hat{\beta} = \frac{n\left(\sum_{i=1}^{n} x_i y_i\right) - \left(\sum_{i=1}^{n} x_i\right)\left(\sum_{i=1}^{n} y_i\right)}{n\left(\sum_{i=1}^{n} x_i^2\right) - \left(\sum_{i=1}^{n} x_i\right)^2} \tag{13.4.19}$$

To simplify the calculation of these estimated regression coefficients, it is customary to determine $\hat{\beta}$ first and then $\hat{\alpha}$ by means of the formula

$$\hat{\alpha} = \frac{\sum_{i=1}^{n} y_i - \hat{\beta} \sum_{i=1}^{n} x_i}{n} \tag{13.4.20}$$

(The reader will be asked to verify in Exercise 2 on page 318 that the two expressions for $\hat{\alpha}$ are equivalent.)

Substituting $\hat{\alpha}$ and $\hat{\beta}$ for α and β in (13.4.17), it follows immediately that the maximum likelihood estimate of σ is

$$\hat{\sigma} = \sqrt{\frac{1}{n} \sum_{i=1}^{n} [y_i - (\hat{\alpha} + \hat{\beta} x_i)]^2} \tag{13.4.21}$$

In actual practice, it is usually easier to find $\hat{\sigma}$ by means of the formula

$$\hat{\sigma}^2 = (1 - r^2)\hat{\sigma}_2^2 \tag{13.4.22}$$

where r is the sample correlation coefficient given by (13.4.12) and $\hat{\sigma}_2$ is given by (13.4.10). It will be left as an exercise, Exercise 3 on page 318, to show that (13.4.21) and (13.4.22) are equivalent.

Having obtained estimators for the regression coefficients, let us now investigate their use in testing hypotheses concerning α and β, and in the construction of confidence intervals for these two parameters. Since problems involving β are usually of more immediate concern (the null hypothesis $\beta = 0$ is equivalent to the null hypothesis $\rho = 0$) we shall discuss some of the sampling theory connected with $\hat{\beta}$ in the text. Corresponding theory concerning $\hat{\alpha}$ is discussed in Exercises 4 and 5 on page 319.

To study the sampling distribution of the maximum likelihood estimator $\hat{\beta}$, let us use (13.4.19) to write

$$\hat{\beta} = \frac{n \sum_{i=1}^{n} [x_i - \bar{x}]\mathbf{y}_i}{n\left(\sum_{i=1}^{n} x_i^2\right) - \left(\sum_{i=1}^{n} x_i\right)^2} = \sum_{i=1}^{n} \left[\frac{x_i - \bar{x}}{n\hat{\sigma}_1^2}\right]\mathbf{y}_i \qquad (13.4.23)$$

where $\hat{\sigma}_1^2$ is given by (13.4.10). It can thus be seen by inspection that $\hat{\beta}$ is a *linear combination* of the independent random variables $\mathbf{y}_i$ having the normal distributions (13.4.14). Hence, according to Exercise 6 on page 173 the random variable $\hat{\beta}$, itself, has a normal distribution and according to Theorem 7.2

$$\begin{aligned} E(\hat{\beta}) &= \sum_{i=1}^{n} \left[\frac{x_i - \bar{x}}{n\hat{\sigma}_1^2}\right] E(\mathbf{y}_i \mid x_i) \\ &= \sum_{i=1}^{n} \left[\frac{x_i - \bar{x}}{n\hat{\sigma}_1^2}\right] (\alpha + \beta x_i) = \beta \end{aligned} \qquad (13.4.24)$$

and

$$\begin{aligned} \operatorname{var}(\hat{\beta}) &= \sum_{i=1}^{n} \left[\frac{x_i - \bar{x}}{n\hat{\sigma}_1^2}\right]^2 \operatorname{var}(\mathbf{y}_i \mid x_i) \\ &= \sum_{i=1}^{n} \left[\frac{x_i - \bar{x}}{n\hat{\sigma}_1^2}\right]^2 \sigma^2 = \frac{\sigma^2}{n\hat{\sigma}_1^2} \end{aligned} \qquad (13.4.25)$$

In order to apply this theory to the construction of confidence intervals for β or tests concerning β, we shall have to make use of the following theorem, a proof of which is referred to in the Bibliography on page 327

THEOREM 13.1:

Under the assumptions of normal regression analysis, $n\hat{\sigma}^2/\sigma^2$, with $\hat{\sigma}^2$ given by (13.4.21), is a value assumed by a random variable having the chi-square distribution with $n - 2$ degrees of freedom. Furthermore, the two random variables $n\hat{\boldsymbol{\sigma}}^2/\sigma^2$ and $\hat{\beta}$ are independent.

Making use of this theorem as well as the fact that $\hat{\beta}$ has a normal distribution whose mean and variance are given by (13.4.24) and (13.4.25), the definition of the t distribution in Section 8.2.4 leads to the result that

$$t = \frac{(\hat{\beta} - \beta)/(\sigma/\sqrt{n}\,\hat{\sigma}_1)}{\sqrt{\dfrac{n\hat{\sigma}^2}{\sigma^2}\Big/ n - 2}} = \frac{(\hat{\beta} - \beta)\,\hat{\sigma}_1\sqrt{n - 2}}{\hat{\sigma}} \qquad (13.4.26)$$

is a value assumed by a random variable having the t distribution with $n - 2$ degrees of freedom.

Using the t statistic given by (13.4.26), we can now construct a $1 - \alpha$ confidence interval for β by manipulating the double inequality $-t_{\alpha/2,n-2} \leq t \leq t_{\alpha/2,n-2}$ so that the middle term is β while the other two terms to not involve this parameter. The result is

$$\hat{\beta} - t_{\alpha/2,n-2}\frac{\hat{\sigma}}{\sqrt{n - 2}\,\hat{\sigma}_1} \leq \beta \leq \hat{\beta} + t_{\alpha/2,n-2}\frac{\hat{\sigma}}{\sqrt{n - 2}\,\hat{\sigma}_1} \qquad (13.4.27)$$

Similarly, to test the null hypothesis $\beta = \beta_0$ against one of the alternatives $\beta > \beta_0$, $\beta < \beta_0$, or $\beta \neq \beta_0$ the appropriate critical regions of size α are $t \geq t_{\alpha,n-2}$, $t \leq -t_{\alpha,n-2}$, and $|t| \geq t_{\alpha/2,n-2}$, where t must be calculated according to (13.4.26) with β_0 substituted for β.

To illustrate the methods discussed in the preceding paragraph, let us consider the following data on road width, x, and accident frequency, y, treating the road widths as constants, the accident frequencies as values assumed by random variables, and assuming that the conditions underlying normal regression analysis can be met: (road widths in feet and accident frequencies per hundred million vehicle miles)

x	y
26	92
30	85
44	78
50	81
62	54
68	51
74	40

Since $n = 7$,

$$\sum_{i=1}^{n} x_i = 354, \quad \sum_{i=1}^{n} y_i = 481, \quad \sum_{i=1}^{n} x_i^2 = 19{,}956,$$

$$\sum_{i=1}^{n} y_i^2 = 35{,}451, \quad \text{and} \quad \sum_{i=1}^{n} x_i y_i = 22{,}200$$

substitution into (13.4.19) and (13.4.20) yields

$$\hat{\beta} = \frac{7(22200) - (354)(481)}{7(19956) - (354)^2} = -1.035$$

$$\hat{\alpha} = \frac{481 - (-1.035)(354)}{7} = 121.1$$

and the resulting *estimated* regression equation becomes

$$y = 121.1 - 1.035x$$

Using this equation, we might predict, for example, that on a 100 mile stretch of road having a width of 70 feet there will be $121.1 - 1.035(70) = 48.7$ accidents among the next one million cars. How to evaluate the "goodness" of such a prediction is indicated in Exercise 12 below.

In order to construct a 0.95 confidence interval for β, we first calculate $\hat{\sigma}_1$, $\hat{\sigma}_2$, r, and $\hat{\sigma}$ according to (13.4.10), (13.4.12), and (13.4.22), getting $\hat{\sigma}_1 = 17.1$, $\hat{\sigma}_2 = 18.6$, $r = -0.96$, and $\hat{\sigma} = 5.25$. Substituting the values obtained for $\hat{\sigma}_1$ and $\hat{\sigma}$ together with $t_{.025,5} = 2.571$ and $\hat{\beta} = -1.035$ into (13.4.27), we obtain

$$-1.39 \leq \beta \leq -0.68$$

An alternate (and easier) way of calculating such a confidence interval for β is given in Exercise 10 below.

EXERCISES

1. Verify that the system of equations given by (13.4.15) and (13.4.16) yield the solutions given by (13.4.18) and (13.4.19).

2. Verify that (13.4.18) and (13.4.20) are equivalent.

3. Verify that (13.4.21) and (13.4.22) are equivalent.

4. (a) Show that (13.4.20) can be written in the form

$$\hat{\alpha} = \sum_{i=1}^{n} \left[\frac{\hat{\sigma}_1^2 + \bar{x}^2 - x_i \bar{x}}{n\,\hat{\sigma}_1^2} \right] y_i$$

(b) Show that $\hat{\alpha}$ has a normal distribution with

$$E(\hat{\alpha}) = \alpha \qquad \text{and} \qquad \operatorname{var}(\hat{\alpha}) = \frac{\sigma^2(\hat{\sigma}_1^2 + \bar{x}^2)}{n\hat{\sigma}_1^2}$$

(c) Use Theorem 7.3 to show that

$$\operatorname{cov}(\hat{\alpha}, \hat{\beta}) = \frac{-\sigma^2 \bar{x}}{n\hat{\sigma}_1^2}$$

5. Using the result obtained in part (b) of Exercise 4, show that

$$z = \frac{(\hat{\alpha} - \alpha)\hat{\sigma}_1\sqrt{n}}{\sigma\sqrt{\hat{\sigma}_1^2 + \bar{x}^2}}$$

is a value assumed by a random variable having the standard normal distribution. Assuming that $\hat{\alpha}$ is independent of $n\hat{\sigma}^2/\sigma^2$, the random variable referred to in Theorem 13.1, show that

$$t = \frac{(\hat{\alpha} - \alpha)\hat{\sigma}_1\sqrt{n-2}}{\hat{\sigma}\sqrt{\hat{\sigma}_1^2 + \bar{x}^2}} \tag{13.4.28}$$

is a value assumed by a random variable having the t distribution with $n - 2$ degrees of freedom.

6. Using the t statistic (13.4.28) of Exercise 5, test the null hypothesis $\alpha = 120$ against the alternative hypothesis $\alpha \neq 120$ for the illustration on page 318. Use a level of significance of 0.05.

7. Using the t statistic (13.4.28) of Exercise 5, construct a 0.95 confidence interval for α for the illustration on page 318.

8. The following are the ages, x, and second-hand prices, y, charged for a certain make of two-door sedan: (ages in years and prices in dollars)

x	1	3	9	2	5	5	8	1
y	1685	1175	285	1395	795	685	495	1855

Assuming that the conditions underlying normal regression analysis can be met, estimate the coefficients of the regression line of $\mathbf{y}$ on x. Also construct a 0.95 confidence interval for β.

9. A manufacturer of optical equipment has the following data on the unit cost (in dollars) of certain custom-made lenses and the number of units made in each order:

Number of units x	1	3	5	10	12
Cost per unit y	58	55	40	37	22

Assuming that the conditions underlying normal regression analysis are met, estimate the regression coefficients and use the estimated regression equation to predict the unit cost in an order of 8 of these lenses. Also test the null hypothesis $\beta = -3$ against the alternative hypothesis $\beta \neq -3$ at a level of significance of 0.01.

10. (a) Verify that the t statistic given by (13.4.26) can be written in the form

$$t = \left(1 - \frac{\beta}{\hat{\beta}}\right)\frac{r\sqrt{n-2}}{\sqrt{1-r^2}}$$

(b) Use the result obtained in (a) to derive the following $1 - \alpha$ confidence limits for β:

$$\hat{\beta}\left[1 \pm t_{\alpha/2,n-2}\frac{\sqrt{1-r^2}}{r\sqrt{n-2}}\right]$$

(c) Use the confidence limits obtained in (b) to verify the confidence interval for β obtained for the illustration on page 318.

11. Use part (a) of Exercise 10 to show that if the assumptions underlying normal regression analysis are met and $\beta = 0$, then $\mathbf{r}^2$ has a *beta distribution.* Also show that the mean of this distribution is $1/(n-1)$.

12. (*Limits of prediction*) Suppose that in a problem in which the assumptions underlying normal regression analysis are met, $\hat{\alpha}$ and $\hat{\beta}$ have been calculated for a given set of paired data. We now want to use the estimated regression equation to predict y for a given value of x, say, $x = x_0$. It is assumed that $f(y \mid x_0)$ is normal with the mean $\alpha + \beta x_0$ and the variance σ^2, where α, β, and σ are the same as in the likelihood function for the given data.

(a) Use (13.4.24), (13.4.25), and the results obtained in Exercise 4 to show that $\mathbf{y} - \hat{\alpha} - \hat{\beta}x_0$ is a random variable having a normal distribution with 0 mean and the variance

$$\sigma^2\left[1 + \frac{1}{n} + \frac{(x_0 - \bar{x})^2}{n\hat{\sigma}_1^2}\right]$$

(b) Assuming that $\mathbf{y} - \hat{\alpha} - \hat{\beta}x_0$ and $n\hat{\sigma}^2/\sigma^2$, the random variable referred to in Theorem 13.1, are independent, show that

$$t = \frac{(y - \hat{\alpha} - \hat{\beta}x_0)\sqrt{n - 2}}{\hat{\sigma}\sqrt{1 + n + (x_0 - \bar{x})^2/\hat{\sigma}_1^2}} \tag{13.4.29}$$

is a value assumed by a random variable having the t distribution with $n - 2$ degrees of freedom.

(c) Solve the double inequality $-t_{\alpha/2,n-2} \leq t \leq t_{\alpha/2,n-2}$, with t given by (13.4.29), so that the middle term is y and the other two terms can be calculated without knowledge of y. Note that although the resulting double inequality is to be interpreted like a confidence interval, it is not designed to estimate a population parameter. Rather it provides *limits of prediction* for the value of $\mathbf{y}$ which corresponds to x_0.

(d) Use the result of part (c) to find 0.95 *limits of prediction* for predicting the accident frequency for a 100 mile stretch of road 70 feet wide on the basis of the data on page 317.

(e) Use the result of part (c) and the data of Exercise 9 to find 0.95 limits of prediction for the unit cost of lenses in an order of 8.

13.5 The Method of Least Squares

In sections 13.2 and 13.3 we assumed that we were dealing with *known* bivariate distributions and in Section 13.4 only the parameters were unknown. In actual practice, there are many problems where a set of paired data gives the indication that the regression may very well be linear, where we want to find estimates of the regression coefficients, but where we cannot make any assumptions about underlying distributions. Problems of this kind are usually handled with the use of the *method of least squares*, a method of curve fitting suggested early in the 19th century by the French mathematician Adrien Legendre.

To illustrate the method of least squares, let us consider a problem in which the management of a firm wants to predict new salesmen's first year sales, y, on the basis of test scores, x, obtained in a specially designed aptitude test. The following data are available from the company's files, with first year sales in 1000 dollars:

x	y	x	y
48	312	50	288
32	164	26	146
40	280	50	361
34	196	22	149
30	200	43	252

Plotting these data as in Figure 13.5, it is apparent that a straight line provides a reasonably good fit; the points do not all fall on a straight line, but the over-all pattern seems to indicate that there might very well be a linear regression.

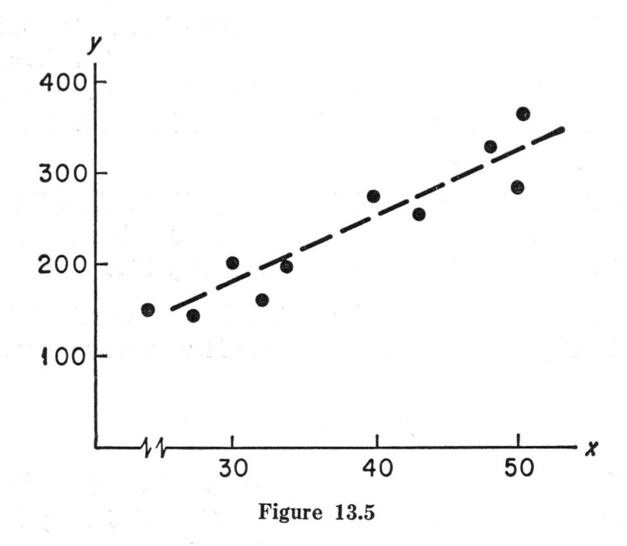

Figure 13.5

Deciding, thus, that a straight line will give a good approximation of the regression of first year sales on aptitude scores, we now face the problem of finding the line (the equation of the line) which in some sense provides the best possible fit. In other words, we face the problem of estimating the regression coefficients α and β in $y = \alpha + \beta x$, so that the resulting line provides the best possible fit. The criterion which we shall use for deciding which line provides the best fit is the *criterion of least squares*; as we shall use it here, this criterion demands that *the sum of the squares of the vertical*

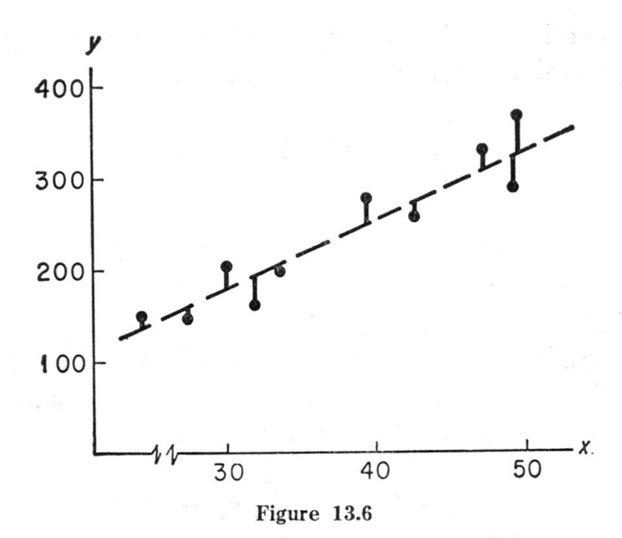

Figure 13.6

deviations from the points to the line (the heavy lines of Figure 13.6) *be a minimum.* Given a set of paired data (x_1, y_1), (x_2, y_2), $\cdots$, and (x_n, y_n), the method of least squares, thus, selects those values of α and β in $y = \alpha + \beta x$ which make

$$\sum_{i=1}^{n} [y_i - (\alpha + \beta x_i)]^2 \tag{13.5.1}$$

a minimum. Differentiating partially with respect to α and β, and equating these partial derivatives to zero, we obtain

$$\sum_{i=1}^{n} (-2)[y_i - (\alpha + \beta x_i)] = 0 \tag{13.5.2}$$

and

$$\sum_{i=1}^{n} (-2)x_i[y_i - (\alpha + \beta x_i)] = 0 \tag{13.5.3}$$

Solving these two equations for α and β, we obtain the *least squares estimates* which we shall write as α' and β'.

As can be seen by inspection, (13.5.2) and (13.5.3) are equivalent to (13.4.15) and (13.4.16), the two equations which yielded the maximum likelihood estimates of α and β under the assumptions of normal regression analysis. *Hence, the least squares estimates α' and β', obtained without any assumptions about underlying distributions, are identical with $\hat{\alpha}$ and $\hat{\beta}$ as given by* (13.4.18) *and* (13.4.19).

In actual practice, the least squares estimates are usually obtained by solving the simultaneous linear equations

$$\sum_{i=1}^{n} y_i = \alpha' n + \beta' \sum_{i=1}^{n} x_i \tag{13.5.4}$$

$$\sum_{i=1}^{n} x_i y_i = \alpha' \sum_{i=1}^{n} x_i + \beta' \sum_{i=1}^{n} x_i^2 \tag{13.5.5}$$

It will be left to the reader to verify that these two equations, called the *normal equations*, are equivalent to (13.5.2) and (13.5.3).

Continuing now with the illustration concerning the salesmen's test scores and first year sales, we find that $n = 10$,

$$\sum_{i=1}^{n} x_i = 375, \qquad \sum_{i=1}^{n} y_i = 2348$$

$$\sum_{i=1}^{n} x_i^2 = 14{,}993, \qquad \text{and} \qquad \sum_{i=1}^{n} x_i y_i = 94{,}448$$

and that, therefore, the two normal equations are

$$2348 = 10\alpha' + 375\beta'$$

$$94448 = 375\alpha' + 14993\beta'$$

Solving for α' and β' we get $\alpha' = -23.20$ and $\beta' = 6.88$, and we, thus, find that the equation of the least squares line is

$$y = -23.20 + 6.88x$$

Using this equation, we could predict that an applicant receiving a score of 45 on the special aptitude test will have first year sales of $y = -23.20 + 6.88(45) = 286.2$ thousand dollars. *However, not having made any assumptions about underlying distributions, we cannot evaluate the "goodness" of this prediction in terms of limits of prediction, and we cannot test hypotheses or construct confidence intervals for the regression coefficients.*

The method of least squares is used in many problems of curve fitting, which are more general than the one treated in this section. In Exercise 4 below, the reader will be asked to use the method of least squares to estimate the parameters α, β, and γ in the parabolic regression equation $y = \alpha + \beta x + \gamma x^2$, and in Exercises 5 and 6 he will be asked to estimate the parameters of regression equations representing exponential functions and power functions. In Exercise 7 the method of least squares will be used to estimate the parameters in a multiple regression equation having the form $z = \alpha + \beta x + \gamma y$.

EXERCISES

1. In the study of the stress-strain curve of a certain alloy an engineer obtained the following results on the stress, x, in hundred thousand psi and the strain, y, in thousandths of an inch:

x	y	x	y
0.1	1	1.0	10
0.3	4	1.2	11
0.5	6	1.5	17
0.8	8		

Find least squares estimates of the coefficients of the regression line of **y** on **x**.

2. The following are the grades which 10 students obtained in a midterm examination and in a final examination in a college course in statistics:

x (*midterm*)	y (*final*)	x (*midterm*)	y (*final*)
65	71	62	65
92	89	72	78
54	62	43	35
80	74	57	59
21	17	91	97

Find least squares estimates of the coefficients of the regression line of **y** on **x**. Also plot the given data and the graph of the line to get a visual impression of the "goodness" of the fit.

3. There are many problems where there is good reason to assume that the regression line must pass through the origin. To handle problems of this kind, use the method of least squares to estimate β in $y = \beta x$ for a given set of paired data $(x_1, y_1), (x_2, y_2), \ldots, (x_n, y_n)$. Apply the result to the data of Exercise 1, where there is theoretical reason to assume that the regression line must pass through the origin.

4. (*Parabolic curve fitting*) Suppose that plotting the points (x_1, y_1), $(x_2, y_2), \ldots,$ and (x_n, y_n) makes it apparent that a parabola will give a good fit, namely, that the regression equation is of the form $y = \alpha + \beta x + \gamma x^2$. Show that the method of least squares leads to the following normal equations, where α', β', and γ' are the least square estimates of the corresponding parameters:

$$\sum_{i=1}^{n} y_i = \alpha' n + \beta' \sum_{i=1}^{n} x_i + \gamma' \sum_{i=1}^{n} x_i^2$$

$$\sum_{i=1}^{n} x_i y_i = \alpha' \sum_{i=1}^{n} x_i + \beta' \sum_{i=1}^{n} x_i^2 + \gamma' \sum_{i=1}^{n} x_i^3$$

$$\sum_{i=1}^{n} x_i^2 y_i = \alpha' \sum_{i=1}^{n} x_i^2 + \beta' \sum_{i=1}^{n} x_i^3 + \gamma' \sum_{i=1}^{n} x_i^4$$

Use these equations to fit a parabola to the following data on core drillings made at one-foot intervals along the length of a vacuum-cast ingot to determine the amount of hydrogen present: (core location, x, in feet from base and amount of hydrogen present, y, in parts per million)

x	y	x	y
1	1.28	6	0.65
2	1.53	7	0.87
3	1.03	8	0.81
4	0.81	9	1.10
5	0.74	10	1.03

5. (*Fitting of exponential curve*) If a set of paired data gives the indication that the regression equation is of the form $y = \alpha \cdot \beta^x$, it is customary to use the method of this section to fit a straight line of the form $\log y = \log \alpha + x \cdot \log \beta$ to the points $(x_i, \log y_i)$. Use this technique to fit an exponential curve to the following data on the growth of a certain plant: (time, x, in weeks and height, y, in inches)

x	1	2	3	4	5	6	7	8
y	1.00	1.20	1.80	2.50	3.60	4.70	6.60	9.10

6. (*Fitting of power function*) If a set of paired data gives the indication that the regression equation might be of the form $y = \alpha \cdot x^\beta$, it is customary to use the method of this section to fit a linear equation in $\log x$ and $\log y$, namely, $\log y = \log \alpha + \beta \cdot \log x$, to the points $(\log x_i, \log y_i)$. Use this method to fit a so-called power function of the form $y = \alpha \cdot x^\beta$ to the following data:

x	1	2	4	6	10
y	110	62	38	21	9

7. (*Multiple linear regression*) In some problems it is desired to fit a plane having the equation $z = \alpha + \beta x + \gamma y$ to a set of data consisting of the triplets (x_i, y_i, z_i) for $i = 1, 2, \ldots,$ and n. Minimizing

$$\sum_{i=1}^{n} [z_i - (\alpha + \beta x_i + \gamma y_i)]^2$$

derive a set of normal equations for the least squares estimates α', β', and γ'. Use these equations to fit a plane of this kind to the points (1, 1, 1), (0, 2, −5), (2, 1, 3), (3, 2, 2), and (4, 1, 12).

BIBLIOGRAPHY

A detailed treatment of the various mathematical and statistical properties of the bivariate normal surface may be found in

Yule, G. U., and M. G. Kendall, *An Introduction to the Theory of Statistics*, 14th ed., New York: Hafner Publishing Co., 1950, Chapter 10.

A derivation of the maximum likelihood estimates given by (13.4.10) and (13.4.11) may be found in

Hoel, P., *Introduction to Mathematical Statistics*, 2nd ed., New York: John Wiley & Sons, Inc., 1954, Chapter 8.

The distribution of $\frac{1}{2} \cdot \ln \frac{1 + \mathbf{r}}{1 - \mathbf{r}}$ is discussed in

Kendall, M. G., *The Advanced Theory of Statistics*, Vol. I, 5th ed., London: Charles Griffin & Co., 1952, Chapter 14.

A proof of Theorem 13.1, based on Cochran's Theorem, is given in

Wilks, S. S., *Mathematical Statistics*, Princeton, N. J.: Princeton University Press, 1947, Chapter 8.

Chapter **14**

Introduction to Analysis of Variance

14.1 Introduction

Anyone who has at one time been engaged in applied research knows how difficult it is to plan an experiment so that it can actually serve the purpose for which it is designed. All too often it happens that an experiment purported to test one thing tests another or that an experiment which is not properly designed cannot serve any useful purpose at all. For instance, let us refer to Exercise 3 on page 270, which deals with the comparison of two kinds of gasoline. Even if the difference between the two sample means is statistically significant, can we really conclude that there is a difference in the actual average mileage yields of the two kinds of gasoline? *Is it not possible that the observed difference between the means may be accounted for by the fact that the gasolines were tested in different cars, by different drivers, perhaps, over different terrains*? Any one of these factors can make it difficult, even impossible, to analyze and interpret the experiment in an intelligent fashion.

There are essentially two ways of handling problems of this kind. One is to perform a rigorously controlled experiment in which all variables except the one with which we are concerned are held fixed. For instance, all of the test runs in the gasoline experiment could be made with the same car (which is rigorously inspected after each run), with the same driver, and over the same route. In that case, if there is a significant difference between the average mileages obtained with the two kinds of gasoline, we know that it is *not* due to differences in cars, drivers, or routes. On the positive side we know that one gasoline performs better than the other *if it is used in a specific kind of car, by a specific driver, and over a specific route.* This really does not tell us very much, and generally speaking, it is not the kind of information we want.

The second way of handling this problem is to *design* the experiment in such a way that we can not only compare the merits of the two kinds of gasoline under more general conditions, but that we can also test whether the other variables affect their performance. To illustrate how this might be done, suppose that the test runs are performed in two cars, a low-priced car L and a high-priced car H, by two drivers, a good driver Mr. G and a poor driver Mr. P, and over two routes, a city route C and a rural route R. As before, each test run is performed with 1 gallon of gasoline, but now there are 16 test runs, 8 with Brand A and 8 with Brand B, and they are planned as follows:

Test run	*Gasoline*	*Car*	*Driver*	*Route*
1	B	L	G	C
2	B	H	P	C
3	A	H	P	C
4	B	L	P	R
5	A	H	G	C
6	B	H	G	C
7	B	L	G	R
8	A	L	P	R
9	A	L	G	R
10	A	H	P	R
11	B	L	P	C
12	A	L	P	C
13	A	H	G	R
14	B	H	G	R
15	A	L	G	C
16	B	H	P	R

This means that the first test run is performed with gasoline B in the low-priced car, by the good driver, over the city route; the second test run is performed with gasoline B in the high-priced car, by the poor driver, over the city route; and so forth. It is customary to refer to this kind of scheme as completely balanced: *each gasoline is used once with each possible combination of cars, drivers, and routes.*

Another important feature of the above scheme is that we protected ourselves by *randomization.* First we wrote down the 16 possible ways in which one can select one of two gasolines, one of two cars, one of two drivers, and one of two routes. Then we randomly selected the order in which these test runs are to be performed, using random numbers or some other gambling device. Had we not randomized the experiment in this fashion, extraneous factors might conceivably upset the results. For instance, had we first run the 8 tests with gasoline A and then the 8 tests with gasoline B, the results might be affected by the deterioration of equipment, driver fatigue, or differences in traffic conditions along the chosen routes. We would, similarly, have asked for trouble if we had performed the first 8 tests with car L and the others with car H, if we had performed the first 8 tests with driver G and the others with driver P, and so forth.

Another factor which is of importance in the design of an experiment is that of *replication* or *repetition.* In order to be able to decide whether an observed difference between sample means is significant or whether a sample mean differs significantly from some assumed value μ_0, we must have an estimate of chance variation, or as it is usually called, the *experimental error.* Such an estimate is usually obtained by repeating all or parts of the experimental scheme. In our illustration we might, thus, perform 32 test runs, 2 of each of the 16 possible combinations listed in the scheme above. (This problem will be touched upon again on page 343.)

The purpose of this example has been to introduce some of the basic ideas of experimental design. Generally speaking, the analysis of an experiment depends partially on the experimental design and partially on assumptions concerning the distributions of underlying random variables. (The latter are also referred to as assumptions concerning the *mathematical model.*) As we saw in Chapters 9 through 13, most of the standard procedures, that is, tests of hypotheses and methods of estimation, require assumptions about the population, or populations, from which the samples are obtained. Specification of these assumptions, thus, constitutes another important aspect of the proper use of statistics in experimentation.

The subjects of experimental design and, correspondingly, the analysis of experimental data are so vast that we can at best touch upon some of the basic ideas. In Sections 14.2 and 14.3 we shall introduce a method of analyzing experimental data called the *analysis of variance*; it is undoubtedly the most important technique of experimental statistics. In Section 14.4 we shall briefly touch upon some further considerations.

14.2 One-Way Analysis of Variance

In Section 12.2.2 we considered the problem of deciding whether differences between the means of two samples may be attributed to chance; now let us consider the problem of deciding whether differences among the means of more than two samples may be attributed to chance. For instance, we may want to decide whether there really is a difference in the performance of 3 kinds of tires if 5 tires made by Company A lasted on the average 22,300 miles, 5 tires made by Company B lasted on the average 21,400 miles, while 5 tires made by Company C lasted on the average 20,650 miles. Similarly, we may want to test whether there really is a difference in the average mechanical aptitude of the students of 4 large schools on the basis of scores obtained in an appropriate test by 10 students selected at random from each school. Suppose, for example, that the results obtained in the test are:

School 1	*School* 2	*School* 3	*School* 4
73	84	69	65
57	95	80	58
95	96	73	82
78	62	62	86
86	80	50	35
61	87	71	52
80	100	84	70
98	74	66	79
64	85	52	43
78	77	73	60

The means of these four samples are 77, 84, 68, and 63; what we would like to know is whether the discrepancies among these means may reasonably be attributed to chance or whether they are indicative of differences among the means of the corresponding populations.

To treat problems of this kind in a general fashion, suppose that we have independent random samples of size n from k populations and that x_{ij} is the jth observation of the sample from the ith population. In the analysis which follows we shall assume that the corresponding random variables $\mathbf{x}_{ij}$ have independent normal distributions with the means μ_i and the common variance σ^2. Stating this assumption somewhat differently, we can specify the underlying model by writing

$$x_{ij} = \mu_i + e_{ij} \qquad \text{for} \qquad \begin{matrix} i = 1, 2, \ldots, k \\ j = 1, 2, \ldots, n \end{matrix} \tag{14.2.1}$$

where the e_{ij} are values assumed by independent random variables having normal distributions with 0 means and the common variance σ^2. With an eye on more general problems to be discussed later, we can also write (14.2.1) as

$$x_{ij} = \mu + \alpha_i + e_{ij} \qquad \text{for} \qquad \begin{matrix} i = 1, 2, \ldots, k \\ j = 1, 2, \ldots, n \end{matrix} \tag{14.2.2}$$

where

$$\sum_{i=1}^{k} \alpha_i = 0$$

It is customary to refer to μ as the *grand mean* and to α_i as the *effect* of the ith population. Note that we simply wrote the mean of the ith population as $\mu_i = \mu + \alpha_i$ and that

$$\sum_{i=1}^{k} \alpha_i = 0$$

because we shall want the mean of the μ_i to equal the grand mean μ.

The null hypothesis which we shall want to test is that the means of the k populations are all equal or, in other words,

$$H_0\colon\ \alpha_i = 0 \qquad \text{for} \quad i = 1, 2, \ldots, k$$

The alternative hypothesis is that the means are not all equal or, in other words,

$$H_A\colon\ \alpha_i \neq 0 \qquad \text{for at least one value of } i$$

The method which we shall use to test these hypotheses is based on an analysis of the total variability of the data. If the null hypothesis is true, then

$$\sum_{i=1}^{k} \sum_{j=1}^{n} (x_{ij} - \bar{x})^2$$

which is $(nk - 1)$ times the variance of all the data, is due entirely to chance variation. Here $\bar{x}$ is the mean of all the data, namely,

$$\bar{x} = \frac{1}{k \cdot n} \sum_{i=1}^{k} \sum_{j=1}^{n} x_{ij}$$

If the null hypothesis is not true, then part of this *sum of squares* can be attributed to differences among the means of the k populations. To be more specific, let us write

$$\sum_{i=1}^{k} \sum_{j=1}^{n} (x_{ij} - \bar{x})^2 = \sum_{i=1}^{k} \sum_{j=1}^{n} [(x_{ij} - \bar{x}_{i.}) + (\bar{x}_{i.} - \bar{x})]^2 \quad (14.2.3)$$

where

$$\bar{x}_{i.} = \frac{1}{n} \sum_{j=1}^{n} x_{ij}$$

is the mean of the sample from the ith population. If we now expand the righthand member of (14.2.3), we get

$$\begin{aligned} \sum_{i=1}^{k} \sum_{j=1}^{n} (x_{ij} - \bar{x})^2 &= \sum_{i=1}^{k} \sum_{j=1}^{n} (x_{ij} - \bar{x}_{i.})^2 + \sum_{i=1}^{k} \sum_{j=1}^{n} (\bar{x}_{i.} - \bar{x})^2 \\ &\quad + 2 \sum_{i=1}^{k} \sum_{j=1}^{n} (x_{ij} - \bar{x}_{i.})(\bar{x}_{i.} - \bar{x}) \\ &= \sum_{i=1}^{k} \sum_{j=1}^{n} (x_{ij} - \bar{x}_{i.})^2 + n \sum_{i=1}^{k} (\bar{x}_{i.} - \bar{x})^2 \\ &\quad + 2 \sum_{i=1}^{k} (\bar{x}_{i.} - \bar{x}) \sum_{j=1}^{n} (x_{ij} - \bar{x}_{i.}) \end{aligned}$$

and since

$$\sum_{j=1}^{n} (x_{ij} - \bar{x}_{i.}) = 0$$

for each value of i, we finally obtain the identity

$$\begin{aligned} &\sum_{i=1}^{k} \sum_{j=1}^{n} (x_{ij} - \bar{x})^2 \\ &\qquad = \sum_{i=1}^{k} \sum_{j=1}^{n} (x_{ij} - \bar{x}_{i.})^2 + n \sum_{i=1}^{k} (\bar{x}_{i.} - \bar{x})^2 \end{aligned} \quad (14.2.4)$$

It is customary to refer to the lefthand member of (14.2.4) as the *total sum of squares* SST, to the first term of the righthand member as the *error sum of squares* SSE, and to the second term of the righthand member as the *between samples sum of squares* SSB. We can, thus, write $SST = SSE + SSB$. Note that we have accomplished what we originally set out to do: *we have decomposed* SST, *a measure of the total variability of the data, into the sum of two components: the first component,* SSE, *measures chance variation (the variability within the samples) regardless of whether the null hypothesis is true; the second component,* SSB, *measures chance variation if the null hypothesis is true, but it can be attributed in part to differences among the population means if the null hypothesis is false.*

Under the null hypothesis and the model assumed in (14.2.2), the nk observations x_{ij} may be looked upon as *one* random sample from a normal population with the mean μ and the variance σ^2. Hence, according to Theorem 8.6, the random variable

$$\frac{1}{\sigma^2} \sum_{i=1}^{k} \sum_{j=1}^{n} (\mathbf{x}_{ij} - \bar{\mathbf{x}})^2$$

has a chi-square distribution with $nk - 1$ degrees of freedom. Referring to the same theorem we also find that the random variables

$$\frac{1}{\sigma^2} \sum_{j=1}^{n} (\mathbf{x}_{ij} - \bar{\mathbf{x}}_{i.})^2$$

for $i = 1, 2, \ldots$, and k have independent chi-square distributions with $n - 1$ degrees of freedom and, hence, according to Theorem 8.4 that the random variable

$$\frac{1}{\sigma^2} \sum_{i=1}^{k} \sum_{j=1}^{n} (\mathbf{x}_{ij} - \bar{\mathbf{x}}_{i.})^2$$

has a chi-square distribution with $k(n - 1)$ degrees of freedom. Finally, since under the null hypothesis the $\bar{x}_{i.}$ are values assumed by independent random variables having a normal distribution with the mean μ and the variance σ^2/n, it follows according to Theorem 8.6 that the random variable

$$\frac{n}{\sigma^2} \sum_{i=1}^{k} (\bar{\mathbf{x}}_{i.} - \bar{\mathbf{x}})^2$$

has a chi-square distribution with $k - 1$ degrees of freedom.

In order to proceed to the test of the null hypothesis formulated on page 332, we shall have to accept without proof that the random variables

$$\frac{1}{\sigma^2}\sum_{i=1}^{k}\sum_{j=1}^{n}(\mathbf{x}_{ij}-\bar{\mathbf{x}}_{i.})^2 \quad \text{and} \quad \frac{n}{\sigma^2}\sum_{i=1}^{k}(\bar{\mathbf{x}}_{i.}-\bar{\mathbf{x}})^2$$

are *independent.* Using this result, a proof of which is referred to in the Bibliography on page 350, and Theorem 8.7, it follows that

$$\frac{SSB/(k-1)\sigma^2}{SSE/k(n-1)\sigma^2} = \frac{k(n-1)SSB}{(k-1)SSE}$$

is a value assumed by a random variable having the F distribution with $k - 1$ and $k(n - 1)$ degrees of freedom. Consequently, we reject the null hypothesis that the α_i are all equal to zero if

$$F = \frac{k(n-1)SSB}{(k-1)SSE} \tag{14.2.5}$$

is greater than or equal to $F_{\alpha,k-1,k(n-1)}$. We are rejecting the null hypothesis for values falling into the righthand tail of the F distributions, inasmuch as this rejects the null hypothesis when SSB, *the variation between the samples,* is too large.

The analysis which we have outlined in this section is usually presented in the following kind of table, called an *analysis of variance table*:

Source of variation	*Degrees of freedom*	*Sum of squares*	*Mean square*	*F*
Between samples	$k-1$	SSB	$MSB = \dfrac{SSB}{k-1}$	$\dfrac{MSB}{MSE}$
Error	$k(n-1)$	SSE	$MSE = \dfrac{SSE}{k(n-1)}$	
Total	$kn-1$	SST		

Here the *mean squares* are the sums of squares divided by the corresponding degrees of freedom.

Let us now return to the illustration on page 331, where we wanted to test whether there is a difference in the average mechanical aptitude of the students of four schools. We could calculate SSB and SSE by substituting directly into the two terms on the right-hand side of (14.2.4), but to simplify the calculations we shall instead use the short-cut formulas the reader will be asked to derive in Exercise 1 below. We, thus, get

$$SST = \sum_{i=1}^{k} \sum_{j=1}^{n} x_{ij}^2 - \frac{1}{k \cdot n}\left[\sum_{i=1}^{k} \sum_{j=1}^{n} x_{ij}\right]^2 \qquad (14.2.6)$$

$$= 222{,}276 - 213{,}160 = 9{,}116$$

$$SSB = \frac{1}{n} \sum_{i=1}^{k} \left[\sum_{j=1}^{n} x_{ij}\right]^2 - \frac{1}{k \cdot n}\left[\sum_{i=1}^{k} \sum_{j=1}^{n} x_{ij}\right]^2 \qquad (14.2.7)$$

$$= 215{,}780 - 213{,}160 = 2{,}620$$

and

$$SSE = SST - SSB$$

$$= 9{,}116 - 2{,}620 = 6{,}496$$

Hence

$$F = \frac{4(9)(2{,}620)}{3(6{,}496)} = 4.84$$

and since this exceeds $F_{.05,3,36}$ the null hypothesis must be rejected. (Actually, $F_{.05,3,36}$ is not given in Table VI, but it must fall between $F_{.05,3,30} = 2.92$ and $F_{.05,3,40} = 2.84$, which are both exceeded by $F = 4.84$.) We conclude that the average mechanical aptitudes of the students in the four schools are not all equal.

The parameters of the model, that is, the grand mean μ and the α_i, are usually estimated by the method of least squares. In other words, the estimates which are generally given for μ and the α_i are the values which minimize

$$\sum_{i=1}^{k} \sum_{j=1}^{n} [x_{ij} - (\mu + \alpha_i)]^2 \qquad (14.2.8)$$

subject to the restriction that

$$\sum_{i=1}^{k} \alpha_i = 0$$

This may be done by using the method of Lagrange multipliers, referred to in the Bibliography on page 350 (see also Exercise 6 below).

EXERCISES

1. Derive the short-cut computing formulas for SST and SSB given by (14.2.6) and (14.2.7).

2. Random samples of 8 sets of tires each of 3 different brands required the following braking distances while going at 30 miles per hour:

Brand A	*Brand B*	*Brand C*
26	26	24
28	31	27
25	27	25
23	25	26
25	28	25
27	29	23
24	26	27
28	26	25

Use a level of significance of 0.05 to test the null hypothesis that the true average braking distance (while going at 30 miles per hour) is the same for the three brands of tires.

3. The following are 5 consecutive weeks' earnings (in dollars) of 3 salesmen employed by a given firm:

Mr. Jones	*Mr. Smith*	*Mr. Brown*
172	203	161
185	172	149
165	187	183
194	183	156
212	179	144

Use a level of significance of 0.05 to test whether the differences among the average weekly earnings of these three salesmen are significant.

4. If the sample sizes are unequal in a one-way analysis of variance and there are n_i observations in the sample from the ith population, show that

$$\sum_{i=1}^{k} \sum_{j=1}^{n_i} (x_{ij} - \bar{x})^2 = \sum_{i=1}^{k} \sum_{j=1}^{n_i} (x_{ij} - \bar{x}_{i.})^2 + \sum_{i=1}^{k} n_i (\bar{x}_{i.} - \bar{x})^2$$

analogous to (14.2.4). Also show that the number of degrees of freedom corresponding to SST, SSE, and SSB are $N - 1$, $N - k$, and $k - 1$,

where $$N = \sum_{i=1}^{k} n_i$$

5. The following are the amounts of corn (in bushels per acre) obtained for 4 test plots of one variety, 6 test plots of a second variety, 6 test plots of a third variety, and 3 test plots of a fourth variety:

Variety A	*Variety B*	*Variety C*	*Variety D*
82.5	72.3	75.1	90.3
69.4	77.6	80.2	88.6
73.9	58.0	69.7	72.4
89.8	62.7	87.3	
	69.5	94.6	
	81.0	69.2	

Use the theory of Exercise 4 to test the null hypothesis that there is no difference in the true average yield of the four varieties of corn. Let $\alpha = 0.05$.

6. Using Lagrange multipliers (see Bibliography on page 350) show that the least squares estimates for μ and the α_i in (14.2.2) are $\mu' = \bar{x}$ and $\alpha_i' = \bar{x}_{i.} - \bar{x}$.

7. Show that for $k = 2$ the F test of this section is equivalent to the t test on page 268.

14.3 Two-Way Analysis of Variance

To give an example of a two-way analysis of variance, let us consider a problem in which it is desired to investigate the effect of k different kinds of fuels and n different kinds of launchers on the range of a certain rocket. Referring to the fuels as A_i for $i = 1, 2, \ldots, k$ and to the launchers as B_j for $j = 1, 2, \ldots, n$, suppose that one rocket is fired for each possible combination of fuels and launchers, that the firing of the nk rockets is randomized, and that x_{ij} is the range obtained with the ith fuel and the jth launcher. A possible model for this kind of problem is to look upon the x_{ij} as values assumed by independent random variables having normal distributions with the means μ_{ij} and the variance σ^2, where

$$\mu_{ij} = \mu + \alpha_i + \beta_j \tag{14.3.1}$$

and

$$\sum_{i=1}^{k} \alpha_i = 0 \quad \text{and} \quad \sum_{j=1}^{n} \beta_j = 0$$

Analogous to (14.2.2) we could also specify these assumptions by writing

$$x_{ij} = \mu + \alpha_i + \beta_j + e_{ij} \quad \text{for} \quad \begin{array}{l} i = 1, 2, \ldots, k \\ j = 1, 2, \ldots, n \end{array} \tag{14.3.2}$$

where the e_{ij} are values assumed by independent random variables having normal distributions with 0 means and the common variance σ^2. Note that in this model the *effects* of the two variables, that is, the α_i and β_j, are added to μ; in Exercise 1 on page 346 the reader will be asked to show that the restriction

$$\sum_{i=1}^{k} \alpha_i = 0$$

arises from the fact that we shall want the *mean* of the μ_{ij} for a fixed value of j to equal $\mu + \beta_j$. (A similar reason can be given for the restriction imposed on the β_j.)

The null hypotheses we shall want to test are (1) that the α_i are all equal to 0 and (2) that the β_j are all equal to 0; the corresponding alternative hypotheses are that the respective parameters are not all equal to 0. The tests of these hypotheses are based on the following analysis of the total variability of the data, decomposing it into terms attributed to differences among the A's, differences among the B's, and chance (experimental error):

$$\sum_{i=1}^{k}\sum_{j=1}^{n} (x_{ij} - \bar{x})^2 = n \sum_{i=1}^{k} (\bar{x}_{i.} - \bar{x})^2 + k \sum_{j=1}^{n} (\bar{x}_{.j} - \bar{x})^2$$

$$+ \sum_{i=1}^{k}\sum_{j=1}^{n} (x_{ij} - \bar{x}_{i.} - \bar{x}_{.j} + \bar{x})^2 \tag{14.3.3}$$

Here

$$\bar{x}_{.j} = \frac{1}{k} \sum_{i=1}^{k} x_{ij}$$

and the other symbols are as defined in Section 14.2. The reader will be asked to verify this identity in Exercise 2 on page 346.

Writing (14.3.3) as $SST = SSA + SSB + SSE$, it can be shown that if the null hypothesis concerning the α_i is true, then SSA/σ^2 and SSE/σ^2 are values assumed by independent random variables having chi-square distributions with $k - 1$ and $(n - 1)(k - 1)$ degrees of freedom; if this null hypothesis is not true, then SSA can be attributed, at least in part, to differences among the A's, that is, differences among the fuels. Similarly, if the null hypothesis concerning the β_j is true, it can be shown that SSB/σ^2 and SSE/σ^2 are values assumed by independent random variables having chi-square distributions with $n - 1$ and $(n - 1)(k - 1)$ degrees of freedom; if this null hypothesis is not true, then SSB can be attributed, at least in part, to differences among the B's, that is, differences among the launchers. If both of the null hypotheses are true, it can be shown, furthermore, that SST/σ^2 is a value assumed by a random variable having a chi-square distribution with $nk - 1$ degrees of freedom.

In accordance with Theorem 8.7, the test of the null hypothesis concerning the α_i can, thus, be based on the statistic

$$F_A = \frac{SSA/(k - 1)}{SSE/(n - 1)(k - 1)} = \frac{(n - 1)SSA}{SSE} \qquad (14.3.4)$$

which, under the null hypothesis that the α_i are all equal to 0, is a value assumed by a random variable having the F distribution with $k - 1$ and $(n - 1)(k - 1)$ degrees of freedom. We reject this null hypothesis if F_A is greater than or equal to $F_{\alpha, k-1, (n-1)(k-1)}$.

Similarly, the test of the null hypothesis that the β_j are all equal to 0 can be based on the statistic

$$F_B = \frac{SSB/(n - 1)}{SSE/(n - 1)(k - 1)} = \frac{(k - 1)SSB}{SSE} \qquad (14.3.5)$$

which, under the null hypothesis that the β_j are all equal to 0, is a value assumed by a random variable having the F distribution with $n - 1$ and $(n - 1)(k - 1)$ degrees of freedom. We reject this null hypothesis if F_B is greater than or equal to $F_{\alpha, n-1, (n-1)(k-1)}$.

The *analysis of variance table* for this kind of a two-way analysis is usually presented in the following fashion:

Source of variation	*Degrees of freedom*	*Sum of squares*	*Mean square*	F
Between A's	$k - 1$	SSA	$MSA = \dfrac{SSA}{k - 1}$	$\dfrac{MSA}{MSE}$
Between B's	$n - 1$	SSB	$MSB = \dfrac{SSB}{n - 1}$	$\dfrac{MSB}{MSE}$
Error	$(n - 1)(k - 1)$	SSE	$MSE = \dfrac{SSE}{(n - 1)(k - 1)}$	
Total	$nk - 1$	SST		

Here the *mean squares* are again the sums of squares divided by the respective degrees of freedom.

To illustrate this technique, suppose that an experiment designed to test four fuels and 3 launchers yielded the results shown in the following table: (ranges in nautical miles)

		Launcher		
		B_1	B_2	B_3
Fuel	A_1	58.2	56.2	65.3
	A_2	49.1	54.1	51.6
	A_3	60.1	70.9	39.2
	A_4	75.8	58.2	48.7

The necessary sums of squares can be obtained by substituting directly into the respective terms of (14.3.3) or by using the short-cut formulas the reader will be asked to derive in Exercise 3 on page 346. In either case, we get $SST = 1113.42$, $SSA = 157.59$,

$SSB = 223.85$, $SSE = 731.98$, and the following analysis of variance table:

Source of variation	*Degrees of freedom*	*Sum of squares*	*Mean square*	*F*
Between A's	3	157.59	52.53	0.43
Between B's	2	223.85	111.93	0.92
Error	6	731.98		
Total	11	1113.42		

Since $F_A = 0.43$ is less than $F_{.05,3,6} = 4.76$ and $F_B = 0.92$ is less than $F_{.05,2,6} = 5.14$, neither null hypothesis can be rejected. We conclude that the performance of the rocket is *not* affected by differences among the fuels or differences among the launchers.

The model which we used for the above experiment has a serious disadvantage. *It does not allow for the possibility that there might be joint effects of the two variables, that is, so-called interactions.* With reference to our example, the model does not allow for the possibility that a particular fuel might yield a very high range *if and only if* it is used in conjunction with a particular launcher. Note, for example, the very high value obtained with fuel A_4 and launcher B_1, and the very low value obtained with fuel A_3 and launcher B_3. As the experiment was designed, we have no choice but to attribute these discrepancies to chance.

To account for possible joint effects of the two variables, or interactions, let us look upon the range obtained with fuel A_i and launcher B_j as a value assumed by a random variable having a normal distribution with the mean

$$\mu_{ij} = \mu + \alpha_i + \beta_j + \gamma_{ij} \tag{14.3.6}$$

where

$$\sum_{i=1}^{k} \alpha_i = 0, \quad \sum_{j=1}^{n} \beta_j = 0, \quad \sum_{i=1}^{k} \gamma_{ij} = 0$$

for each j, and

$$\sum_{j=1}^{n} \gamma_{ij} = 0$$

for each i. In order to test hypotheses concerning the α_i, the β_j, as well as the γ_{ij}, it is necessary to *replicate*, that is, to take more than one observation of each combination of fuels and launchers; otherwise we would not have an estimate of the experimental error. Letting x_{ijr} stand for the rth value obtained with fuel A_i and launcher B_j, and taking m observations of each kind, the appropriate model becomes

$$x_{ijr} = \mu + \alpha_i + \beta_j + \gamma_{ij} + e_{ijr} \tag{14.3.7}$$

for $i = 1, 2, \ldots,$ and k, $j = 1, 2, \ldots,$ and n, $r = 1, 2, \ldots,$ and m, where the e_{ijr} are values assumed by independent random variables having normal distributions with 0 means and the common variance σ^2.

The null hypotheses we shall want to test are (1) that the α_i are all equal to 0, (2) that the β_j are all equal to 0, and (3) that the γ_{ij} are all equal to 0; the corresponding alternative hypotheses are that the respective parameters are not all equal to 0. The tests of these hypotheses are based on the following analysis of the total variability of the data, decomposing it into terms which can be attributed to differences among the A's, differences among the B's, interactions (joint effects), and chance (experimental error):

$$\begin{aligned}\sum_{i=1}^{k}\sum_{j=1}^{n}\sum_{r=1}^{m}(x_{ijr} - \bar{x})^2 &= nm\sum_{i=1}^{k}(\bar{x}_{i..} - \bar{x})^2 + km\sum_{j=1}^{n}(\bar{x}_{.j.} - \bar{x})^2 \\ &\quad + m\sum_{i=1}^{k}\sum_{j=1}^{n}(\bar{x}_{ij.} - \bar{x}_{i..} - \bar{x}_{.j.} + \bar{x})^2 \\ &\quad + \sum_{i=1}^{k}\sum_{j=1}^{n}\sum_{r=1}^{m}(x_{ijr} - \bar{x}_{ij.})^2\end{aligned} \tag{14.3.8}$$

Here $\bar{x}$ is again the mean of all the data, $\bar{x}_{i..}$ is the mean of all the data for fuel A_i, $\bar{x}_{.j.}$ is the mean of all the data for launcher B_j, and $\bar{x}_{ij.}$ is the mean of all the data for fuel A_i used in combination with launcher B_j. Writing (14.3.8) as $SST = SSA + SSB + SSI + SSE$, it can be shown that the test of the null hypothesis concerning the α_i can be based on the statistic

$$F_A = \frac{SSA/(k-1)}{SSE/kn(m-1)} = \frac{kn(m-1)SSA}{(k-1)SSE} \tag{14.3.9}$$

which, under the null hypothesis that the α_i are all equal to 0, is a value assumed by a random variable having the F distribution with

$k - 1$ and $kn(m - 1)$ degrees of freedom. We reject this null hypothesis if F_A is greater than or equal to $F_{\alpha,k-1,kn(m-1)}$. Similarly, the test of the null hypothesis concerning the β_j can be based on the statistic

$$F_B = \frac{SSB/(n-1)}{SSE/kn(m-1)} = \frac{kn(m-1)SSB}{(n-1)SSE} \tag{14.3.10}$$

which, under the null hypothesis that the β_j are all equal to 0, is a value assumed by a random variable having the F distribution with $n - 1$ and $kn(m - 1)$ degrees of freedom. We reject this null hypothesis if F_B is greater than or equal to $F_{\alpha,n-1,kn(m-1)}$. Finally, to test the null hypothesis concerning the γ_{ij} we use the statistic

$$F_I = \frac{SSI/(k-1)(n-1)}{SSE/kn(m-1)} = \frac{kn(m-1)SSI}{(k-1)(n-1)SSE} \tag{14.3.11}$$

which, under the null hypothesis that the γ_{ij} are all equal to 0, is a value assumed by a random variable having the F distribution with $(k - 1)(n - 1)$ and $kn(m - 1)$ degrees of freedom. We reject this null hypothesis if F_I is greater than or equal to $F_{\alpha,(k-1)(n-1),kn(m-1)}$.

The *analysis of variance table* for this kind of a two-way analysis is usually presented in the following fashion:

Source of variation	*Degrees of freedom*	*Sum of squares*	*Mean square*	*F*
Between A's	$k - 1$	SSA	$MSA = \frac{SSA}{k-1}$	$\frac{MSA}{MSE}$
Between B's	$n - 1$	SSB	$MSB = \frac{SSB}{n-1}$	$\frac{MSB}{MSE}$
Interaction	$(k - 1)(n - 1)$	SSI	$MSI = \frac{SSI}{(k-1)(n-1)}$	$\frac{MSI}{MSE}$
Error	$kn(m - 1)$	SSE	$MSE = \frac{SSE}{kn(m-1)}$	
Total	$mkn - 1$	SST		

To illustrate the use of this two-way interaction model, suppose that in the rocket example 2 rockets were fired for each combination of fuels and launchers, that the 24 rockets were fired in a randomized order, and that the results were as shown in the following table· (figures are again in nautical miles)

		Launcher		
		B_1	B_2	B_3
Fuel	A_1	58.2 52.6	56.2 41.2	65.3 60.8
	A_2	49.1 42.8	54.1 50.5	51.6 48.4
	A_3	60.1 58.3	70.9 73.2	39.2 40.7
	A_4	75.8 71.5	58.2 51.0	48.7 41.4

Using short-cut formulas to calculate the necessary sums of squares (see Exercise 7 below), we get $SSA = 261.68$, $SSB = 370.98$, $SSI = 1768.69$, $SSE = 236.95$, $SST = 2638.30$, and the three F statistics are

$$F_A = 4.42 \qquad F_B = 9.39 \qquad F_I = 14.93$$

Since $F_{.05,3,12} = 3.49$, $F_{.05,2,12} = 3.89$, and $F_{.05,6,12} = 3.00$, we find that all three of the null hypotheses can be rejected.

The fact that there are significant interactions is most important. It means that there are differences in the performance of the rocket due to particular combinations of fuels and launchers. Hence, one has to be careful not to say, for example, that one fuel is better than another, since this may be true only if the fuel is used in combination with a particular launcher. Another important feature of the above results is that most of the variability which we attributed to chance in the first example of this section, where we used the model given by (14.3.2), should really have been attributed to interactions.

EXERCISES

1. Show that for the model given by (14.3.2) the conditions

$$\frac{1}{k}\sum_{i=1}^{k}\mu_{ij} = \mu + \beta_j \qquad \text{and} \qquad \frac{1}{n}\sum_{j=1}^{n}\mu_{ij} = \mu + \alpha_i$$

lead to the restrictions that the sum of the α_i as well as the sum of the β_j must equal 0.

2. Verify the identity given by (14.3.3).

3. Show that for the model given by (14.3.2) one can calculate SST with (14.2.6) and SSA and SSB with formulas analogous to (14.2.7).

4. The following are the yields of three varieties of wheat (in pounds per plot) obtained with three different kinds of fertilizer:

		Variety of wheat		
		B_1	B_2	B_3
	A_1	46.3	41.9	43.7
Fertilizer	A_2	33.8	37.4	35.8
	A_3	36.9	37.5	32.0

Use a level of significance of 0.05 to test the null hypothesis that there is no difference in the average yield of the three varieties of wheat and the null hypothesis that there is no difference in the effectiveness of the three fertilizers.

5. The following are the number of defective pieces produced by four workmen operating, in turn, four different machines:

		Workman			
		B_1	B_2	B_3	B_4
	A_1	26	27	31	26
	A_2	19	21	27	18
Machine	A_3	23	28	26	24
	A_4	22	26	25	19

Use a level of significance of 0.05 to test whether the differences in the performance of the workmen are significant and also whether the differences in the performance of the machines are significant.

6. Verify the identity given by (14.3.8).

7. Derive short-cut formulas for obtaining the sums of squares of the analysis of variance of the interaction model and use them to verify the numerical values given for the example in the text on page 345.

8. Suppose that in an experiment analogous to that of Exercise 5 each workman operates each machine on three different days and that the results obtained are as follows: (figures are number of defectives produced each day)

		Workman			
		B_1	B_2	B_3	B_4
Machine	A_1	26, 28, 25	28, 25, 31	30, 29, 33	25, 26, 28
	A_2	19, 24, 21	21, 27, 23	27, 25, 24	15, 13, 21
	A_3	23, 26, 24	34, 37, 29	26, 28, 24	25, 29, 26
	A_4	20, 23, 22	26, 28, 24	32, 28, 29	18, 20, 24

Use a level of significance of 0.05 to test for significant differences among the workmen, significant differences among the machines, and interactions.

9. (*Latin squares*) *A latin square* is a square array in which each letter (or other symbol) appears once in each row and once in each column. The following is an example of a latin square of side 4:

$$\begin{matrix} A & B & C & D \\ B & C & D & A \\ C & D & A & B \\ D & A & B & C \end{matrix}$$

Looking upon the rows R_i of a latin square of side r as the levels of one variable, the columns C_j as the levels of a second variable, and $A, B, C, \ldots,$ as r "treatments," that is, levels of a third variable, it is possible to test hypotheses concerning all three of these variables on the basis of as few as r^2 observations, provided there are no interactions. Writing the observation in the ith row and jth column as

$x_{ij(k)}$, the model which we use for an experiment of this kind is

$$x_{ij(k)} = \mu + \alpha_i + \beta_j + \tau_k + e_{ij}$$

for i, j, and $k = 1, 2, \ldots, r$. The e_{ij} are values assumed by independent random variables having normal distributions with 0 means and the common variance σ^2, and

$$\sum_{i=1}^{r} \alpha_i = \sum_{j=1}^{r} \beta_j = \sum_{k=1}^{r} \tau_k = 0$$

We now refer to the α_i as the "row effects," the β_j as the "column effects," and the τ_k as the "treatment effects." (Note that for a given latin square knowledge of i and j automatically determines k.)

(a) Formulate the three null hypotheses which we shall want to test concerning the parameters of this model and the corresponding alternatives.

(b) Show that

$$\sum_{i=1}^{r} \sum_{j=1}^{r} (x_{ij(k)} - \bar{x})^2 = r \sum_{i=1}^{r} (\bar{x}_{i.} - \bar{x})^2 + r \sum_{j=1}^{r} (\bar{x}_{.j} - \bar{x})^2$$

$$+ r \sum_{k=1}^{r} (\bar{x}_{(k)} - \bar{x})^2$$

$$+ \sum_{i=1}^{r} \sum_{j=1}^{r} (x_{ij(k)} - \bar{x}_{i.} - \bar{x}_{.j} - \bar{x}_{(k)} + 2\bar{x})^2$$

where $\bar{x}_{(k)}$ is the mean of all the data corresponding to the kth treatment and the other means are as defined for (14.3.3).

(c) Construct an analysis of variance table for this kind of experiment, referring to the sums of squares of part (b) as SST, SSR, SSC, $SS(T_r)$, and SSE. The number of degrees of freedom for SSE may be obtained by subtracting the sum of the degrees of freedom for SSR, SSC, and $SS(T_r)$ from the number of degrees of freedom for SST.

10. Suppose that the experiment of Exercise 5 was actually designed as a latin square of side 4 like the one given in Exercise 9, with A, B, C, and D standing for the use of raw materials supplied by four different firms. Use the method of analysis obtained in Exercise 9 to test for significant differences among the workmen, significant differences among the machines, and significant differences among the raw materials supplied by the four firms. Use $\alpha = 0.05$.

14.4 Some Further Considerations

The topics which we have presented in this chapter gave us a brief introduction to some of the fundamental ideas of experimental design and the analysis of variance. The subject is vast and new methods are developed constantly, as their need arises in experiments where the conditions underlying so-called standard techniques cannot be met.

The designs which we discussed all had the special feature that there were observations corresponding to all "treatment combinations," that is, for all possible combinations of the values assumed by the variables. To show that this can be very impractical or even impossible, we have only to consider an experiment in which we want to compare the yield of 20 varieties of corn and, at the same time, the effect of 12 fertilizers. To use a model like the one given by (14.3.2), we would have to plant 240 plots and it does not require much imagination to see that it would be extremely difficult to find that many plots for which soil composition, irrigation, slope, . . ., are constant or otherwise controllable. Consequently, there is a need for designs which make it possible to test hypotheses concerning the most relevant (though not all) parameters of a model on the basis of experiments which can be performed, that is, experiments which are feasible from a practical point of view. This leads to the construction of so-called *incomplete block designs,* which are discussed in some of the general references listed below.

Further complications arise when there are extraneous variables which can be measured although they cannot be controlled. For example, in a study comparing a number of "teaching machines" it may be impossible to use individuals with identical I.Q.'s, but, at least, their I.Q.'s are known. In that case we might have to use an *analysis of covariance* model like

$$x_{ij} = \mu + \alpha_i + \beta y_i + e_{ij}$$

where y_i is the known I.Q. of the ith individual. Note that here the estimation of β is essentially a problem of regression analysis.

Other difficulties arise when the α_i and β_j in (14.3.2) are not constants, but values assumed by random variables. This might happen, for example, when there are 20 varieties of corn and 12 kinds of fertilizer and we randomly select, say, 5 varieties of corn and 3 kinds of fertilizer for consideration in an experiment. These are just some of the generalizations of the methods which we have presented in this chapter. They are treated in detail in the general texts on experimental statistics listed below.

BIBLIOGRAPHY

A proof of the independence of the random variables whose values constitute the various sums of squares in an analysis of variance (for example, SSB and SSE on page 335) may be found in

Scheffe, H., *The Analysis of Variance,* New York: John Wiley & Sons, Inc., 1959.

The method of Lagrange multipliers is discussed in many texts on advanced calculus, for example, in

Widder, D. V., *Advanced Calculus,* 2nd ed., Englewood Cliffs, N. J.: Prentice-Hall, Inc., 1961, Chapter 4.

The following are some general texts dealing with experimental design and the analysis of variance

Cochran, W. G., and G. M. Cox, *Experimental Design,* 2nd ed, New York: John Wiley & Sons, Inc., 1957.

Finney, D. J., *Experimental Design and its Statistical Basis,* Chicago: University of Chicago Press, 1955.

Fisher, R. A., *Statistical Methods for Research Workers,* 10th ed., New York: Hafner Publishing Co., 1948

Kempthorne, O., *The Design and Analysis of Experiments,* New York: John Wiley & Sons, Inc., 1952.

Ostle, B., *Statistics in Research,* Ames, Iowa: Iowa State College Press, 1954.

Snedecor, G. W., *Statistical Methods,* 5th ed., Ames, Iowa: Iowa State College Press, 1956.

Appendix

Sums and Products

To simplify expressions involving sums and products, the $\sum$ and $\prod$ notations are widely used in statistics. By definition, if a and b are positive integers and $b \geq a$, then

$$\sum_{i=a}^{b} x_i = x_a + x_{a+1} + x_{a+2} + \ldots + x_b$$

$$\prod_{i=a}^{b} x_i = x_a \cdot x_{a+1} \cdot x_{a+2} \cdot \ldots \cdot x_b$$

When using this notation, it is helpful to apply the following rules, which can all be verified by writing both sides of the respective equations in full, that is, without the $\sum$ and $\prod$ notations:

$$\sum_{i=1}^{n} kx_i = k \sum_{i=1}^{n} x_i \tag{A.1}$$

$$\sum_{i=1}^{n} k = nk \tag{A.2}$$

$$\sum_{i=1}^{n} (x_i + y_i) = \sum_{i=1}^{n} x_i + \sum_{i=1}^{n} y_i \tag{A.3}$$

$$\prod_{i=1}^{n} kx_i = k^n \prod_{i=1}^{n} x_i \tag{A.4}$$

$$\prod_{i=1}^{n} k = k^n \tag{A.5}$$

$$\prod_{i=1}^{n} x_i y_i = \left(\prod_{i=1}^{n} x_i\right)\left(\prod_{i=1}^{n} y_i\right) \tag{A.6}$$

$$\ln \prod_{i=1}^{n} x_i = \sum_{i=1}^{n} \ln x_i \tag{A.7}$$

The following are two special sums, the sum of the first n positive integers and the sum of their squares, which can be proved by mathematical induction:

$$\sum_{i=1}^{n} i = 1 + 2 + \ldots + n = \frac{n(n+1)}{2} \tag{A.8}$$

$$\sum_{i=1}^{n} i^2 = 1^2 + 2^2 + \ldots + n^2 = \frac{n(n+1)(2n+1)}{6} \tag{A.9}$$

Double sums, triple sums, . . ., are also widely used in statistics; repeatedly applying the definition we have, for example,

$$\begin{aligned}\sum_{i=1}^{3} \sum_{j=1}^{4} x_{ij} &= \sum_{i=1}^{3} (x_{i1} + x_{i2} + x_{i3} + x_{i4}) \\ &= x_{11} + x_{12} + x_{13} + x_{14} + x_{21} + x_{22} \\ &\quad + x_{23} + x_{24} + x_{31} + x_{32} + x_{33} + x_{34}\end{aligned}$$

When working with double sums, the following rule is of special interest:

$$\sum_{i<j}\sum x_i x_j = \tfrac{1}{2}\left[\left(\sum_{i=1}^{n} x_i\right)^2 - \sum_{i=1}^{n} x_i^2\right] \tag{A.10}$$

where

$$\sum_{i<j}\sum x_i x_j = \sum_{i=1}^{n-1} \sum_{j=i+1}^{n} x_i x_j \tag{A.11}$$

Statistical Tables

I. Binomial Probabilities

II. Poisson Probabilities

III. Areas under the Normal Distribution

IV. Values of $t_{\alpha,v}$

V. Values of $\chi^2_{\alpha,v}$

VI. Values of F_{α,v_1,v_2}

VII. Binomial Coefficients

TABLE I

Binomial Probabilities*

n	x	θ .05	.10	.15	.20	.25	.30	.35	.40	.45	.50
1	0	.9500	.9000	.8500	.8000	.7500	.7000	.6500	.6000	.5500	.5000
	1	.0500	.1000	.1500	.2000	.2500	.3000	.3500	.4000	.4500	.5000
2	0	.9025	.8100	.7225	.6400	.5625	.4900	.4225	.3600	.3025	.2500
	1	.0950	.1800	.2550	.3200	.3750	.4200	.4550	.4800	.4950	.5000
	2	.0025	.0100	.0225	.0400	.0625	.0900	.1225	.1600	.2025	.2500
3	0	.8574	.7290	.6141	.5120	.4219	.3430	.2746	.2160	.1664	.1250
	1	.1354	.2430	.3251	.3840	.4219	.4410	.4436	.4320	.4084	.3750
	2	.0071	.0270	.0574	.0960	.1406	.1890	.2389	.2880	.3341	.3750
	3	.0001	.0010	.0034	.0080	.0156	.0270	.0429	.0640	.0911	.1250
4	0	.8145	.6561	.5220	.4096	.3164	.2401	.1785	.1296	.0915	.0625
	1	.1715	.2916	.3685	.4096	.4219	.4116	.3845	.3456	.2995	.2500
	2	.0135	.0486	.0975	.1536	.2109	.2646	.3105	.3456	.3675	.3750
	3	.0005	.0036	.0115	.0256	.0469	.0756	.1115	.1536	.2005	.2500
	4	.0000	.0001	.0005	.0016	.0039	.0081	.0150	.0256	.0410	.0625
5	0	.7738	.5905	.4437	.3277	.2373	.1681	.1160	.0778	.0503	.0312
	1	.2036	.3280	.3915	.4096	.3955	.3602	.3124	.2592	.2059	.1562
	2	.0214	.0729	.1382	.2048	.2637	.3087	.3364	.3456	.3369	.3125
	3	.0011	.0081	.0244	.0512	.0879	.1323	.1811	.2304	.2757	.3125
	4	.0000	.0004	.0022	.0064	.0146	.0284	.0488	.0768	.1128	.1562
	5	.0000	.0000	.0001	.0003	.0010	.0024	.0053	.0102	.0185	.0312
6	0	.7351	.5314	.3771	.2621	.1780	.1176	.0754	.0467	.0277	.0156
	1	.2321	.3543	.3993	.3932	.3560	.3025	.2437	.1866	.1359	.0938
	2	.0305	.0984	.1762	.2458	.2966	.3241	.3280	.3110	.2780	.2344
	3	.0021	.0146	.0415	.0819	.1318	.1852	.2355	.2765	.3032	.3125
	4	.0001	.0012	.0055	.0154	.0330	.0595	.0951	.1382	.1861	.2344
	5	.0000	.0001	.0004	.0015	.0044	.0102	.0205	.0369	.0609	.0938
	6	.0000	.0000	.0000	.0001	.0002	.0007	.0018	.0041	.0083	.0156
7	0	.6983	.4783	.3206	.2097	.1335	.0824	.0490	.0280	.0152	.0078
	1	.2573	.3720	.3960	.3670	.3115	.2471	.1848	.1306	.0872	.0547
	2	.0406	.1240	.2097	.2753	.3115	.3177	.2985	.2613	.2140	.1641
	3	.0036	.0230	.0617	.1147	.1730	.2269	.2679	.2903	.2918	.2734
	4	.0002	.0026	.0109	.0287	.0577	.0972	.1442	.1935	.2388	.2734
	5	.0000	.0002	.0012	.0043	.0115	.0250	.0466	.0774	.1172	.1641
	6	.0000	.0000	.0001	.0004	.0013	.0036	.0084	.0172	.0320	.0547
	7	.0000	.0000	.0000	.0000	.0001	.0002	.0006	.0016	.0037	.0078
8	0	.6634	.4305	.2725	.1678	.1001	.0576	.0319	.0168	.0084	.0039
	1	.2793	.3826	.3847	.3355	.2670	.1977	.1373	.0896	.0548	.0312
	2	.0515	.1488	.2376	.2936	.3115	.2965	.2587	.2090	.1569	.1094
	3	.0054	.0331	.0839	.1468	.2076	.2541	.2786	.2787	.2568	.2188
	4	.0004	.0046	.0185	.0459	.0865	.1361	.1875	.2322	.2627	.2734

* Entries in this table are values of $\binom{n}{x}\theta^x(1-\theta)^{n-x}$ for the indicated values of n, x, and θ. Reproduced by permission from *Handbook of Probability and Statistics with Tables*, by Burington and May, 1953, McGraw-Hill Book Co., Inc.

TABLE I (continued)

n	x	θ .05	.10	.15	.20	.25	.30	.35	.40	.45	.50
8	5	.0000	.0004	.0026	.0092	.0231	.0467	.0808	.1239	.1719	.2188
	6	.0000	.0000	.0002	.0011	.0038	.0100	.0217	.0413	.0703	.1094
	7	.0000	.0000	.0000	.0001	.0004	.0012	.0033	.0079	.0164	.0312
	8	.0000	.0000	.0000	.0000	.0000	.0001	.0002	.0007	.0017	.0039
9	0	.6302	.3874	.2316	.1342	.0751	.0404	.0207	.0101	.0046	.0020
	1	.2985	.3874	.3679	.3020	.2253	.1556	.1004	.0605	.0339	.0176
	2	.0629	.1722	.2597	.3020	.3003	.2668	.2162	.1612	.1110	.0703
	3	.0077	.0446	.1069	.1762	.2336	.2668	.2716	.2508	.2119	.1641
	4	.0006	.0074	.0283	.0661	.1168	.1715	.2194	.2508	.2600	.2461
	5	.0000	.0008	.0050	.0165	.0389	.0735	.1181	.1672	.2128	.2461
	6	.0000	.0001	.0006	.0028	.0087	.0210	.0424	.0743	.1160	.1641
	7	.0000	.0000	.0000	.0003	.0012	.0039	.0098	.0212	.0407	.0703
	8	.0000	.0000	.0000	.0000	.0001	.0004	.0013	.0035	.0083	.0176
	9	.0000	.0000	.0000	.0000	.0000	.0000	.0001	.0003	.0008	.0020
10	0	.5987	.3487	.1969	.1074	.0563	.0282	.0135	.0060	.0025	.0010
	1	.3151	.3874	.3474	.2684	.1877	.1211	.0725	.0403	.0207	.0098
	2	.0746	.1937	.2759	.3020	.2816	.2335	.1757	.1209	.0763	.0439
	3	.0105	.0574	.1298	.2013	.2503	.2668	.2522	.2150	.1665	.1172
	4	.0010	.0112	.0401	.0881	.1460	.2001	.2377	.2508	.2384	.2051
	5	.0001	.0015	.0085	.0264	.0584	.1029	.1536	.2007	.2340	.2461
	6	.0000	.0001	.0012	.0055	.0162	.0368	.0689	.1115	.1596	.2051
	7	.0000	.0000	.0001	.0008	.0031	.0090	.0212	.0425	.0746	.1172
	8	.0000	.0000	.0000	.0001	.0004	.0014	.0043	.0106	.0229	.0439
	9	.0000	.0000	.0000	.0000	.0000	.0001	.0005	.0016	.0042	.0098
	10	.0000	.0000	.0000	.0000	.0000	.0000	.0000	.0001	.0003	.0010
11	0	.5688	.3138	.1673	.0859	.0422	.0198	.0088	.0036	.0014	.0005
	1	.3293	.3835	.3248	.2362	.1549	.0932	.0518	.0266	.0125	.0054
	2	.0867	.2131	.2866	.2953	.2581	.1998	.1395	.0887	.0513	.0269
	3	.0137	.0710	.1517	.2215	.2581	.2568	.2254	.1774	.1259	.0806
	4	.0014	.0158	.0536	.1107	.1721	.2201	.2428	.2365	.2060	.1611
	5	.0001	.0025	.0132	.0388	.0803	.1321	.1830	.2207	.2360	.2256
	6	.0000	.0003	.0023	.0097	.0268	.0566	.0985	.1471	.1931	.2256
	7	.0000	.0000	.0003	.0017	.0064	.0173	.0379	.0701	.1128	.1611
	8	.0000	.0000	.0000	.0002	.0011	.0037	.0102	.0234	.0462	.0806
	9	.0000	.0000	.0000	.0000	.0001	.0005	.0018	.0052	.0126	.0269
	10	.0000	.0000	.0000	.0000	.0000	.0000	.0002	.0007	.0021	.0054
	11	.0000	.0000	.0000	.0000	.0000	.0000	.0000	.0000	.0002	.0005
12	0	.5404	.2824	.1422	.0687	.0317	.0138	.0057	.0022	.0008	.0002
	1	.3413	.3766	.3012	.2062	.1267	.0712	.0368	.0174	.0075	.0029
	2	.0988	.2301	.2924	.2835	.2323	.1678	.1088	.0639	.0339	.0161
	3	.0173	.0852	.1720	.2362	.2581	.2397	.1954	.1419	.0923	.0537
	4	.0021	.0213	.0683	.1329	.1936	.2311	.2367	.2128	.1700	.1208
	5	.0002	.0038	.0193	.0532	.1032	.1585	.2039	.2270	.2225	.1934
	6	.0000	.0005	.0040	.0155	.0401	.0792	.1281	.1766	.2124	.2256
	7	.0000	.0000	.0006	.0033	.0115	.0291	.0591	.1009	.1489	.1934
	8	.0000	.0000	.0001	.0005	.0024	.0078	.0199	.0420	.0762	.1208
	9	.0000	.0000	.0000	.0001	.0004	.0015	.0048	.0125	.0277	.0537

TABLE I (continued)

n	x	.05	.10	.15	.20	.25	.30	.35	.40	.45	.50
						θ					
12	10	.0000	.0000	.0000	.0000	.0000	.0002	.0008	.0025	.0068	.0161
	11	.0000	.0000	.0000	.0000	.0000	.0000	.0001	.0003	.0010	.0029
	12	.0000	.0000	.0000	.0000	.0000	.0000	.0000	.0000	.0001	.0002
13	0	.5133	.2542	.1209	.0550	.0238	.0097	.0037	.0013	.0004	.0001
	1	.3512	.3672	.2774	.1787	.1029	.0540	.0259	.0113	.0045	.0016
	2	.1109	.2448	.2937	.2680	.2059	.1388	.0836	.0453	.0220	.0095
	3	.0214	.0997	.1900	.2457	.2517	.2181	.1651	.1107	.0660	.0349
	4	.0028	.0277	.0838	.1535	.2097	.2337	.2222	.1845	.1350	.0873
	5	.0003	.0055	.0266	.0691	.1258	.1803	.2154	.2214	.1989	.1571
	6	.0000	.0008	.0063	.0230	.0559	.1030	.1546	.1968	.2169	.2095
	7	.0000	.0001	.0011	.0058	.0186	.0442	.0833	.1312	.1775	.2095
	8	.0000	.0000	.0001	.0011	.0047	.0142	.0336	.0656	.1089	.1571
	9	.0000	.0000	.0000	.0001	.0009	.0034	.0101	.0243	.0495	.0873
	10	.0000	.0000	.0000	.0000	.0001	.0006	.0022	.0065	.0162	.0349
	11	.0000	.0000	.0000	.0000	.0000	.0001	.0003	.0012	.0036	.0095
	12	.0000	.0000	.0000	.0000	.0000	.0000	.0000	.0001	.0005	.0016
	13	.0000	.0000	.0000	.0000	.0000	.0000	.0000	.0000	.0000	.0001
14	0	.4877	.2288	.1028	.0440	.0178	.0068	.0024	.0008	.0002	.0001
	1	.3593	.3559	.2539	.1539	.0832	.0407	.0181	.0073	.0027	.0009
	2	.1229	.2570	.2912	.2501	.1802	.1134	.0634	.0317	.0141	.0056
	3	.0259	.1142	.2056	.2501	.2402	.1943	.1366	.0845	.0462	.0222
	4	.0037	.0349	.0998	.1720	.2202	.2290	.2022	.1549	.1040	.0611
	5	.0004	.0078	.0352	.0860	.1468	.1963	.2178	.2066	.1701	.1222
	6	.0000	.0013	.0093	.0322	.0734	.1262	.1759	.2066	.2088	.1833
	7	.0000	.0002	.0019	.0092	.0280	.0618	.1082	.1574	.1952	.2095
	8	.0000	.0000	.0003	.0020	.0082	.0232	.0510	.0918	.1398	.1833
	9	.0000	.0000	.0000	.0003	.0018	.0066	.0183	.0408	.0762	.1222
	10	.0000	.0000	.0000	.0000	.0003	.0014	.0049	.0136	.0312	.0611
	11	.0000	.0000	.0000	.0000	.0000	.0002	.0010	.0033	.0093	.0222
	12	.0000	.0000	.0000	.0000	.0000	.0000	.0001	.0005	.0019	.0056
	13	.0000	.0000	.0000	.0000	.0000	.0000	.0000	.0001	.0002	.0009
	14	.0000	.0000	.0000	.0000	.0000	.0000	.0000	.0000	.0000	.0001
15	0	.4633	.2059	.0874	.0352	.0134	.0047	.0016	.0005	.0001	.0000
	1	.3658	.3432	.2312	.1319	.0668	.0305	.0126	.0047	.0016	.0005
	2	.1348	.2669	.2856	.2309	.1559	.0916	.0476	.0219	.0090	.0032
	3	.0307	.1285	.2184	.2501	.2252	.1700	.1110	.0634	.0318	.0139
	4	.0049	.0428	.1156	.1876	.2252	.2186	.1792	.1268	.0780	.0417
	5	.0006	.0105	.0449	.1032	.1651	.2061	.2123	.1859	.1404	.0916
	6	.0000	.0019	.0132	.0430	.0917	.1472	.1906	.2066	.1914	.1527
	7	.0000	.0003	.0030	.0138	.0393	.0811	.1319	.1771	.2013	.1964
	8	.0000	.0000	.0005	.0035	.0131	.0348	.0710	.1181	.1647	.1964
	9	.0000	.0000	.0001	.0007	.0034	.0116	.0298	.0612	.1048	.1527
	10	.0000	.0000	.0000	.0001	.0007	.0030	.0096	.0245	.0515	.0916
	11	.0000	.0000	.0000	.0000	.0001	.0006	.0024	.0074	.0191	.0417
	12	.0000	.0000	.0000	.0000	.0000	.0001	.0004	.0016	.0052	.0139
	13	.0000	.0000	.0000	.0000	.0000	.0000	.0001	.0003	.0010	.0032
	14	.0000	.0000	.0000	.0000	.0000	.0000	.0000	.0000	.0001	.0005
	15	.0000	.0000	.0000	.0000	.0000	.0000	.0000	.0000	.0000	.0000

TABLE I (continued)

		θ									
n	x	.05	.10	.15	.20	.25	.30	.35	.40	.45	.50
16	0	.4401	.1853	.0743	.0281	.0100	.0033	.0010	.0003	.0001	.0000
	1	.3706	.3294	.2097	.1126	.0535	.0228	.0087	.0030	.0009	.0002
	2	.1463	.2745	.2775	.2111	.1336	.0732	.0353	.0150	.0056	.0018
	3	.0359	.1423	.2285	.2463	.2079	.1465	.0888	.0468	.0215	.0085
	4	.0061	.0514	.1311	.2001	.2252	.2040	.1553	.1014	.0572	.0278
	5	.0008	.0137	.0555	.1201	.1802	.2099	.2008	.1623	.1123	.0667
	6	.0001	.0028	.0180	.0550	.1101	.1649	.1982	.1983	.1684	.1222
	7	.0000	.0004	.0045	.0197	.0524	.1010	.1524	.1889	.1969	.1746
	8	.0000	.0001	.0009	.0055	.0197	.0487	.0923	.1417	.1812	.1964
	9	.0000	.0000	.0001	.0012	.0058	.0185	.0442	.0840	.1318	.1746
	10	.0000	.0000	.0000	.0002	.0014	.0056	.0167	.0392	.0755	.1222
	11	.0000	.0000	.0000	.0000	.0002	.0013	.0049	.0142	.0337	.0667
	12	.0000	.0000	.0000	.0000	.0000	.0002	.0011	.0040	.0115	.0278
	13	.0000	.0000	.0000	.0000	.0000	.0000	.0002	.0008	.0029	.0085
	14	.0000	.0000	.0000	.0000	.0000	.0000	.0000	.0001	.0005	.0018
	15	.0000	.0000	.0000	.0000	.0000	.0000	.0000	.0000	.0001	.0002
	16	.0000	.0000	.0000	.0000	.0000	.0000	.0000	.0000	.0000	.0000
17	0	.4181	.1668	.0631	.0225	.0075	.0023	.0007	.0002	.0000	.0000
	1	.3741	.3150	.1893	.0957	.0426	.0169	.0060	.0019	.0005	.0001
	2	.1575	.2800	.2673	.1914	.1136	.0581	.0260	.0102	.0035	.0010
	3	.0415	.1556	.2359	.2393	.1893	.1245	.0701	.0341	.0144	.0052
	4	.0076	.0605	.1457	.2093	.2209	.1868	.1320	.0796	.0411	.0182
	5	.0010	.0175	.0668	.1361	.1914	.2081	.1849	.1379	.0875	.0472
	6	.0001	.0039	.0236	.0680	.1276	.1784	.1991	.1839	.1432	.0944
	7	.0000	.0007	.0065	.0267	.0668	.1201	.1685	.1927	.1841	.1484
	8	.0000	.0001	.0014	.0084	.0279	.0644	.1134	.1606	.1883	.1855
	9	.0000	.0000	.0003	.0021	.0093	.0276	.0611	.1070	.1540	.1855
	10	.0000	.0000	.0000	.0004	.0025	.0095	.0263	.0571	.1008	.1484
	11	.0000	.0000	.0000	.0001	.0005	.0026	.0090	.0242	.0525	.0944
	12	.0000	.0000	.0000	.0000	.0001	.0006	.0024	.0081	.0215	.0472
	13	.0000	.0000	.0000	.0000	.0000	.0001	.0005	.0021	.0068	.0182
	14	.0000	.0000	.0000	.0000	.0000	.0000	.0001	.0004	.0016	.0052
	15	.0000	.0000	.0000	.0000	.0000	.0000	.0000	.0001	.0003	.0010
	16	.0000	.0000	.0000	.0000	.0000	.0000	.0000	.0000	.0000	.0001
	17	.0000	.0000	.0000	.0000	.0000	.0000	.0000	.0000	.0000	.0000
18	0	.3972	.1501	.0536	.0180	.0056	.0016	.0004	.0001	.0000	.0000
	1	.3763	.3002	.1704	.0811	.0338	.0126	.0042	.0012	.0003	.0001
	2	.1683	.2835	.2556	.1723	.0958	.0458	.0190	.0069	.0022	.0006
	3	.0473	.1680	.2406	.2297	.1704	.1046	.0547	.0246	.0095	.0031
	4	.0093	.0700	.1592	.2153	.2130	.1681	.1104	.0614	.0291	.0117
	5	.0014	.0218	.0787	.1507	.1988	.2017	.1664	.1146	.0666	.0327
	6	.0002	.0052	.0301	.0816	.1436	.1873	.1941	.1655	.1181	.0708
	7	.0000	.0010	.0091	.0350	.0820	.1376	.1792	.1892	.1657	.1214
	8	.0000	.0002	.0022	.0120	.0376	.0811	.1327	.1734	.1864	.1669
	9	.0000	.0000	.0004	.0033	.0139	.0386	.0794	.1284	.1694	.1855

TABLE I (continued)

		θ									
n	*x*	.05	.10	.15	.20	.25	.30	.35	.40	.45	.50
18	10	.0000	.0000	.0001	.0008	.0042	.0149	.0385	.0771	.1248	.1669
	11	.0000	.0000	.0000	.0001	.0010	.0046	.0151	.0374	.0742	.1214
	12	.0000	.0000	.0000	.0000	.0002	.0012	.0047	.0145	.0354	.0708
	13	.0000	.0000	.0000	.0000	.0000	.0002	.0012	.0045	.0134	.0327
	14	.0000	.0000	.0000	.0000	.0000	.0000	.0002	.0011	.0039	.0117
	15	.0000	.0000	.0000	.0000	.0000	.0000	.0000	.0002	.0009	.0031
	16	.0000	.0000	.0000	.0000	.0000	.0000	.0000	.0000	.0001	.0006
	17	.0000	.0000	.0000	.0000	.0000	.0000	.0000	.0000	.0000	.0001
	18	.0000	.0000	.0000	.0000	.0000	.0000	.0000	.0000	.0000	.0000
19	0	.3774	.1351	.0456	.0144	.0042	.0011	.0003	.0001	.0000	.0000
	1	.3774	.2852	.1529	.0685	.0268	.0093	.0029	.0008	.0002	.0000
	2	.1787	.2852	.2428	.1540	.0803	.0358	.0138	.0046	.0013	.0003
	3	.0533	.1796	.2428	.2182	.1517	.0869	.0422	.0175	.0062	.0018
	4	.0112	.0798	.1714	.2182	.2023	.1491	.0909	.0467	.0203	.0074
	5	.0018	.0266	.0907	.1636	.2023	.1916	.1468	.0933	.0497	.0222
	6	.0002	.0069	.0374	.0955	.1574	.1916	.1844	.1451	.0949	.0518
	7	.0000	.0014	.0122	.0443	.0974	.1525	.1844	.1797	.1443	.0961
	8	.0000	.0002	.0032	.0166	.0487	.0981	.1489	.1797	.1771	.1442
	9	.0000	.0000	.0007	.0051	.0198	.0514	.0980	.1464	.1771	.1762
	10	.0000	.0000	.0001	.0013	.0066	.0220	.0528	.0976	.1449	.1762
	11	.0000	.0000	.0000	.0003	.0018	.0077	.0233	.0532	.0970	.1442
	12	.0000	.0000	.0000	.0000	.0004	.0022	.0083	.0237	.0529	.0961
	13	.0000	.0000	.0000	.0000	.0001	.0005	.0024	.0085	.0233	.0518
	14	.0000	.0000	.0000	.0000	.0000	.0001	.0006	.0024	.0082	.0222
	15	.0000	.0000	.0000	.0000	.0000	.0000	.0001	.0005	.0022	.0074
	16	.0000	.0000	.0000	.0000	.0000	.0000	.0000	.0001	.0005	.0018
	17	.0000	.0000	.0000	.0000	.0000	.0000	.0000	.0000	.0001	.0003
	18	.0000	.0000	.0000	.0000	.0000	.0000	.0000	.0000	.0000	.0000
	19	.0000	.0000	.0000	.0000	.0000	.0000	.0000	.0000	.0000	.0000
20	0	.3585	.1216	.0388	.0115	.0032	.0008	.0002	.0000	.0000	.0000
	1	.3774	.2702	.1368	.0576	.0211	.0068	.0020	.0005	.0001	.0000
	2	.1887	.2852	.2293	.1369	.0669	.0278	.0100	.0031	.0008	.0002
	3	.0596	.1901	.2428	.2054	.1339	.0716	.0323	.0123	.0040	.0011
	4	.0133	.0898	.1821	.2182	.1897	.1304	.0738	.0350	.0139	.0046
	5	.0022	.0319	.1028	.1746	.2023	.1789	.1272	.0746	.0365	.0148
	6	.0003	.0089	.0454	.1091	.1686	.1916	.1712	.1244	.0746	.0370
	7	.0000	.0020	.0160	.0545	.1124	.1643	.1844	.1659	.1221	.0739
	8	.0000	.0004	.0046	.0222	.0609	.1144	.1614	.1797	.1623	.1201
	9	.0000	.0001	.0011	.0074	.0271	.0654	.1158	.1597	.1771	.1602
	10	.0000	.0000	.0002	.0020	.0099	.0308	.0686	.1171	.1593	.1762
	11	.0000	.0000	.0000	.0005	.0030	.0120	.0336	.0710	.1185	.1602
	12	.0000	.0000	.0000	.0001	.0008	.0039	.0136	.0355	.0727	.1201
	13	.0000	.0000	.0000	.0000	.0002	.0010	.0045	.0146	.0366	.0739
	14	.0000	.0000	.0000	.0000	.0000	.0002	.0012	.0049	.0150	.0370
	15	.0000	.0000	.0000	.0000	.0000	.0000	.0003	.0013	.0049	.0148
	16	.0000	.0000	.0000	.0000	.0000	.0000	.0000	.0003	.0013	.0046
	17	.0000	.0000	.0000	.0000	.0000	.0000	.0000	.0000	.0002	.0011
	18	.0000	.0000	.0000	.0000	.0000	.0000	.0000	.0000	.0000	.0002
	19	.0000	.0000	.0000	.0000	.0000	.0000	.0000	.0000	.0000	.0000
	20	.0000	.0000	.0000	.0000	.0000	.0000	.0000	.0000	.0000	.0000

TABLE II

Poisson Probabilities*

	λ									
x	0.1	0.2	0.3	0.4	0.5	0.6	0.7	0.8	0.9	1.0
0	.9048	.8187	.7408	.6703	.6065	.5488	.4966	.4493	.4066	.3679
1	.0905	.1637	.2222	.2681	.3033	.3293	.3476	.3595	.3659	.3679
2	.0045	.0164	.0333	.0536	.0758	.0988	.1217	.1438	.1647	.1839
3	.0002	.0011	.0033	.0072	.0126	.0198	.0284	.0383	.0494	.0613
4	.0000	.0001	.0002	.0007	.0016	.0030	.0050	.0077	.0111	.0153
5	.0000	.0000	.0000	.0001	.0002	.0004	.0007	.0012	.0020	.0031
6	.0000	.0000	.0000	.0000	.0000	.0000	.0001	.0002	.0003	.0005
7	.0000	.0000	.0000	.0000	.0000	.0000	.0000	.0000	.0000	.0001

	λ									
x	1.1	1.2	1.3	1.4	1.5	1.6	1.7	1.8	1.9	2.0
0	.3329	.3012	.2725	.2466	.2231	.2019	.1827	.1653	.1496	.1353
1	.3662	.3614	.3543	.3452	.3347	.3230	.3106	.2975	.2842	.2707
2	.2014	.2169	.2303	.2417	.2510	.2584	.2640	.2678	.2700	.2707
3	.0738	.0867	.0998	.1128	.1255	.1378	.1496	.1607	.1710	.1804
4	.0203	.0260	.0324	.0395	.0471	.0551	.0636	.0723	.0812	.0902
5	.0045	.0062	.0084	.0111	.0141	.0176	.0216	.0260	.0309	.0361
6	.0008	.0012	.0018	.0026	.0035	.0047	.0061	.0078	.0098	.0120
7	.0001	.0002	.0003	.0005	.0008	.0011	.0015	.0020	.0027	.0034
8	.0000	.0000	.0001	.0001	.0001	.0002	.0003	.0005	.0006	.0009
9	.0000	.0000	.0000	.0000	.0000	.0000	.0001	.0001	.0001	.0002

	λ									
x	2.1	2.2	2.3	2.4	2.5	2.6	2.7	2.8	2.9	3.0
0	.1225	.1108	.1003	.0907	.0821	.0743	.0672	.0608	.0550	.0498
1	.2572	.2438	.2306	.2177	.2052	.1931	.1815	.1703	.1596	.1494
2	.2700	.2681	.2652	.2613	.2565	.2510	.2450	.2384	.2314	.2240
3	.1890	.1966	.2033	.2090	.2138	.2176	.2205	.2225	.2237	.2240
4	.0992	.1082	.1169	.1254	.1336	.1414	.1488	.1557	.1622	.1680
5	.0417	.0476	.0538	.0602	.0668	.0735	.0804	.0872	.0940	.1008
6	.0146	.0174	.0206	.0241	.0278	.0319	.0362	.0407	.0455	.0504
7	.0044	.0055	.0068	.0083	.0099	.0118	.0139	.0163	.0188	.0216
8	.0011	.0015	.0019	.0025	.0031	.0038	.0047	.0057	.0068	.0081
9	.0003	.0004	.0005	.0007	.0009	.0011	.0014	.0018	.0022	.0027
10	.0001	.0001	.0001	.0002	.0002	.0003	.0004	.0005	.0006	.0008
11	.0000	.0000	.0000	.0000	.0000	.0001	.0001	.0001	.0002	.0002
12	.0000	.0000	.0000	.0000	.0000	.0000	.0000	.0000	.0000	.0001

* Entries in this table are values of $(e^{-\lambda}\lambda^x/x!)$ for the indicated values of x and λ. Reproduced by permission from *Handbook of Probability and Statistics with Tables*, by Burington and May, 1953, McGraw-Hill Book Co., Inc.

TABLE II (continued)

x	λ 3.1	3.2	3.3	3.4	3.5	3.6	3.7	3.8	3.9	4.0
0	.0450	.0408	.0369	.0334	.0302	.0273	.0247	.0224	.0202	.0183
1	.1397	.1304	.1217	.1135	.1057	.0984	.0915	.0850	.0789	.0733
2	.2165	.2087	.2008	.1929	.1850	.1771	.1692	.1615	.1539	.1465
3	.2237	.2226	.2209	.2186	.2158	.2125	.2087	.2046	.2001	.1954
4	.1734	.1781	.1823	.1858	.1888	.1912	.1931	.1944	.1951	.1954
5	.1075	.1140	.1203	.1264	.1322	.1377	.1429	.1477	.1522	.1563
6	.0555	.0608	.0662	.0716	.0771	.0826	.0881	.0936	.0989	.1042
7	.0246	.0278	.0312	.0348	.0385	.0425	.0466	.0508	.0551	.0595
8	.0095	.0111	.0129	.0148	.0169	.0191	.0215	.0241	.0269	.0298
9	.0033	.0040	.0047	.0056	.0066	.0076	.0089	.0102	.0116	.0132
10	.0010	.0013	.0016	.0019	.0023	.0028	.0033	.0039	.0045	.0053
11	.0003	.0004	.0005	.0006	.0007	.0009	.0011	.0013	.0016	.0019
12	.0001	.0001	.0001	.0002	.0002	.0003	.0003	.0004	.0005	.0006
13	.0000	.0000	.0000	.0000	.0001	.0001	.0001	.0001	.0002	.0002
14	.0000	.0000	.0000	.0000	.0000	.0000	.0000	.0000	.0000	.0001

x	λ 4.1	4.2	4.3	4.4	4.5	4.6	4.7	4.8	4.9	5.0
0	.0166	.0150	.0136	.0123	.0111	.0101	.0091	.0082	.0074	.0067
1	.0679	.0630	.0583	.0540	.0500	.0462	.0427	.0395	.0365	.0337
2	.1393	.1323	.1254	.1188	.1125	.1063	.1005	.0948	.0894	.0842
3	.1904	.1852	.1798	.1743	.1687	.1631	.1574	.1517	.1460	.1404
4	.1951	.1944	.1933	.1917	.1898	.1875	.1849	.1820	.1789	.1755
5	.1600	.1633	.1662	.1687	.1708	.1725	.1738	.1747	.1753	.1755
6	.1093	.1143	.1191	.1237	.1281	.1323	.1362	.1398	.1432	.1462
7	.0640	.0686	.0732	.0778	.0824	.0869	.0914	.0959	.1002	.1044
8	.0328	.0360	.0393	.0428	.0463	.0500	.0537	.0575	.0614	.0653
9	.0150	.0168	.0188	.0209	.0232	.0255	.0280	.0307	.0334	.0363
10	.0061	.0071	.0081	.0092	.0104	.0118	.0132	.0147	.0164	.0181
11	.0023	.0027	.0032	.0037	.0043	.0049	.0056	.0064	.0073	.0082
12	.0008	.0009	.0011	.0014	.0016	.0019	.0022	.0026	.0030	.0034
13	.0002	.0003	.0004	.0005	.0006	.0007	.0008	.0009	.0011	.0013
14	.0001	.0001	.0001	.0001	.0002	.0002	.0003	.0003	.0004	.0005
15	.0000	.0000	.0000	.0000	.0001	.0001	.0001	.0001	.0001	.0002

x	λ 5.1	5.2	5.3	5.4	5.5	5.6	5.7	5.8	5.9	6.0
0	.0061	.0055	.0050	.0045	.0041	.0037	.0033	.0030	.0027	.0025
1	.0311	.0287	.0265	.0244	.0225	.0207	.0191	.0176	.0162	.0149
2	.0793	.0746	.0701	.0659	.0618	.0580	.0544	.0509	.0477	.0446
3	.1348	.1293	.1239	.1185	.1133	.1082	.1033	.0985	.0938	.0892
4	.1719	.1681	.1641	.1600	.1558	.1515	.1472	.1428	.1383	.1339

TABLE II (continued)

x	λ = 5.1	5.2	5.3	5.4	5.5	5.6	5.7	5.8	5.9	6.0
5	.1753	.1748	.1740	.1728	.1714	.1697	.1678	.1656	.1632	.1606
6	.1490	.1515	.1537	.1555	.1571	.1584	.1594	.1601	.1605	.1606
7	.1086	.1125	.1163	.1200	.1234	.1267	.1298	.1326	.1353	.1377
8	.0692	.0731	.0771	.0810	.0849	.0887	.0925	.0962	.0998	.1033
9	.0392	.0423	.0454	.0486	.0519	.0552	.0586	.0620	.0654	.0688
10	.0200	.0220	.0241	.0262	.0285	.0309	.0334	.0359	.0386	.0413
11	.0093	.0104	.0116	.0129	.0143	.0157	.0173	.0190	.0207	.0225
12	.0039	.0045	.0051	.0058	.0065	.0073	.0082	.0092	.0102	.0113
13	.0015	.0018	.0021	.0024	.0028	.0032	.0036	.0041	.0046	.0052
14	.0006	.0007	.0008	.0009	.0011	.0013	.0015	.0017	.0019	.0022
15	.0002	.0002	.0003	.0003	.0004	.0005	.0006	.0007	.0008	.0009
16	.0001	.0001	.0001	.0001	.0001	.0002	.0002	.0002	.0003	.0003
17	.0000	.0000	.0000	.0000	.0000	.0001	.0001	.0001	.0001	.0001

x	λ = 6.1	6.2	6.3	6.4	6.5	6.6	6.7	6.8	6.9	7.0
0	.0022	.0020	.0018	.0017	.0015	.0014	.0012	.0011	.0010	.0009
1	.0137	.0126	.0116	.0106	.0098	.0090	.0082	.0076	.0070	.0064
2	.0417	.0390	.0364	.0340	.0318	.0296	.0276	.0258	.0240	.0223
3	.0848	.0806	.0765	.0726	.0688	.0652	.0617	.0584	.0552	.0521
4	.1294	.1249	.1205	.1162	.1118	.1076	.1034	.0992	.0952	.0912
5	.1579	.1549	.1519	.1487	.1454	.1420	.1385	.1349	.1314	.1277
6	.1605	.1601	.1595	.1586	.1575	.1562	.1546	.1529	.1511	.1490
7	.1399	.1418	.1435	.1450	.1462	.1472	.1480	.1486	.1489	.1490
8	.1066	.1099	.1130	.1160	.1188	.1215	.1240	.1263	.1284	.1304
9	.0723	.0757	.0791	.0825	.0858	.0891	.0923	.0954	.0985	.1014
10	.0441	.0469	.0498	.0528	.0558	.0588	.0618	.0649	.0679	.0710
11	.0245	.0265	.0285	.0307	.0330	.0353	.0377	.0401	.0426	.0452
12	.0124	.0137	.0150	.0164	.0179	.0194	.0210	.0227	.0245	.0264
13	.0058	.0065	.0073	.0081	.0089	.0098	.0108	.0119	.0130	.0142
14	.0025	.0029	.0033	.0037	.0041	.0046	.0052	.0058	.0064	.0071
15	.0010	.0012	.0014	.0016	.0018	.0020	.0023	.0026	.0029	.0033
16	.0004	.0005	.0005	.0006	.0007	.0008	.0010	.0011	.0013	.0014
17	.0001	.0002	.0002	.0002	.0003	.0003	.0004	.0004	.0005	.0006
18	.0000	.0001	.0001	.0001	.0001	.0001	.0001	.0002	.0002	.0002
19	.0000	.0000	.0000	.0000	.0000	.0000	.0000	.0001	.0001	.0001

x	λ = 7.1	7.2	7.3	7.4	7.5	7.6	7.7	7.8	7.9	8.0
0	.0008	.0007	.0007	.0006	.0006	.0005	.0005	.0004	.0004	.0003
1	.0059	.0054	.0049	.0045	.0041	.0038	.0035	.0032	.0029	.0027
2	.0208	.0194	.0180	.0167	.0156	.0145	.0134	.0125	.0116	.0107
3	.0492	.0464	.0438	.0413	.0389	.0366	.0345	.0324	.0305	.0286
4	.0874	.0836	.0799	.0764	.0729	.0696	.0663	.0632	.0602	.0573
5	.1241	.1204	.1167	.1130	.1094	.1057	.1021	.0986	.0951	.0916
6	.1468	.1445	.1420	.1394	.1367	.1339	.1311	.1282	.1252	.1221
7	.1489	.1486	.1481	.1474	.1465	.1454	.1442	.1428	.1413	.1396
8	.1321	.1337	.1351	.1363	.1373	.1382	.1388	.1392	.1395	.1396
9	.1042	.1070	.1096	.1121	.1144	.1167	.1187	.1207	.1224	.1241

TABLE II (continued)

x	λ 7.1	7.2	7.3	7.4	7.5	7.6	7.7	7.8	7.9	8.0
10	.0740	.0770	.0800	.0829	.0858	.0887	.0914	.0941	.0967	.0993
11	.0478	.0504	.0531	.0558	.0585	.0613	.0640	.0667	.0695	.0722
12	.0283	.0303	.0323	.0344	.0366	.0388	.0411	.0434	.0457	.0481
13	.0154	.0168	.0181	.0196	.0211	.0227	.0243	.0260	.0278	.0296
14	.0078	.0086	.0095	.0104	.0113	.0123	.0134	.0145	.0157	.0169
15	.0037	.0041	.0046	.0051	.0057	.0062	.0069	.0075	.0083	.0090
16	.0016	.0019	.0021	.0024	.0026	.0030	.0033	.0037	.0041	.0045
17	.0007	.0008	.0009	.0010	.0012	.0013	.0015	.0017	.0019	.0021
18	.0003	.0003	.0004	.0004	.0005	.0006	.0006	.0007	.0008	.0009
19	.0001	.0001	.0001	.0002	.0002	.0002	.0003	.0003	.0003	.0004
20	.0000	.0000	.0001	.0001	.0001	.0001	.0001	.0001	.0001	.0002
21	.0000	.0000	.0000	.0000	.0000	.0000	.0000	.0000	.0001	.0001

x	λ 8.1	8.2	8.3	8.4	8.5	8.6	8.7	8.8	8.9	9.0
0	.0003	.0003	.0002	.0002	.0002	.0002	.0002	.0002	.0001	.0001
1	.0025	.0023	.0021	.0019	.0017	.0016	.0014	.0013	.0012	.0011
2	.0100	.0092	.0086	.0079	.0074	.0068	.0063	.0058	.0054	.0050
3	.0269	.0252	.0237	.0222	.0208	.0195	.0183	.0171	.0160	.0150
4	.0544	.0517	.0491	.0466	.0443	.0420	.0398	.0377	.0357	.0337
5	.0882	.0849	.0816	.0784	.0752	.0722	.0692	.0663	.0635	.0607
6	.1191	.1160	.1128	.1097	.1066	.1034	.1003	.0972	.0941	.0911
7	.1378	.1358	.1338	.1317	.1294	.1271	.1247	.1222	.1197	.1171
8	.1395	.1392	.1388	.1382	.1375	.1366	.1356	.1344	.1332	.1318
9	.1256	.1269	.1280	.1290	.1299	.1306	.1311	.1315	.1317	.1318
10	.1017	.1040	.1063	.1084	.1104	.1123	.1140	.1157	.1172	.1186
11	.0749	.0776	.0802	.0828	.0853	.0878	.0902	.0925	.0948	.0970
12	.0505	.0530	.0555	.0579	.0604	.0629	.0654	.0679	.0703	.0728
13	.0315	.0334	.0354	.0374	.0395	.0416	.0438	.0459	.0481	.0504
14	.0182	.0196	.0210	.0225	.0240	.0256	.0272	.0289	.0306	.0324
15	.0098	.0107	.0116	.0126	.0136	.0147	.0158	.0169	.0182	.0194
16	.0050	.0055	.0060	.0066	.0072	.0079	.0086	.0093	.0101	.0109
17	.0024	.0026	.0029	.0033	.0036	.0040	.0044	.0048	.0053	.0058
18	.0011	.0012	.0014	.0015	.0017	.0019	.0021	.0024	.0026	.0029
19	.0005	.0005	.0006	.0007	.0008	.0009	.0010	.0011	.0012	.0014
20	.0002	.0002	.0002	.0003	.0003	.0004	.0004	.0005	.0005	.0006
21	.0001	.0001	.0001	.0001	.0001	.0002	.0002	.0002	.0002	.0003
22	.0000	.0000	.0000	.0000	.0001	.0001	.0001	.0001	.0001	.0001

x	λ 9.1	9.2	9.3	9.4	9.5	9.6	9.7	9.8	9.9	10
0	.0001	.0001	.0001	.0001	.0001	.0001	.0001	.0001	.0001	.0000
1	.0010	.0009	.0009	.0008	.0007	.0007	.0006	.0005	.0005	.0005
2	.0046	.0043	.0040	.0037	.0034	.0031	.0029	.0027	.0025	.0023
3	.0140	.0131	.0123	.0115	.0107	.0100	.0093	.0087	.0081	.0076
4	.0319	.0302	.0285	.0269	.0254	.0240	.0226	.0213	.0201	.0189

TABLE II (continued)

x	λ 9.1	9.2	9.3	9.4	9.5	9.6	9.7	9.8	9.9	10
5	.0581	.0555	.0530	.0506	.0483	.0460	.0439	.0418	.0398	.0378
6	.0881	.0851	.0822	.0793	.0764	.0736	.0709	.0682	.0656	.0631
7	.1145	.1118	.1091	.1064	.1037	.1010	.0982	.0955	.0928	.0901
8	.1302	.1286	.1269	.1251	.1232	.1212	.1191	.1170	.1148	.1126
9	.1317	.1315	.1311	.1306	.1300	.1293	.1284	.1274	.1263	.1251
10	.1198	.1210	.1219	.1228	.1235	.1241	.1245	.1249	.1250	.1251
11	.0991	.1012	.1031	.1049	.1067	.1083	.1098	.1112	.1125	.1137
12	.0752	.0776	.0799	.0822	.0844	.0866	.0888	.0908	.0928	.0948
13	.0526	.0549	.0572	.0594	.0617	.0640	.0662	.0685	.0707	.0729
14	.0342	.0361	.0380	.0399	.0419	.0439	.0459	.0479	.0500	.0521
15	.0208	.0221	.0235	.0250	.0265	.0281	.0297	.0313	.0330	.0347
16	.0118	.0127	.0137	.0147	.0157	.0168	.0180	.0192	.0204	.0217
17	.0063	.0069	.0075	.0081	.0088	.0095	.0103	.0111	.0119	.0128
18	.0032	.0035	.0039	.0042	.0046	.0051	.0055	.0060	.0065	.0071
19	.0015	.0017	.0019	.0021	.0023	.0026	.0028	.0031	.0034	.0037
20	.0007	.0008	.0009	.0010	.0011	.0012	.0014	.0015	.0017	.0019
21	.0003	.0003	.0004	.0004	.0005	.0006	.0006	.0007	.0008	.0009
22	.0001	.0001	.0002	.0002	.0002	.0002	.0003	.0003	.0004	.0004
23	.0000	.0001	.0001	.0001	.0001	.0001	.0001	.0001	.0002	.0002
24	.0000	.0000	.0000	.0000	.0000	.0000	.0000	.0001	.0001	.0001

x	λ 11	12	13	14	15	16	17	18	19	20
0	.0000	.0000	.0000	.0000	.0000	.0000	.0000	.0000	.0000	.0000
1	.0002	.0001	.0000	.0000	.0000	.0000	.0000	.0000	.0000	.0000
2	.0010	.0004	.0002	.0001	.0000	.0000	.0000	.0000	.0000	.0000
3	.0037	.0018	.0008	.0004	.0002	.0001	.0000	.0000	.0000	.0000
4	.0102	.0053	.0027	.0013	.0006	.0003	.0001	.0001	.0000	.0000
5	.0224	.0127	.0070	.0037	.0019	.0010	.0005	.0002	.0001	.0001
6	.0411	.0255	.0152	.0087	.0048	.0026	.0014	.0007	.0004	.0002
7	.0646	.0437	.0281	.0174	.0104	.0060	.0034	.0018	.0010	.0005
8	.0888	.0655	.0457	.0304	.0194	.0120	.0072	.0042	.0024	.0013
9	.1085	.0874	.0661	.0473	.0324	.0213	.0135	.0083	.0050	.0029
10	.1194	.1048	.0859	.0663	.0486	.0341	.0230	.0150	.0095	.0058
11	.1194	.1144	.1015	.0844	.0663	.0496	.0355	.0245	.0164	.0106
12	.1094	.1144	.1099	.0984	.0829	.0661	.0504	.0368	.0259	.0176
13	.0926	.1056	.1099	.1060	.0956	.0814	.0658	.0509	.0378	.0271
14	.0728	.0905	.1021	.1060	.1024	.0930	.0800	.0655	.0514	.0387
15	.0534	.0724	.0885	.0989	.1024	.0992	.0906	.0786	.0650	.0516
16	.0367	.0543	.0719	.0866	.0960	.0992	.0963	.0884	.0772	.0646
17	.0237	.0383	.0550	.0713	.0847	.0934	.0963	.0936	.0863	.0760
18	.0145	.0256	.0397	.0554	.0706	.0830	.0909	.0936	.0911	.0844
19	.0084	.0161	.0272	.0409	.0557	.0699	.0814	.0887	.0911	.0888
20	.0046	.0097	.0177	.0286	.0418	.0559	.0692	.0798	.0866	.0888
21	.0024	.0055	.0109	.0191	.0299	.0426	.0560	.0684	.0783	.0846
22	.0012	.0030	.0065	.0121	.0204	.0310	.0433	.0560	.0676	.0769
23	.0006	.0016	.0037	.0074	.0133	.0216	.0320	.0438	.0559	.0669
24	.0003	.0008	.0020	.0043	.0083	.0144	.0226	.0328	.0442	.0557

TABLE II (continued)

	λ									
x	11	12	13	14	15	16	17	18	19	20
25	.0001	.0004	.0010	.0024	.0050	.0092	.0154	.0237	.0336	.0446
26	.0000	.0002	.0005	.0013	.0029	.0057	.0101	.0164	.0246	.0343
27	.0000	.0001	.0002	.0007	.0016	.0034	.0063	.0109	.0173	.0254
28	.0000	.0000	.0001	.0003	.0009	.0019	.0038	.0070	.0117	.0181
29	.0000	.0000	.0001	.0002	.0004	.0011	.0023	.0044	.0077	.0125
30	.0000	.0000	.0000	.0001	.0002	.0006	.0013	.0026	.0049	.0083
31	.0000	.0000	.0000	.0000	.0001	.0003	.0007	.0015	.0030	.0054
32	.0000	.0000	.0000	.0000	.0001	.0001	.0004	.0009	.0018	.0034
33	.0000	.0000	.0000	.0000	.0000	.0001	.0002	.0005	.0010	.0020
34	.0000	.0000	.0000	.0000	.0000	.0000	.0001	.0002	.0006	.0012
35	.0000	.0000	.0000	.0000	.0000	.0000	.0000	.0001	.0003	.0007
36	.0000	.0000	.0000	.0000	.0000	.0000	.0000	.0001	.0002	.0004
37	.0000	.0000	.0000	.0000	.0000	.0000	.0000	.0000	.0001	.0002
38	.0000	.0000	.0000	.0000	.0000	.0000	.0000	.0000	.0000	.0001
39	.0000	.0000	.0000	.0000	.0000	.0000	.0000	.0000	.0000	.0001

TABLE III

Areas Under the Normal Distribution

z	.00	.01	.02	.03	.04	.05	.06	.07	.08	.09
0.0	.0000	.0040	.0080	.0120	.0160	.0199	.0239	.0279	.0319	.0359
0.1	.0398	.0438	.0478	.0517	.0557	.0596	.0636	.0675	.0714	.0753
0.2	.0793	.0832	.0871	.0910	.0948	.0987	.1026	.1064	.1103	.1141
0.3	.1179	.1217	.1255	.1293	.1331	.1368	.1406	.1443	.1480	.1517
0.4	.1554	.1591	.1628	.1664	.1700	.1736	.1772	.1808	.1844	.1879
0.5	.1915	.1950	.1985	.2019	.2054	.2088	.2123	.2157	.2190	.2224
0.6	.2257	.2291	.2324	.2357	.2389	.2422	.2454	.2486	.2517	.2549
0.7	.2580	.2611	.2642	.2673	.2704	.2734	.2764	.2794	.2823	.2852
0.8	.2881	.2910	.2939	.2967	.2995	.3023	.3051	.3078	.3106	.3133
0.9	.3159	.3186	.3212	.3238	.3264	.3289	.3315	.3340	.3365	.3389
1.0	.3413	.3438	.3461	.3485	.3508	.3531	.3554	.3577	.3599	.3621
1.1	.3643	.3665	.3686	.3708	.3729	.3749	.3770	.3790	.3810	.3830
1.2	.3849	.3869	.3888	.3907	.3925	.3944	.3962	.3980	.3997	.4015
1.3	.4032	.4049	.4066	.4082	.4099	.4115	.4131	.4147	.4162	.4177
1.4	.4192	.4207	.4222	.4236	.4251	.4265	.4279	.4292	.4306	.4319
1.5	.4332	.4345	.4357	.4370	.4382	.4394	.4406	.4418	.4429	.4441
1.6	.4452	.4463	.4474	.4484	.4495	.4505	.4515	.4525	.4535	.4545
1.7	.4554	.4564	.4573	.4582	.4591	.4599	.4608	.4616	.4625	.4633
1.8	.4641	.4649	.4656	.4664	.4671	.4678	.4686	.4693	.4699	.4706
1.9	.4713	.4719	.4726	.4732	.4738	.4744	.4750	.4756	.4761	.4767
2.0	.4772	.4778	.4783	.4788	.4793	.4798	.4803	.4808	.4812	.4817
2.1	.4821	.4826	.4830	.4834	.4838	.4842	.4846	.4850	.4854	.4857
2.2	.4861	.4864	.4868	.4871	.4875	.4878	.4881	.4884	.4887	.4890
2.3	.4893	.4896	.4898	.4901	.4904	.4906	.4909	.4911	.4913	.4916
2.4	.4918	.4920	.4922	.4925	.4927	.4929	.4931	.4932	.4934	.4936
2.5	.4938	.4940	.4941	.4943	.4945	.4946	.4948	.4949	.4951	.4952
2.6	.4953	.4955	.4956	.4957	.4959	.4960	.4961	.4962	.4963	.4964
2.7	.4965	.4966	.4967	.4968	.4969	.4970	.4971	.4972	.4973	.4974
2.8	.4974	.4975	.4976	.4977	.4977	.4978	.4979	.4979	.4980	.4981
2.9	.4981	.4982	.4982	.4983	.4984	.4984	.4985	.4985	.4986	.4986
3.0	.4987	.4987	.4987	.4988	.4988	.4989	.4989	.4989	.4990	.4990

TABLE IV

VALUES OF $t_{\alpha,v}$*

ν	$\alpha = .10$	$\alpha = .05$	$\alpha = .025$	$\alpha = .01$	$\alpha = .005$	ν
1	3.078	6.314	12.706	31.821	63.657	1
2	1.886	2.920	4.303	6.965	9.925	2
3	1.638	2.353	3.182	4.541	5.841	3
4	1.533	2.132	2.776	3.747	4.604	4
5	1.476	2.015	2.571	3.365	4.032	5
6	1.440	1.943	2.447	3.143	3.707	6
7	1.415	1.895	2.365	2.998	3.499	7
8	1.397	1.860	2.306	2.896	3.355	8
9	1.383	1.833	2.262	2.821	3.250	9
10	1.372	1.812	2.228	2.764	3.169	10
11	1.363	1.796	2.201	2.718	3.106	11
12	1.356	1.782	2.179	2.681	3.055	12
13	1.350	1.771	2.160	2.650	3.012	13
14	1.345	1.761	2.145	2.624	2.977	14
15	1.341	1.753	2.131	2.602	2.947	15
16	1.337	1.746	2.120	2.583	2.921	16
17	1.333	1.740	2.110	2.567	2.898	17
18	1.330	1.734	2.101	2.552	2.878	18
19	1.328	1.729	2.093	2.539	2.861	19
20	1.325	1.725	2.086	2.528	2.845	20
21	1.323	1.721	2.080	2.518	2.831	21
22	1.321	1.717	2.074	2.508	2.819	22
23	1.319	1.714	2.069	2.500	2.807	23
24	1.318	1.711	2.064	2.492	2.797	24
25	1.316	1.708	2.060	2.485	2.787	25
26	1.315	1.706	2.056	2.479	2.779	26
27	1.314	1.703	2.052	2.473	2.771	27
28	1.313	1.701	2.048	2.467	2.763	28
29	1.311	1.699	2.045	2.462	2.756	29
inf.	1.282	1.645	1.960	2.326	2.576	inf.

* This table is abridged from Table IV of R. A. Fisher, *Statistical Methods for Research Workers*, published by Oliver and Boyd, Ltd., Edinburgh, by permission of the author and publishers.

TABLE V

VALUES OF $\chi^2_{\alpha,\nu}$ *

ν	α = .995	α = .99	α = .975	α = .95	α = .05	α = .025	α = .01	α = .005	ν
1	.0000393	.000157	.000982	.00393	3.841	5.024	6.635	7.879	1
2	.0100	.0201	.0506	.103	5.991	7.378	9.210	10.597	2
3	.0717	.115	.216	.352	7.815	9.348	11.345	12.838	3
4	.207	.297	.484	.711	9.488	11.143	13.277	14.860	4
5	.412	.554	.831	1.145	11.070	12.832	15.086	16.750	5
6	.676	.872	1.237	1.635	12.592	14.449	16.812	18.548	6
7	.989	1.239	1.690	2.167	14.067	16.013	18.475	20.278	7
8	1.344	1.646	2.180	2.733	15.507	17.535	20.090	21.955	8
9	1.735	2.088	2.700	3.325	16.919	19.023	21.666	23.589	9
10	2.156	2.558	3.247	3.940	18.307	20.483	23.209	25.188	10
11	2.603	3.053	3.816	4.575	19.675	21.920	24.725	26.757	11
12	3.074	3.571	4.404	5.226	21.026	23.337	26.217	28.300	12
13	3.565	4.107	5.009	5.892	22.362	24.736	27.688	29.819	13
14	4.075	4.660	5.629	6.571	23.685	26.119	29.141	31.319	14
15	4.601	5.229	6.262	7.261	24.996	27.488	30.578	32.801	15
16	5.142	5.812	6.908	7.962	26.296	28.845	32.000	34.267	16
17	5.697	6.408	7.564	8.672	27.587	30.191	33.409	35.718	17
18	6.265	7.015	8.231	9.390	28.869	31.526	34.805	37.156	18
19	6.844	7.633	8.907	10.117	30.144	32.852	36.191	38.582	19
20	7.434	8.260	9.591	10.851	31.410	34.170	37.566	39.997	20
21	8.034	8.897	10.283	11.591	32.671	35.479	38.932	41.401	21
22	8.643	9.542	10.982	12.338	33.924	36.781	40.289	42.796	22
23	9.260	10.196	11.689	13.091	35.172	38.076	41.638	44.181	23
24	9.886	10.856	12.401	13.848	36.415	39.364	42.980	45.558	24
25	10.520	11.524	13.120	14.611	37.652	40.646	44.314	46.928	25
26	11.160	12.198	13.844	15.379	38.885	41.923	45.642	48.290	26
27	11.808	12.879	14.573	16.151	40.113	43.194	46.963	49.645	27
28	12.461	13.565	15.308	16.928	41.337	44.461	48.278	50.993	28
29	13.121	14.256	16.047	17.708	42.557	45.722	49.588	52.336	29
30	13.787	14.953	16.791	18.493	43.773	46.979	50.892	53.672	30

* This table is based on Table 8 of *Biometrika Tables for Statisticians, Volume I*, by permission of the *Biometrika* trustees.

TABLE VIa

VALUES OF $F_{.05, v_1, v_2}$*

v_1 = Degrees of freedom for numerator

v_2 = Degrees of freedom for denominator	1	2	3	4	5	6	7	8	9	10	12	15	20	24	30	40	60	120	∞
1	161	200	216	225	230	234	237	239	241	242	244	246	248	249	250	251	252	253	254
2	18.5	19.0	19.2	19.2	19.3	19.3	19.4	19.4	19.4	19.4	19.4	19.4	19.4	19.5	19.5	19.5	19.5	19.5	19.5
3	10.1	9.55	9.28	9.12	9.01	8.94	8.89	8.85	8.81	8.79	8.74	8.70	8.66	8.64	8.62	8.59	8.57	8.55	8.53
4	7.71	6.94	6.59	6.39	6.26	6.16	6.09	6.04	6.00	5.96	5.91	5.86	5.80	5.77	5.75	5.72	5.69	5.66	5.63
5	6.61	5.79	5.41	5.19	5.05	4.95	4.88	4.82	4.77	4.74	4.68	4.62	4.56	4.53	4.50	4.46	4.43	4.40	4.37
6	5.99	5.14	4.76	4.53	4.39	4.28	4.21	4.15	4.10	4.06	4.00	3.94	3.87	3.84	3.81	3.77	3.74	3.70	3.67
7	5.59	4.74	4.35	4.12	3.97	3.87	3.79	3.73	3.68	3.64	3.57	3.51	3.44	3.41	3.38	3.34	3.30	3.27	3.23
8	5.32	4.46	4.07	3.84	3.69	3.58	3.50	3.44	3.39	3.35	3.28	3.22	3.15	3.12	3.08	3.04	3.01	2.97	2.93
9	5.12	4.26	3.86	3.63	3.48	3.37	3.29	3.23	3.18	3.14	3.07	3.01	2.94	2.90	2.86	2.83	2.79	2.75	2.71
10	4.96	4.10	3.71	3.48	3.33	3.22	3.14	3.07	3.02	2.98	2.91	2.85	2.77	2.74	2.70	2.66	2.62	2.58	2.54
11	4.84	3.98	3.59	3.36	3.20	3.09	3.01	2.95	2.90	2.85	2.79	2.72	2.65	2.61	2.57	2.53	2.49	2.45	2.40
12	4.75	3.89	3.49	3.26	3.11	3.00	2.91	2.85	2.80	2.75	2.69	2.62	2.54	2.51	2.47	2.43	2.38	2.34	2.30
13	4.67	3.81	3.41	3.18	3.03	2.92	2.83	2.77	2.71	2.67	2.60	2.53	2.46	2.42	2.38	2.34	2.30	2.25	2.21
14	4.60	3.74	3.34	3.11	2.96	2.85	2.76	2.70	2.65	2.60	2.53	2.46	2.39	2.35	2.31	2.27	2.22	2.18	2.13
15	4.54	3.68	3.29	3.06	2.90	2.79	2.71	2.64	2.59	2.54	2.48	2.40	2.33	2.29	2.25	2.20	2.16	2.11	2.07
16	4.49	3.63	3.24	3.01	2.85	2.74	2.66	2.59	2.54	2.49	2.42	2.35	2.28	2.24	2.19	2.15	2.11	2.06	2.01
17	4.45	3.59	3.20	2.96	2.81	2.70	2.61	2.55	2.49	2.45	2.38	2.31	2.23	2.19	2.15	2.10	2.06	2.01	1.96
18	4.41	3.55	3.16	2.93	2.77	2.66	2.58	2.51	2.46	2.41	2.34	2.27	2.19	2.15	2.11	2.06	2.02	1.97	1.92
19	4.38	3.52	3.13	2.90	2.74	2.63	2.54	2.48	2.42	2.38	2.31	2.23	2.16	2.11	2.07	2.03	1.98	1.93	1.88
20	4.35	3.49	3.10	2.87	2.71	2.60	2.51	2.45	2.39	2.35	2.28	2.20	2.12	2.08	2.04	1.99	1.95	1.90	1.84
21	4.32	3.47	3.07	2.84	2.68	2.57	2.49	2.42	2.37	2.32	2.25	2.18	2.10	2.05	2.01	1.96	1.92	1.87	1.81
22	4.30	3.44	3.05	2.82	2.66	2.55	2.46	2.40	2.34	2.30	2.23	2.15	2.07	2.03	1.98	1.94	1.89	1.84	1.78
23	4.28	3.42	3.03	2.80	2.64	2.53	2.44	2.37	2.32	2.27	2.20	2.13	2.05	2.01	1.96	1.91	1.86	1.81	1.76
24	4.26	3.40	3.01	2.78	2.62	2.51	2.42	2.36	2.30	2.25	2.18	2.11	2.03	1.98	1.94	1.89	1.84	1.79	1.73
25	4.24	3.39	2.99	2.76	2.60	2.49	2.40	2.34	2.28	2.24	2.16	2.09	2.01	1.96	1.92	1.87	1.82	1.77	1.71
30	4.17	3.32	2.92	2.69	2.53	2.42	2.33	2.27	2.21	2.16	2.09	2.01	1.93	1.89	1.84	1.79	1.74	1.68	1.62
40	4.08	3.23	2.84	2.61	2.45	2.34	2.25	2.18	2.12	2.08	2.00	1.92	1.84	1.79	1.74	1.69	1.64	1.58	1.51
60	4.00	3.15	2.76	2.53	2.37	2.25	2.17	2.10	2.04	1.99	1.92	1.84	1.75	1.70	1.65	1.59	1.53	1.47	1.39
120	3.92	3.07	2.68	2.45	2.29	2.18	2.09	2.02	1.96	1.91	1.83	1.75	1.66	1.61	1.55	1.50	1.43	1.35	1.25
∞	3.84	3.00	2.60	2.37	2.21	2.10	2.01	1.94	1.88	1.83	1.75	1.67	1.57	1.52	1.46	1.39	1.32	1.22	1.00

* This table is reproduced from M. Merrington and C. M. Thompson, "Tables of percentage points of the inverted beta (*F*) distribution," *Biometrika*, Vol. 33 (1943), by permission of the *Biometrika* trustees.

TABLE VIb

VALUES OF $F_{.01,v_1,v_2}$*

v_1 = Degrees of freedom for numerator; v_2 = Degrees of freedom for denominator

v_2	1	2	3	4	5	6	7	8	9	10	12	15	20	24	30	40	60	120	∞
1	4,052	5,000	5,403	5,625	5,764	5,859	5,928	5,982	6,023	6,056	6,106	6,157	6,209	6,235	6,261	6,287	6,313	6,339	6,366
2	98.5	99.0	99.2	99.2	99.3	99.3	99.4	99.4	99.4	99.4	99.4	99.4	99.4	99.5	99.5	99.5	99.5	99.5	99.5
3	34.1	30.8	29.5	28.7	28.2	27.9	27.7	27.5	27.3	27.2	27.1	26.9	26.7	26.6	26.5	26.4	26.3	26.2	26.1
4	21.2	18.0	16.7	16.0	15.5	15.2	15.0	14.8	14.7	14.5	14.4	14.2	14.0	13.9	13.8	13.7	13.7	13.6	13.5
5	16.3	13.3	12.1	11.4	11.0	10.7	10.5	10.3	10.2	10.1	9.89	9.72	9.55	9.47	9.38	9.29	9.20	9.11	9.02
6	13.7	10.9	9.78	9.15	8.75	8.47	8.26	8.10	7.98	7.87	7.72	7.56	7.40	7.31	7.23	7.14	7.06	6.97	6.88
7	12.2	9.55	8.45	7.85	7.46	7.19	6.99	6.84	6.72	6.62	6.47	6.31	6.16	6.07	5.99	5.91	5.82	5.74	5.65
8	11.3	8.65	7.59	7.01	6.63	6.37	6.18	6.03	5.91	5.81	5.67	5.52	5.36	5.28	5.20	5.12	5.03	4.95	4.86
9	10.6	8.02	6.99	6.42	6.06	5.80	5.61	5.47	5.35	5.26	5.11	4.96	4.81	4.73	4.65	4.57	4.48	4.40	4.31
10	10.0	7.56	6.55	5.99	5.64	5.39	5.20	5.06	4.94	4.85	4.71	4.56	4.41	4.33	4.25	4.17	4.08	4.00	3.91
11	9.65	7.21	6.22	5.67	5.32	5.07	4.89	4.74	4.63	4.54	4.40	4.25	4.10	4.02	3.94	3.86	3.78	3.69	3.60
12	9.33	6.93	5.95	5.41	5.06	4.82	4.64	4.50	4.39	4.30	4.16	4.01	3.86	3.78	3.70	3.62	3.54	3.45	3.36
13	9.07	6.70	5.74	5.21	4.86	4.62	4.44	4.30	4.19	4.10	3.96	3.82	3.66	3.59	3.51	3.43	3.34	3.25	3.17
14	8.86	6.51	5.56	5.04	4.70	4.46	4.28	4.14	4.03	3.94	3.80	3.66	3.51	3.43	3.35	3.27	3.18	3.09	3.00
15	8.68	6.36	5.42	4.89	4.56	4.32	4.14	4.00	3.89	3.80	3.67	3.52	3.37	3.29	3.21	3.13	3.05	2.96	2.87
16	8.53	6.23	5.29	4.77	4.44	4.20	4.03	3.89	3.78	3.69	3.55	3.41	3.26	3.18	3.10	3.02	2.93	2.84	2.75
17	8.40	6.11	5.19	4.67	4.34	4.10	3.93	3.79	3.68	3.59	3.46	3.31	3.16	3.08	3.00	2.92	2.83	2.75	2.65
18	8.29	6.01	5.09	4.58	4.25	4.01	3.84	3.71	3.60	3.51	3.37	3.23	3.08	3.00	2.92	2.84	2.75	2.66	2.57
19	8.19	5.93	5.01	4.50	4.17	3.94	3.77	3.63	3.52	3.43	3.30	3.15	3.00	2.92	2.84	2.76	2.67	2.58	2.49
20	8.10	5.85	4.94	4.43	4.10	3.87	3.70	3.56	3.46	3.37	3.23	3.09	2.94	2.86	2.78	2.69	2.61	2.52	2.42
21	8.02	5.78	4.87	4.37	4.04	3.81	3.64	3.51	3.40	3.31	3.17	3.03	2.88	2.80	2.72	2.64	2.55	2.46	2.36
22	7.95	5.72	4.82	4.31	3.99	3.76	3.59	3.45	3.35	3.26	3.12	2.98	2.83	2.75	2.67	2.58	2.50	2.40	2.31
23	7.88	5.66	4.76	4.26	3.94	3.71	3.54	3.41	3.30	3.21	3.07	2.93	2.78	2.70	2.62	2.54	2.45	2.35	2.26
24	7.82	5.61	4.72	4.22	3.90	3.67	3.50	3.36	3.26	3.17	3.03	2.89	2.74	2.66	2.58	2.49	2.40	2.31	2.21
25	7.77	5.57	4.68	4.18	3.86	3.63	3.46	3.32	3.22	3.13	2.99	2.85	2.70	2.62	2.53	2.45	2.36	2.27	2.17
30	7.56	5.39	4.51	4.02	3.70	3.47	3.30	3.17	3.07	2.98	2.84	2.70	2.55	2.47	2.39	2.30	2.21	2.11	2.01
40	7.31	5.18	4.31	3.83	3.51	3.29	3.12	2.99	2.89	2.80	2.66	2.52	2.37	2.29	2.20	2.11	2.02	1.92	1.80
60	7.08	4.98	4.13	3.65	3.34	3.12	2.95	2.82	2.72	2.63	2.50	2.35	2.20	2.12	2.03	1.94	1.84	1.73	1.60
120	6.85	4.79	3.95	3.48	3.17	2.96	2.79	2.66	2.56	2.47	2.34	2.19	2.03	1.95	1.86	1.76	1.66	1.53	1.38
∞	6.63	4.61	3.78	3.32	3.02	2.80	2.64	2.51	2.41	2.32	2.18	2.04	1.88	1.79	1.70	1.59	1.47	1.32	1.00

* This table is reproduced from M. Merrington and C. M. Thompson, "Tables of percentage points of the inverted beta (*F*) distribution," *Biometrika*, Vol. 33 (1943), by permission of the *Biometrika* trustees.

TABLE VII

Binomial Coefficients

n	$\binom{n}{0}$	$\binom{n}{1}$	$\binom{n}{2}$	$\binom{n}{3}$	$\binom{n}{4}$	$\binom{n}{5}$	$\binom{n}{6}$	$\binom{n}{7}$	$\binom{n}{8}$	$\binom{n}{9}$	$\binom{n}{10}$
0	1										
1	1	1									
2	1	2	1								
3	1	3	3	1							
4	1	4	6	4	1						
5	1	5	10	10	5	1					
6	1	6	15	20	15	6	1				
7	1	7	21	35	35	21	7	1			
8	1	8	28	56	70	56	28	8	1		
9	1	9	36	84	126	126	84	36	9	1	
10	1	10	45	120	210	252	210	120	45	10	1
11	1	11	55	165	330	462	462	330	165	55	11
12	1	12	66	220	495	792	924	792	495	220	66
13	1	13	78	286	715	1287	1716	1716	1287	715	286
14	1	14	91	364	1001	2002	3003	3432	3003	2002	1001
15	1	15	105	455	1365	3003	5005	6435	6435	5005	3003
16	1	16	120	560	1820	4368	8008	11440	12870	11440	8008
17	1	17	136	680	2380	6188	12376	19448	24310	24310	19448
18	1	18	153	816	3060	8568	18564	31824	43758	48620	43758
19	1	19	171	969	3876	11628	27132	50388	75582	92378	92378
20	1	20	190	1140	4845	15504	38760	77520	125970	167960	184756

Answers to Odd-Numbered Exercises

Page 15

1. (a) (1, 1), (1, 2), (1, 3), (1, 4), (2, 1), (2, 2), (2, 3), (2, 4), (3, 1), (3, 2), (3, 3), (3, 4), (4, 1), (4, 2), (4, 3), (4, 4);
(b) (1, 1), (1, 2), (1, 3), (1, 4), (2, 1), (3, 1), (4, 1);
(c) (1, 1), (2, 2), (3, 3), (4, 4);
(d) (2, 2), (2, 4), (4, 2), (4, 4);
(e) (1, 1), (1, 3), (3, 1), (3, 3);
(f) (1, 1);
(g) (1, 1), (2, 2), (3, 3), (4, 4), (2, 4), (4, 2);
(h) (2, 2), (2, 3), (2, 4), (3, 2), (3, 3), (3, 4), (4, 2), (4, 3), (4, 4);
(i) ϕ;
(j) S;
(k) (1, 1), (1, 3), (3, 1);
(l) (1, 1), (1, 3), (3, 1).

3. (a) {Evans, French, Green, Hughes};
(b) {Burns, Davis, Evans, Green};
(c) {Allen, Hughes};
(d) {Carlson, Davis, Green, Hughes}.

5. (a) {French, Hughes};
(b) {Burns, Carlson, French, Green};
(c) {Evans, French, Green};
(d) {Burns, Carlson, French, Green, Hughes};
(e) {French};
(f) {Allen, Burns, Carlson, Davis, French, Hughes};
(g) {French};
(h) {French};
(i) {Allen, Davis, Hughes}.

7. {(0, 2), (1, 2), (2, 2), (2, 0), (2, 1)} and {(0, 0), (0, 2), (2, 0), (2, 2)}.

Page 28

1. (a) 4; (b) 16; (c) 12.

3. 15,818,400.

5. 9.

9. (a) 7,392; (b) 44,352.

11. 60,060.

13. 444,600.

15. 21 and 6

17. (a) n^r; (b) $\binom{r-1}{r-n}$.

25. (a) 1680; (b) 12,600; (c) 90.

Page 40

1. (a) The sum of the probabilities is less than 1;
(b) $P(C \cup D)$ cannot be less than $P(C)$;
(c) $P(D \cap E)$ must equal 0;
(d) $P(E)$ cannot be negative and $P(A) + P(B) + P(C) + P(D)$ cannot exceed 1;
(e) $P(C)$ cannot exceed 1.

3. (a) 0.70; (b) 0.40; (c) 0.20; (d) 0.90.

5. $P(\phi) = 0$, $P(S) = 1$, $P(A \cup B) = 0.90$, $P(A \cup C) = 0.70$, $P(B \cup C) = 0.40$.

11. (a) 1/26; (b) 1/2; (c) 3/13; (d) 1/13; (e) 15/52.

13. 2/3 and 2/9.

15. 3/8.

Page 51

1. (a) The probability that if one of the wealthy club members is elected, he has ulcers;
(b) The probability that if a club member with ulcers is elected, he is a college graduate and wealthy;
(c) The probability that the person elected is wealthy, given that he is neither a college graduate nor does he have ulcers;
(d) The probability that if the person elected is a college graduate he is not wealthy but he has ulcers.

3. (a) 0.74; (b) 0; (c) 0; (d) 0.26.

5. (a) 0.20; (b) 0.09; (c) 0.56; (d) 0.44.

9. (a) they are pairwise independent; (b) they are not independent.

Page 58

3. 0.2735.

5. 0.66.

7. 0.32.

9. 2/3.

Page 65

1. $f(-3) = 1/8, f(-1) = 3/8, f(1) = 3/8, f(3) = 1/8$.

3. $f(0) = 1/2, f(1) = 1/4, f(2) = 1/8, f(3) = 1/8$;

$$F(x) = \begin{cases} 0 & \text{for } x < 0 \\ 1/2 & \text{for } 0 \leq x < 1 \\ 3/4 & \text{for } 1 \leq x < 2 \\ 7/8 & \text{for } 2 \leq x < 3 \\ 1 & \text{for } 3 \leq x \end{cases}$$

Page 75

1. (a) 625/3888; (b) 7500/7776;

3. 32,805/131,072.

9. (a) 385/969; (b) 682/969; (c) 106/1938.

11. 0.0023 and 0.0016;

13. (a) 2/3; (b) 2/3; (c) 7/12.

15. 21/256.

Page 78

1. (a) 0.1009; (b) 0.0573; (c) 0.2254.

3. 0.5139 and 0.2241.

5. 0.77.

7. 0.3679, 0.3679, and 0.1839.

9. 0.3012 and 0.2214.

11. 100/631.

13. 0.37.

15. 0.187.

Page 88

1. (a) $f(1) = 1/3, f(2) = 11/27, f(3) = 7/27$;
(b) $g(1) = 11/27, g(2) = 7/27, g(3) = 1/3$;
(c) $f_1(1 \mid 2) = 1/7, f_1(2 \mid 2) = 3/7, f_1(3 \mid 2) = 3/7$;
(d) $f_2(1 \mid 1) = 5/9, f_2(2 \mid 1) = 1/9, f_2(3 \mid 1) = 1/3$.

3. (a) 0; (b) 0; (c) 20/27; (d) 0; (e) 11/27; (f) 1.

5. 315/8192.

7. $\dfrac{10!}{4!3!2!2!}\left(\dfrac{9}{16}\right)^4\left(\dfrac{3}{16}\right)^5\left(\dfrac{1}{16}\right)$.

9. $\dfrac{\prod_{i=1}^{k}\binom{a_i}{x_i}}{\binom{N}{n}}$.

Page 93

1. $1.60.

3. 2.89.

Page 98

1. $\mu = 3/2$ and $\sigma^2 = 3/4$.

9. $k = \sqrt{20}$.

Page 104

1. The probability is less than 1/9; the actual probability is 0.0004.

7. $\mu = (n + 1)/2$ and $\sigma^2 = (n^2 - 1)/12$.

11. $\mu_2' = \mu_{(2)}' + \mu_{(1)}'$; $\mu_3' = \mu_{(3)}' + 3\mu_{(2)}' + \mu_{(1)}'$;
$\mu_4' = \mu_{(4)}' + 6\mu_{(3)}' + 7\mu_{(2)}' + \mu_{(1)}'$.

Page 111

1. $\mu_3' = n\theta + 3n(n-1)\theta^2 + n(n-1)(n-2)\theta^3$; $\mu_3 = n\theta(1-\theta)(1-2\theta)$;

$$\alpha_3 = \frac{1 - 2\theta}{\sqrt{n\theta(1-\theta)}};$$

(a) $\alpha_3 = 0$ for $\theta = 1/2$; (b) $\alpha_3 \to 0$ when n is large.

3. No; $M_x(0)$ must equal 1.

Page 113

1. 50/729.

Page 115

1. The second location.

3. Confirmed pessimists would locate the store in the first location, being worried about a possible loss of \$5000 in the second location; confirmed optimists would locate the store in the second location, hoping for the \$25,000 profit.

5. If 2% are defective, it is more profitable not to test; if 6% are defective, it is more profitable to test.

Page 124

1. $f(x) = \begin{cases} 1/x^2 & \text{for } x > 1 \\ 0 & \text{for } x < 1 \end{cases}$ it is undefined at $x = 1$.

3. $k = 6$; 0.896.

5. $F(x) = \begin{cases} 0 & \text{for } x \leq 0 \\ x^2/2 & \text{for } 0 < x \leq 1 \\ 2x - \dfrac{x^2}{2} - 1 & \text{for } 1 < x \leq 2 \\ 1 & \text{for } x \geq 2 \end{cases}$

7. $f(x) = \begin{cases} 0 & \text{for } x < 0 \\ xe^{-x} & \text{for } x > 0 \end{cases}$

Page 130

1. $c = \theta(\ln 2)$.

Page 131

1. 1/2.

3. $\dfrac{4(\sqrt{e} - 1)}{e^2} = 0.35$.

5. $(13/3)e^{-10/3} = 0.15$.

Page 141

1. $k = 12.$

3. $k = 2;\ f(x_1) = \begin{cases} (1 + x_1)^{-2} & \text{for } x_1 > 0 \\ 0 & \text{for } x_1 < 0 \end{cases}$

$$g(x_2) = \begin{cases} (1 + x_2)^{-2} & \text{for } x_2 > 0 \\ 0 & \text{for } x_2 < 0 \end{cases}$$

$$f(x_1 \mid x_2) = \begin{cases} 2(1 + x_2)^2(1 + x_1 + x_2)^{-3} & \text{for } x_1 > 0 \\ 0 & \text{for } x_1 < 0 \end{cases}$$

5. $f(x_1) = \begin{cases} 2(1 - x_1) & \text{for } 0 < x_1 < 1 \\ 0 & \text{elsewhere} \end{cases}$

$$g(x_2) = \begin{cases} 2x_2 & \text{for } 0 < x_2 < 1 \\ 0 & \text{elsewhere} \end{cases}$$

they are not independent; 1/2.

7. They are not independent.

9. $2(e^{-1/2} - e^{-1}) = 0.48.$

Page 150

5. μ exists, σ^2 does not exist.

7. $\mu_r' = \dfrac{\Gamma(\alpha + \beta)\Gamma(\alpha + r)}{\Gamma(\alpha)\Gamma(\alpha + \beta + r)};\quad \mu = \dfrac{\alpha}{\alpha + \beta};\quad \sigma^2 = \dfrac{\alpha\beta}{(\alpha + \beta)^2(\alpha + \beta + 1)}.$

9. (a) 0.0037; (b) 0.9582; (c) 0.7454; (d) 0.0301; (e) 0.0974; (f) 0.3730.

11. 0.9544 and 0.997^+.

13. 2.4548.

15. 0.2843 and 323.6 hours.

Page 156

3. $M_x(t) = \dfrac{1}{1 - t}$

5. α_3 and α_4 are so-called shape parameters; they are invariant under linear transformations.

Page 160

1. $e^{-\sqrt{\lambda}t}e^{\lambda(e^{t/\sqrt{\lambda}}-1)}$.

3. 0.19.

5. 0.026.

7. 0.40.

Page 161

1. 0.

Page 162

1. $x = v_1 + \dfrac{(a+c)(v_2 - v_1)}{a+b+c}$; 32.

Page 170

1. $$f(y) = \begin{cases} \dfrac{1}{\theta_1 - \theta_2}[e^{-y/\theta_1} - e^{-y/\theta_2}] & \text{for } y > 0 \\ 0 & \text{elsewhere} \end{cases}$$

5. $$f(y) = \begin{cases} y & \text{for } 0 < y < 1 \\ 2 - y & \text{for } 1 \leq y < 2 \\ 0 & \text{elsewhere} \end{cases}$$

Page 173

3. $M_x(t) = \dfrac{\theta^n e^{nt}}{[1 - e^t(1-\theta)]^n}$; the negative binomial distribution.

Page 178

1. (a) $\mu = 11$ and $\sigma^2 = 228$; (b) $\mu = 20$ and $\sigma^2 = 389$.

7. The probability is greater than or equal to 15/16.

Page 181

1. The difference will not exceed 10.

Page 187

5. Table III does not give a value for $z = 4$, but the probability exceeds 0.997^+.

Page 192

3. 0.83

7. 0.035.

Page 197

7. $e^{-1.22} = 0.295$.

Page 203

7. 5/16.

11. No; $t = 4\frac{1}{6}$ is greater than might reasonably be expected, it exceeds $t_{.005,24} = 2.797$.

Page 207

3. $\mu = (5\alpha + \beta)/6$.

5. (a) $$f(u_r, u_s) = \frac{n!f(u_r)f(u_s)}{(r-1)!(s-r-1)!(n-s)!} \times \left[\int_{-\infty}^{u_r} f(x)\,dx\right]^{r-1}\left[\int_{u_r}^{u_s} f(x)\,dx\right]^{s-r-1}\left[\int_{u_s}^{\infty} f(x)\,dx\right]^{n-s}$$

for $-\infty < u_r < u_s < \infty$;

(c) $$g(u_1, u_n) = \frac{n(n-1)}{\theta^2} e^{-(u_1+u_n)/\theta}\left[e^{-(u_1/\theta)} - e^{-(u_n/\theta)}\right]^{n-2}$$

for $0 < u_1 < u_n < \infty$.

Page 212

1. $$\rho(\theta, \delta_2) = \begin{cases} 1 & \text{for } \theta = 0 \\ 0 & \text{for } \theta = 1 \\ 1 & \text{for } \theta = 2 \end{cases}$$

3. $$\rho(\theta, \delta_3) = \begin{cases} 1/2 & \text{for } \theta = 0 \\ 1/4 & \text{for } \theta = 1 \\ 1/2 & \text{for } \theta = 2 \end{cases}$$

5. 5/12.

Page 220

5. The relative efficiency is 7/6.

Page 225

1. (a) $\bar{\mathbf{x}}$; (b) $\bar{\mathbf{x}}$.

3. The maximum likelihood estimate of θ is given by the largest value in the sample.

5. $$\frac{-n}{\ln \prod_{i=1}^{n} x_i}$$

Page 229

1. $k = \dfrac{-1}{\ln(1-\alpha)}$

3. $c = \dfrac{1 + \sqrt{1-\alpha}}{\alpha}$

Page 231

1. $1924 < \mu < 2046$.

3. $2.690 < \mu < 2.720$.

5. $\$55.14 < \mu < \$61.14$.

7. $(\bar{x}_1 - \bar{x}_2) \pm z_{\alpha/2}\sqrt{(\sigma_1^2/n_1) + (\sigma_2^2/n_2)}$

Page 233

1. $0.085 < \theta < 0.221$.

3. $0.234 < \theta < 0.306$.

5. $0.243 < \theta < 0.298$.

9. $$\left(\frac{x_1}{n_1} - \frac{x_2}{n_2}\right) \pm 1.96\sqrt{\frac{\frac{x_1}{n_1}\left(1 - \frac{x_1}{n_1}\right)}{n_1} + \frac{\frac{x_2}{n_2}\left(1 - \frac{x_2}{n_2}\right)}{n_2}}$$

Page 235

1. $0.00057 < \sigma^2 < 0.004$.

3. $2.2 < \sigma < 11.5$.

5. $10.46 < \sigma < 12.74$.

Page 245

1. Type I error: predict incorrectly that Candidate Y will win;
Type II error: predict incorrectly that Candidate X will win.

3. $\alpha = e^{-2} = 0.135, \quad \beta = 1 - e^{-(1/5)} = 0.181.$

7. The critical region is $\sum_{i=1}^{n} x_i > K$; to find K one can make use of the fact that under the null hypothesis $\sum_{i=1}^{n} \mathbf{x}_i$ has a gamma distribution with $\alpha = n$ and $\beta = \theta_0$.

9. H_A is accepted if the number of successes is 42 or more; the probability of committing a Type II error is 0.38.

Page 255

1. (a) $\alpha = 2/5$; (b)

θ	0	1	2	4	5	6
β	0	1/3	8/15	8/15	1/3	0

3. The two critical regions are of the same size, but the one where H_0 is rejected if the two marbles are of different colors is non-admissible.

5. Ω is the set of the positive real numbers and ω is the set $\{\mu_0\}$;

$$\lambda = \left(\frac{\mu_0}{\bar{x}}\right)^{n\bar{x}} e^{n(\bar{x}-\mu_0)}$$

Page 264

1. $z = -2.88$; reject the null hypothesis.

3. $t = -4$; reject the null hypothesis.

7. The control limits are 1.473 and 1.527.

Page 270

1. -0.458; (a) 0.82; (b) 0.44; (c) 0.026.

3. $t = 1.17$; the null hypothesis cannot be rejected.

5. $t = 3.64$; the diet is effective.

Page 274

1. $\chi^2 = 34.56$; null hypothesis cannot be rejected.

3. $F = 1.18$; accept null hypothesis.

5. $F = 3.86$; null hypothesis cannot be rejected.

Page 279

1. (a) $k_{.05} = 12$; 0.88 and 0.63; (b) $k'_{.01} = 6$; 0.75 and 0.61; (c) $k'_{.025} = 7$ and $k_{.025} = 17$; 0.94 and 0.95.

3. $z = 2.21$; reject the null hypothesis.

7. Accept the null hypothesis.

9. $\chi^2 = 3.96$; difference is significant.

Page 286

3. They are not independent.

5. $\chi^2 = 9$; cannot reject the null hypothesis.

7. Good fit.

Page 292

1. Reject the null hypothesis. **3.** Cannot reject the null hypothesis.

5. Cannot reject the null hypothesis that the two populations have equal means.

7. Reject the null hypothesis that the two populations have equal variances.

Page 307

5. (a) 0.20; (b) $1 - e^{-0.32} = 0.27$.

Page 312

3. (a) $\dfrac{1 + r - (1 - r)e^{(\pm 2z_{\alpha/2})/\sqrt{n-3}}}{1 + r + (1 - r)e^{(\pm 2z_{\alpha/2})/\sqrt{n-3}}}$; (b) $0.73 - 0.98$.

5. $r = 0.83$; $0.69 - 0.91$. **7.** 0.84.

Page 318

7. $102.3 < \alpha < 139.9$.

9. $\hat{\alpha} = 60.75$ and $\hat{\beta} = -2.96$; \$37.07; accept the null hypothesis.

Page 325

1. $\alpha' = 0.282$ and $\beta' = 10.19$. **3.** $\beta' = \dfrac{\sum xy}{\sum x^2}$.

5. $y = (0.68)(1.38)^x$.

7. $\sum z = n\alpha + \beta \sum x + \gamma \sum y$

$\sum xz = \alpha \sum x + \beta \sum x^2 + \gamma \sum xy$

$\sum yz = \alpha \sum y + \beta \sum xy + \gamma \sum y^2$;

$\alpha = 134/55$, $\beta = 338/110$, $\gamma = -47/11$.

Page 337

3. $F = 5.0$; reject the null hypothesis that there are no differences.

5. $F = 1.74$; cannot reject the null hypothesis that there are no differences.

Page 346

5. $F_A = 8.58$ and $F_B = 7.70$; there are significant differences in the performance of the workmen as well as the machines.

7. Letting $\dfrac{1}{nmk}\left[\sum_{i=1}^{k}\sum_{j=1}^{n}\sum_{r=1}^{m} x_{ijr}\right]^2 = C$,

$$SSA = \frac{1}{nm}\sum_{i=1}^{k}\left[\sum_{j=1}^{n}\sum_{r=1}^{m} x_{ijr}\right]^2 - C;$$

$$SSB = \frac{1}{km}\sum_{j=1}^{n}\left[\sum_{i=1}^{k}\sum_{r=1}^{m} x_{ijr}\right]^2 - C$$

$$SSI = \frac{1}{m}\sum_{i=1}^{k}\sum_{j=1}^{n}\left[\sum_{r=1}^{m} x_{ijr}\right]^2 - C - SSA - SSB;$$

$$SST = \sum_{i=1}^{k}\sum_{j=1}^{n}\sum_{r=1}^{m} x_{ijr}^2 - C;$$

$$SSE = SST - SSA - SSB - SSI.$$

9. (a) Test the null hypothesis that the α_i are all equal to 0 against the alternative that they are not; test the null hypothesis that the β_j are all equal to 0 against the alternative that they are not; test the null hypothesis that the τ_k are all equal to 0 against the alternative that they are not.

(c)

Source of variation	Degrees of freedom	Sum of squares	Mean square	F
Rows	$r - 1$	SSR	$MSR = \dfrac{SSR}{r-1}$	$\dfrac{MSR}{MSE}$
Columns	$r - 1$	SSC	$MSC = \dfrac{SSC}{r-1}$	$\dfrac{MSC}{MSE}$
Treatments	$r - 1$	$SS(\text{Tr})$	$MS(\text{Tr}) = \dfrac{SS(\text{Tr})}{r-1}$	$\dfrac{MS(\text{Tr})}{MSE}$
Error	$(r-1)(r-2)$	SSE	$MSE = \dfrac{SSE}{(r-1)(r-2)}$	
Total	$r^2 - 1$	SST		

Index

D

E

F

G

H

I

J

L

P

R

S

T

U

V

W